Prentice Hall
LITERATURE
Timeless Voices, Timeless Themes

Formal Assessment

PLATINUM

Prentice
Hall

Upper Saddle River, New Jersey
Glenview, Illinois
Needham, Massachusetts

ACKNOWLEDGMENTS

Grateful acknowledgment is made to the following for copyrighted material:

Bantam Books
From A SEPARATE PEACE by John Knowles. Copyright © 1959 by John Knowles.

The Ecco Press
"Gooseberries" by Anton Chekhov from THE ESSENTIAL TALES OF CHEKHOV, edited by Richard Ford, translated by Constance Garnett.

Harcourt, Inc.
From "Mushrooms in the City" from MARCOVALDO by Italo Calvino. English translation copyright © 1983 by Harcourt Brace Jovanovich, Inc., and Martin Secker & Warburg Limited.

HarperCollins Publishers
"The Sonnet-Ballad" from THE WORLD OF GWENDOLYN BROOKS by Gwendolyn Brooks. Copyright © 1971 by Gwendolyn Brooks.

Library of America
From "Paul's Case" by Willa Cather from WILLA CATHER—STORIES, POEMS AND OTHER WRITINGS, edited by Sharon O'Brien. Copyright © 1992 by Literary Classics of the United States, Inc., New York, NY.

McGraw-Hill Book Company, Inc.
From "The Creative Process in Music" from WHAT TO LISTEN FOR IN MUSIC by Aaron Copland. Copyright © 1939, 1957 by the McGraw-Hill Book Company, Inc.

The New American Library
From "Hercules" from MYTHOLOGY by Edith Hamilton. Copyright © 1940, 1942 by Edith Hamilton.

Note: Every effort has been made to locate the copyright owner of material reprinted in this book. Omissions brought to our attention will be corrected in subsequent printings.

ISBN 0-13-058379-0

6 7 8 9 10   05

CONTENTS

UNIT 1: ON THE EDGE

UNIT 2: STRIVING FOR SUCCESS

UNIT 3: CLASHING FORCES

UNIT 4: TURNING POINTS

UNIT 5: EXPANDING HORIZONS

UNIT 6: SHORT STORIES

UNIT 7: NONFICTION

UNIT 8: DRAMA

UNIT 9: POETRY

UNIT 10: EPICS AND LEGENDS

Name _____ Date _____

"Contents of the Dead Man's Pocket" by Jack Finney

Selection Test

Critical Reading

In the blank, write the letter of the one best answer.

_____ 1. At the beginning of the story, what seems to be the most important thing in Tom Benecke's life?
a. his research on past shopping trends   c. getting paid at the end of the week
b. going to the movies with his wife   d. his long-term professional goals

_____ 2. Which of the following events happened first in "Contents of the Dead Man's Pocket"?
a. Tom contemplated what the police would find in his pockets.
b. He counted customers passing by displays in the grocery store.
c. He watched his wife get ready to go out alone.
d. He sat down to write a memo about store displays.

_____ 3. Which event in "Contents of the Dead Man's Pocket" causes Tom to panic?
a. He thinks about the contents of his pockets.
b. He sees the street below him.
c. The paper flies out the window.
d. Tom sees a man in an apartment across the street.

_____ 4. What do the following lines from "Contents of the Dead Man's Pocket" reveal about Tom?
He kissed her then and, for an instant, holding her close, smelling the perfume she
had used, he was tempted to go with her; it was not actually true that he had to
work tonight, though he very much wanted to.
a. He constantly lies to his wife.
b. He isn't really interested in the movie she wants to see.
c. He likes to be with his wife only when she wears perfume.
d. He is fond of his wife but has given work a higher priority.

_____ 5. If it is not clear why an author has presented certain information, you should
a. reread the sentence or paragraph several times until the reason becomes clear.
b. read ahead to see if the information takes on significance later.
c. use an encyclopedia to research the information.
d. e-mail the author and request an explanation.

_____ 6. To Tom, the contents of his pockets represent
a. his love for his wife.   c. his opportunities for advancement.
b. the accomplishments of his life.   d. all of his personal possessions.

_____ 7. In "Contents of the Dead Man's Pocket," Tom struggles most with his _____.
a. neighbors   b. wife   c. fear   d. job

_____ 8. Often a seemingly minor detail mentioned early in a short story becomes very important later. Which of the following is a good example of such a detail?
a. The window is hard to open.   c. Clare goes out for the evening.
b. It is hot in the apartment.   d. Tom puts on his coat to go out.

_____ 9. What is the best way to clarify a detail when reading a passage?
  a. Reread the sentence or paragraph in which the detail occurs.
  b. Stop reading and consult a dictionary.
  c. Summarize the entire passage in your own words.
  d. Skip to the end of the passage to see if the detail is explained there.

_____ 10. "Contents of the Dead Man's Pocket" is mostly about
  a. a man who risks his life to save his job.
  b. the contents of Tom Benecke's pockets.
  c. a man and woman whose marriage is falling apart.
  d. a man whose ambitions nearly kill him.

_____ 11. Why is the following passage from "Contents of the Dead Man's Pocket" suspenseful?
    For a single moment he knelt, knee bones against stone on the very edge of the
    ledge, body swaying and touching nowhere else, fighting for balance. Then he lost
    it, his shoulders plunging backward, and he flung his arms forward, his hands
    smashing against the window casing on either side; and—his body moving back-
    ward—his fingers clutched the narrow wood stripping of the upper pane.
  a. Tom is in a dangerous spot.
  b. It makes readers think Tom is going to fall.
  c. Tom finally falls from the ledge.
  d. The author doesn't tell what happens.

_____ 12. On the ledge, Tom "flung his arms forward, his hands smashing against the window
    casing on either side; and—his body moving backward—his fingers clutched the nar-
    row wood stripping of the upper pane." The phrase "his body moving backward" has
    the effect of
  a. increasing the suspense.
  b. interrupting the suspense.
  c. convincing the reader that Tom is falling.
  d. slowing the reader down.

_____ 13. Read this passage from "Contents of the Dead Man's Pocket." Then, reread it to clar-
    ify your understanding of Tom's intention. Choose the sentence that best describes
    what he is planning to do.
    His elbow protruding over Lexington Avenue far below, the fingers of his other
    hand pressed down bloodlessly tight against the narrow stripping, he waited, feel-
    ing the sick tenseness and terrible excitement building. It grew and swelled toward
    the moment of action, his nerves tautening. He thought of Clare—just a wordless,
    yearning thought—and then drew his arm back just a bit more, fist so tight his fin-
    gers pained him, and knowing he was going to do it.
  a. Realizing his situation is hopeless, he is preparing to jump.
  b. He is afraid he might slip, so he is tightening his grip on the stripping.
  c. Balancing carefully, he is preparing to slam his fist into the window.
  d. He is planning to wave to a pedestrian on Lexington Avenue.

_____ 14. In "Contents of the Dead Man's Pocket," a moment of high or intense suspense oc-
    curs when
  a. Clare leaves.
  b. Tom looks down and panics.
  c. Tom stares through the window into his living room.
  d. Tom sees the yellow paper fly out the window a second time.

____ 15. Which of the following contributes the most to the suspense in "Contents of the Dead Man's Pocket"?
   a. Tom's thoughts about falling
   b. descriptions of the pain Tom experiences in his fingers and knees
   c. the actions of the man in the window across the street
   d. waiting to see if anyone responds to the coins Tom dropped

Vocabulary and Grammar

____ 16. In "Contents of the Dead Man's Pocket," Tom has a grimace on his face while he is out on the ledge because
   a. he is cold.
   b. he misses Clare.
   c. he is thinking about his promotion.
   d. he is stricken with fear.

____ 17. Tom loses the deftness in his hands, which means he loses
   a. the ability to move his hands skillfully.
   b. all movement in his hands.
   c. all feeling in his hands.
   d. all the warmth in his hands.

____ 18. Tom moves "almost imperceptibly" along the ledge. *Imperceptibly* means he is moving
   a. backwards.
   b. so slowly that the movement can hardly be seen.
   c. hand over hand.
   d. with a shuffling motion.

____ 19. Identify the concrete nouns in the following sentence.
   Then, with utmost delicacy, with a focused concentration of all his senses, he increased even further the strain on his fingertips hooked to these slim edgings of wood.
   a. fingertips, edgings, and wood
   b. senses, fingertips, and wood
   c. delicacy, senses, and fingertips
   d. concentration, strain, and wood

____ 20. Choose the sentence that contains an abstract noun.
   a. The open window dropped shudderingly in its frame.
   b. The yellow paper fluttered along the ledge.
   c. The realization struck him that he might have to wait for Clare to return.
   d. Dropping his palms to the sill, he stared into his living room.

Essay Questions

21. In an essay, describe Tom's goals and values at the beginning of the story. Then state what his values seem to be at the end of the story. Explain why Tom's experience altered his values.

22. Writers create suspense by allowing questions to form in readers' minds. Explain in an essay how the author, Jack Finney, begins to create suspense immediately in the first paragraph. What questions form in your mind? Then discuss how Finney maintains suspense throughout the story. Use specific details from the story to support your ideas.

23. Tom's frightful experience on the ledge forces him to examine his values. Although most people will never be in a life or death situation on an eleventh-story ledge, there are events in people's lives that cause them to change their values. How does that happen? In an essay, explain processes by which people examine—and sometimes adjust—their values.

"View From the Summit" by Edmund Hillary
"The Dream Comes True" from *The Tiger of the Snows* by Tenzing Norgay

Selection Test

Critical Reading

In the blank, write the letter of the one best answer.

_____ 1. In "View From the Summit," Hillary describes walking on breakable crust as "one of the most unpleasant mountaineering conditions." Why would it be especially difficult to walk in these conditions?
   a. When the surface shatters, climbers stagger forward.
   b. There is a greater chance of avalanche.
   c. There is no secure place to establish a belay.
   d. The crusty snow is extremely slippery.

_____ 2. In "View From the Summit," when Hillary notices that Norgay is moving slowly and seems in distress, what does he do?
   a. Hillary examines Norgay's oxygen equipment.
   b. Hillary has Norgay take the lead so he can keep an eye on him.
   c. Hillary loosens the belay so that Norgay can move more easily.
   d. Hillary takes the lead so Norgay can follow in his tracks.

_____ 3. What does Hillary imply in "View From the Summit" when, recalling his reaction to reaching the summit, he says, "In typical Anglo-Saxon fashion, I stretched out my arm for a handshake, but this was not enough for Tenzing who threw his arms around my shoulders . . ."?
   a. Hillary implies that Norgay was insulted by his handshake.
   b. Hillary implies that Norgay overreacted when he reached the summit.
   c. Hillary implies Anglo Saxons tend to be reserved.
   d. Hillary implies that he was put off by Norgay's exuberance.

_____ 4. Which of the following statements made by Hillary about Norgay is a fact?
   a. Norgay surged on "with impressive strength" through the snow.
   b. Norgay was "moving rather slowly" and "in some distress" when his oxygen mask froze up.
   c. Norgay plowed a knee-deep path "to the top of the bulge at 28,000 feet."
   d. Norgay "made his way laboriously" between the ice cornice and the rock.

_____ 5. Choose the statement that best captures the author's perspective of the following passage from "View From the Summit."
   Although it would be relatively useless, I got Tenzing to establish a belay; then I eased my way into the crack, facing the rock. I jammed my crampons into the ice behind me and then wriggled my way upward using every little handhold I could find. Puffing for breath, I made steady height—the ice was holding—and forty feet up I pulled myself out of the crack onto the top of the rock face . . . I waved to Tenzing and brought in the rope as he, too, made his way laboriously up the crack and dragged himself out beside me, panting for breath.
   a. Both men managed a difficult climb, but Hillary was in charge, leading the way.
   b. Hillary always went first.
   c. Norgay's arms were weak; he needed the support of the rope to make it up.
   d. Hillary went up first to make sure the route was safe, then pulled Norgay up.

_____ 6. What aspects of the climb does Hillary emphasize in "View From the Summit"?
  I. the amount of oxygen it takes to complete a climb
  II. how difficult their descent will be
  III. the views during the climb and from the mountain top
  IV. the conditions of the snow and rock
  a. I and II   b. II and III   c II and IV   d. III and IV

_____ 7. In "The Dream Comes True," what is Norgay's comment about the trouble with the oxygen masks freezing up?
  a. It happened just once.
  b. It happened to both men periodically throughout the climb.
  c. It happened only to Norgay, not to Hillary.
  d. Hillary was the only one who could fix the problem when it occurred.

_____ 8. In his book, Norgay addresses the issue of who got to the summit first because
  a. he respects Hillary and wants him to get the credit.
  b. he doesn't want the issue to get in the way of the accomplishment.
  c. it was always his dream to climb Mt. Everest.
  d. everyone has been asking questions.

_____ 9. In "View From the Summit" and "The Dream Comes True," Hillary's and Norgay's equipment included
  I. an extra pair of boots   III. an ice ax
  II. rope   IV. a portable kerosene heater
  a. I and II   b. I and III   c. II and III   d. III and IV

_____ 10. What is Norgay's perspective in this passage from "The Dream Comes True"?
  In my opinion our difficulties were the same—and luckily never too great—and we each helped and were helped by the other in equal measure.
  a. The men were unfair to each other.
  b. The men were equal partners.
  c. One climber would have been in real trouble without the other.
  d. The men had no great difficulties and therefore got along well with each other.

_____ 11. In "The Dream Comes True," what is the attitude of Norgay toward Hillary?
  a. He considers Hillary a snob who robbed him of his rightful fame.
  b. He has only words of praise for Hillary.
  c. He respects Hillary but questions the accuracy or fairness of Hillary's book.
  d. He resents being represented as an assistant on the climb.

_____ 12. Norgay's account might be considered the more accurate because
  a. he doesn't use fancy words like "undulations"; he just describes what he sees.
  b. he doesn't confuse the reader with technical descriptions of the oxygen bottles.
  c. he claims much of the responsibility for the success of the climb.
  d. he gives equal credit to himself and Hillary for making the climb together.

_____ 13. Choose the statement that is a fact.
  a. One of the last challenges before reaching the summit was a great rock step.
  b. Norgay was not a very good step cutter.
  c. To reach the summit, Hillary would not have stopped for any reason.
  d. Norgay was just a guide and deserves little credit for the success of the climb.

_____ 14. Why is it important to determine the author's perspective?
  a. to know the author's purpose for writing
  b. to know whether the author is for or against the main topic
  c. to know whether the work is written in first or third person
  d. to be aware of possible slants or biases in the work

____ 15. Which of the following statements is an opinion?
   a. A 400-foot-long snow slope rose steeply up toward the South Summit.
   b. We were wearing every piece of clothing we possessed.
   c. I wiped the snow off the dials and saw that the bottles were less than a third full of oxygen.
   d. Out came all our delicacies, with the tinned apricots being a special treat.

Vocabulary and Grammar

____ 16. In which sentence does the noun function as a predicate nominative?
   a. Norgay cooked chicken noodle soup for dinner.
   b. Hillary squeezed Norgay's mask to dislodge the ice.
   c. Norgay established a belay for Hillary.
   d. Hillary was the first person to reach the summit.

____ 17. In "View From the Summit," Hillary describes a route to the summit of Makalu as "feasible" because it
   a. appears to be extremely dangerous.   c. looks possible.
   b. disappears suddenly.   d. seems questionable.

____ 18. In "View From the Summit," Hillary refers to the last thousand feet of a ridge attempted by earlier British expeditions as a formidable barrier. This suggests that the ridge _____.
   a. was steep   b. inspired fear   c. angled sharply   d. was icy

____ 19. Chose the sentence in which the noun functions are correctly labeled.
            S   S   DO   DO   OP
   a. Hillary and Norgay ate warm soup and tinned apricots in their tent.

            S   PN   DO   DO   DO
   b. Hillary and Norgay ate warm soup and tinned apricots in their tent.

       S   S   OP   OP   DO
   c. Hillary and Norgay ate warm soup and tinned apricots in their tent.

     PN   PN   DO   DO   OP
   d. Hillary and Norgay ate warm soup and tinned apricots in their tent.

____ 20. The word *aperture* means _____.
   a. photograph   b. light   c. shutter speed   d. opening

Essay Questions

21. Reread the passages in "View From the Summit" and "The Dream Comes True" in which Hillary and Norgay describe their thoughts upon reaching the summit of Mt. Everest. What does each man describe? What do the descriptions reveal about each man? In an essay, compare and contrast the two men's views. Then, draw conclusions about the characters of the men based on their descriptions.

22. In his account, Hillary uses terms such as "standard aperture" and "laboriously," whereas Norgay writes in simpler sentences with fewer technical words. Which account did you find more engaging? How did the language contribute to your impression? Answer these questions in an essay, using details from the selections to support your points.

23. In an essay, examine Hillary's account, specifically his representation of and attitude toward Norgay. Is Norgay justified in feeling that Hillary is unfair to him in his account? Use details from both selections to support your argument.

Name _____ Date _____

"The Monkey's Paw" by W.W. Jacobs
"The Bridegroom" by Alexander Pushkin

Selection Test

Critical Reading

In the blank, write the letter of the one best answer.

_____ 1. What is "The Monkey's Paw" about?
    a. a retired sergeant major who brings a magical monkey's paw from India
    b. an unsuspecting son who dies as a result of his mother's greed
    c. a monkey's paw that grants three wishes to three different people
    d. a magical but evil monkey's paw that ruins the quiet life of a family

_____ 2. Which of the following phrases from "The Monkey's Paw" best describes the Whites' lives before the first wish is granted?
    a. "wild scenes and doughty deeds"
    b. "an air of prosaic wholesomeness"
    c. "steeped in shadow and silence"
    d. "the hopeless resignation of the old"

_____ 3. In "The Monkey's Paw," which of the following lines spoken by Mr. White hints that the wishes can only change his life for the worse?
    a. "And what is there special about it?"
    b. "It seems to me I've got all I want."
    c. ". . . there's no harm done, but it gave me a shock all the same."
    d. ". . . the things happened so naturally. . . ."

_____ 4. Which of the following lines from "The Monkey's Paw" is an example of foreshadowing?
    a. "When he went away he was a slip of a youth in the warehouse."
    b. "I should like to see those old temples and fakirs and jugglers. . . ."
    c. "[The monkey's paw] has caused enough mischief already."
    d. "Did you give him anything for it, Father?"

_____ 5. Which of the following lines from "The Monkey's Paw" foreshadows what happens to Herbert?
    a. ". . . I don't see the money . . . and I bet I never shall."
    b. "Why, we're going to be rich, and famous and happy."
    c. "If you only cleared the house, you'd be quite happy. . . ."
    d. "I expect you'll find the cash tied up in a big bag. . . ."

_____ 6. In "The Monkey's Paw," when a stranger comes to the Whites' door, Mrs. White thinks at first he has come to
    a. announce Herbert's death.
    b. give Mr. White 200 pounds.
    c. ask them for the monkey's paw.
    d. present a bill from the tailor.

_____ 7. In "The Monkey's Paw," Herbert is ". . . caught in the machinery. . . ." In this context, machinery may also indicate the effects of _____.
    a. destiny
    b. carelessness
    c. everyday life
    d. industrialization

_____ 8. In "The Monkey's Paw," when Maw and Meggins offers Mr. White compensation, he faints because he
   a. is overcome with grief by Herbert's death.
   b. knows he should have wished for something else.
   c. realizes he sold his son for 200 pounds.
   d. cannot bear the anguished cries of his wife.

_____ 9. In "The Monkey's Paw," why is Mr. White afraid to wish a second time?
   a. He does not believe the paw can grant wishes.
   b. He is so grief stricken that he forgets the paw.
   c. He has become apathetic since Herbert's death.
   d. He realizes his wishes can have only bad consequences.

_____ 10. At the end of "The Monkey's Paw," what does Mrs. White realize just after she opens the front door?
   a. Her husband has made the third wish.
   b. The monkey's paw killed her son.
   c. She no longer wants her son to return.
   d. The knocking sound is not Herbert.

_____ 11. A central idea of "The Bridegroom" is that
   a. parents often fail to understand their children.
   b. matchmakers do not know what real love is.
   c. dreams sometimes reveal what the future holds.
   d. charming exteriors can hide awful truths.

_____ 12. Why does Natasha fear the bridegroom?
   a. He plans to punish her for spying on him.
   b. He is a wealthy lord who bows to no one.
   c. She saw what he did to the other woman.
   d. He threatened her when she was in the hut.

_____ 13. In "The Bridegroom," what is the most likely reason that Natasha chooses at the wedding feast to tell her story as if she dreamt it?
   a. to avoid revealing that she had been in the hut
   b. to make her fears seem real until she can prove them
   c. to make the guests believe that she is a prophetess
   d. to warn the bridegroom that she knows his true intentions

_____ 14. In "The Bridegroom," Pushkin draws upon themes from
   a. supernatural events.   c. social reform.
   b. folklore.   d. upper-class customs.

_____ 15. Which of the following details in "The Bridegroom" foreshadows the groom's fate?
   a. Natasha's disappearance
   b. Natasha's first reaction to the handsome young man
   c. the matchmaker's unexpected visit
   d. Natasha's request to invite the law

Vocabulary and Grammar

_____ 16. Which of the following sentences contains a pronoun that does not agree with its antecedent?
   a. Mr. White tried, unsuccessfully, to distract his son during a chess game.
   b. The visitor brought bad news to the Whites; he told him that their son was dead.
   c. Mr. White could not have known the results of his first wish.
   d. Sergeant Morris took the monkey paw and threw it upon the fire.

____ 17. Which of the following words or phrases is closest in meaning to the word *maligned*?
   a. praised
   b. lingered
   c. flattered
   d. slandered

____ 18. Which of the following words is most nearly opposite in meaning to the word *tumult*?
   a. order
   b. commotion
   c. chaos
   d. tremor

____ 19. Though upset by _____ betrothal to the groom, Natasha devised a plan that would bring the young man to justice.
   a. his   c. her
   b. its   d. their

____ 20. What is the antecedent of the word *them* in the following sentence?
After she calmed down, Natasha asked her parents to prepare a feast for the guests and told them to invite the law.

   a. Natasha   c. guests
   b. parents   d. law

Essay Questions

21. In "The Monkey's Paw," many hints foreshadow future events. In an essay, identify two examples of foreshadowing from the selection, and explain in detail the specific future events they suggest.

22. What might have happened to Natasha had she married the handsome bridegroom? In an essay, explain your prediction and identify evidence in Pushkin's ballad that helped you to make it.

23. "The Monkey's Paw" comes to a disturbing end. What does the father understand that the mother does not? How would the ending be different had Mrs. White opened the door before Mr. White made his third wish? Why were you surprised or not surprised by the story's conclusion? Answer these questions in an essay, and support your main points with details from the story.

Monkey's Paw/Bridegroom

Name _____   Date _____

from "A Walk to the Jetty" from *Annie John* by Jamaica Kincaid

Selection Test

Critical Reading

In the blank, write the letter of the one best answer.

_____   1. Because Kincaid's novel is set in the Caribbean and the narrator leaves home at an
early age, you can infer that this story is _____.
a. autobiographical
b. fictional
c. a parody
d. symbolic

_____   2. What does the following passage reveal about Annie's mother?
"... she ... said that I was wonderful and good and that there would never be
anybody better. If I had just conquered Persia, she couldn't have been more proud
of me."
a. She has too much pride in her daughter.
b. She stifles her daughter's creativity.
c. She dearly loves her daughter.
d. She wants her daughter to have a better life.

_____   3. How has Annie's relationship with her mother changed since her childhood?
a. Annie's reliance on her mother is undiminished.
b. Annie senses an increasing need to be independent of her mother.
c. Annie's mother is less interested in her daughter.
d. Annie's mother wants her daughter to leave home.

_____   4. How is Annie's father different from her mother?
a. He is more talkative and demonstrative.
b. He is quieter and less demonstrative.
c. He loves Annie more than her mother does.
d. He is much older than his wife.

_____   5. What literary technique does Kincaid use in the following passage?
"I was five years old when I first walked on this road unaccompanied by someone
to hold my hand. My mother had placed three pennies in my little basket, and sent
me to the chemist's shop to buy a pennyworth of senna leaves ...."
a. symbolism
b. alliteration
c. simile
d. flashback

_____   6. What memory returns to Annie as she passes by Miss Dulcie's house?
a. her happy apprenticeship with Miss Dulcie
b. her experience learning how to sew
c. her apprenticeship with the difficult seamstress
d. her close relationship with Miss Dulcie

____ 7. What do references to the store that sold grooming aids imported from England and to the discussions about cricket imply?

    a. At the time of this story, the island was a British dependency.

    b. British products and sports were preferred because of their higher quality.

    c. Kincaid's family was originally from England.

    d. Annie John mentioned British products because she wanted to move to England.

____ 8. Which of the following sights prompts Annie to remember her mother reading the biography of Louis Pasteur?

    a. Miss Dulcie's house

    b. the doctor's office

    c. the chemist's shop

    d. the library

____ 9. What can you infer about Annie's father from the following passage?

> "My father kissed me goodbye and told me to be good and to write home often. After he said this, he looked at me, then looked at the floor and swung his left foot, then looked at me again."

    a. He is not very close to his daughter.

    b. He easily expresses his feelings.

    c. He is anxious for his daughter to leave.

    d. He is uncomfortable expressing his feelings.

____ 10. What does the road to the jetty symbolize?

    a. Antiguan customs

    b. Annie's relationship with her parents

    c. Annie's aspirations

    d. Annie's life

____ 11. What can you infer about Annie's relationship with her mother based on the following passage?

> "She then tightened her arms around me and held me to her close, so that I felt that I couldn't breathe. With that, my tears dried up and I was suddenly on my guard."

    a. Annie's growth and creativity are stifled by her mother's great love.

    b. Annie and her mother are very close.

    c. Annie will miss her mother terribly.

    d. They share an open and demonstrative relationship.

____ 12. Why do you think Kincaid wrote *Annie John*?

    a. to make fun of Miss Dulcie

    b. to record her feelings about coming of age and leaving home

    c. to criticize her mother for trying to stifle her creativity

    d. to describe the beauty of her homeland

Vocabulary and Grammar

____ 13. Which of the following pronouns is an example of the objective case?

    a. they

    b. their

    c. them

    d. theirs

____ 14. Which of the following sentences contains a pronoun that uses the possessive case?

    a. The large porcelain dog had a red satin ribbon wrapped around its neck.

    b. It's going to take approximately half an hour to walk to the jetty.

    c. Annie thinks they're probably a strange sight.

    d. The launch will take her out to sea, where she will then board the ship.

_____ 15. Which of the following sentences contains a pronoun in the nominative case?
  a. Annie boarded the ship and then said good-bye to her parents.
  b. She knew that she would never see them again.
  c. The ship carried her away; before long, her mother was just a dot in the launch.
  d. Despite a strong attachment to her mother, Annie longed for independence.

_____ 16. Annie complained that her mother's voice _____ across her skin.
  a. loomed
  b. tickled
  c. raked
  d. flowed

_____ 17. The word *apprenticed* means
  a. appeared in a large or threatening form.
  b. worked a specific length of time in a craft or trade in return for instruction and support.
  c. formed an alliance with.
  d. appreciated another's effort toward a common cause.

Essay Questions

18. In reference to her apprenticeship experience, Annie says, ". . . I placed on the dustheap of my life Miss Dulcie and everything that I had had to do with her." In an essay, explain what Annie means by "dustheap of my life" and what details of her apprenticeship support that meaning.

19. Many of the flashbacks in the story make you aware of Annie's readiness to leave home. In an essay, explain the experiences that Annie had in growing up that prepared her the most for leaving home. Support your answer with details from the story.

20. Consider the many flashbacks and details given about Annie's experiences growing up and her feelings about those experiences. In an essay, explain what inferences can be made about Annie's decision to leave Antigua based upon her childhood experiences.

"The Masque of the Red Death" by Edgar Allan Poe

Selection Test

Critical Reading

In the blank, write the letter of the one best answer.

____ 1. In "The Masque of the Red Death," whom does Prince Prospero invite to his abbey?
    a. the plague victims of his land
    b. a thousand healthy friends
    c. a mysterious, masked guest
    d. talented musicians

____ 2. In "The Masque of the Red Death," the location of the black chamber at the western end of the suite
    a. suggests a mood of exploration and excitement.
    b. minimizes the presence of natural light.
    c. indicates a fascination with the bizarre.
    d. suggests the end of daylight and life.

____ 3. Which phrase best expresses the mental state of the masquers before the apparition of the Red Death?
    a. "happy and dauntless and sagacious"
    b. "gasped in unutterable horror"
    c. "in them beat feverishly the heart of life"
    d. "a gay and magnificent revel"

____ 4. Which of the following best expresses the theme, or main idea, of "The Masque of the Red Death"?
    a. God punished sinners through the plague.
    b. Death should be faced with courage.
    c. Wealth offers no refuge from death.
    d. Human beings are essentially selfish.

____ 5. In the following passage from "The Masque of the Red Death," which words or phrases are context clues that can help you figure out the meaning of *casements*?
    A tall and narrow Gothic window looked out upon a closed corridor which pursued the windings of the suite. These windows are of stained glass whose color varied in accordance with the prevailing hue of the decorations of the chamber into which it opened. . . . The third was green throughout, and so were the casements.
    a. "windows are of stained glass whose color varied in accordance with the prevailing hue"
    b. "tall and narrow"
    c. "a closed corridor which pursued the windings of the suite"
    d. "the third was green"

____ 6. Which of the following details in "The Masque of the Red Death" suggests that the revelers will not live long?
    a. the white room
    b. the locked gates
    c. the prince's dagger
    d. the ebony clock

_____ 7. The dream–like costumes of the revelers in "The Masque of the Red Death" symbolize
   a. repressed fears and desires.
   b. extreme tension and anxiety.
   c. youthful health and beauty.
   d. carefree glamour and luxury.

_____ 8. In the following passage from "The Masque of the Red Death," what is the most likely
   meaning of *voluptuous*?

   > It was a voluptuous scene, that masquerade. But first let me tell of the rooms in
   > which it was held. There were seven—an imperial suite.

   a. terrifying
   b. ordinary
   c. unusual
   d. luxurious

_____ 9. Which sentence or phrase does NOT contain context clues that *spectral* means
   "ghostly"?
   a. "The mask which concealed the visage was made so nearly to resemble the countenance of a stiffened corpse . . ."
   b. "The figure was tall and gaunt, and shrouded from head to foot in the habiliments of the grave."
   c. "[Prince Prospero's] brow reddened with rage."
   d. "In an assembly of phantasms such as I have painted"

_____ 10. In "The Masque of the Red Death," Prince Prospero objects to the masked stranger
   because he
   a. arrives uninvited.
   b. is costumed as a victim of the Red Death.
   c. interrupts the musicians.
   d. refuses to dance.

_____ 11. In "The Masque of the Red Death," what is foreshadowed when Prospero's "brow reddened with rage" at the sight of the intruder?
   a. the destructive power of anger
   b. the red light from the window
   c. the coming dawn in the east
   d. his death from the Red Death

_____ 12. In "The Masque of the Red Death," how does Prince Prospero die?
   a. He is stabbed with a dagger.
   b. He is stricken by the plague.
   c. He is injured in a fall.
   d. He is hanged from the battlements.

Vocabulary and Grammar

_____ 13. Prospero's guests were deprived of nothing. They never experienced the quality
   of _____.
   a. deprived
   b. depriving
   c. deprivation
   d. deprive

_____ 14. Among the revelers, there _____ a feverish _____.
   a. was; air
   b. were; air
   c. was; airs
   d. were; airs

_____ 15. During the _____ ball, the masqueraders danced _____.
   a. lively, gaily
   b. gaily, lively
   c. live, gay
   d. gaily, live

_____ 16. Which sentence contains both an adjective and an adverb?
   a. Courtiers firmly sealed the gates leading into the abbey.
   b. During the fifth or sixth month, the prince hosted a masked ball.
   c. Vivid colors filled every room except the seventh, which was ghastly.
   d. The seventh room was closely shrouded in black velvet tapestries.

_____ 17. Which of the following sentences demonstrates an appropriate usage of *piquancy*?
   a. The man's blood-speckled forehead revealed his piquancy.
   b. The unusual lighting added piquancy to the scene.
   c. The revelers gasped with piquancy at the sight of the masked stranger.
   d. The prince expressed his piquancy by chasing the offender through the suites.

Essay Questions

18. The setting and descriptive details of "The Masque of the Red Death" contain many symbols. Choose at least three symbols from the story, and in an essay, describe what each symbol stands for. In your discussion explain how the symbols give meaning to the story.

19. Is Prospero's attempt to escape death an act of unforgivable arrogance, or is it a normal human response to the inevitable? Consider the details given about Prospero's personality and behavior. In an essay, support your opinion with examples from the story or from your own experience.

20. Poe stresses Prince Prospero's unusual and elaborate tastes. In an essay, explain what significance these details lend to the story's mood and theme.

"Fear" by Gabriela Mistral
"The street" by Octavio Paz
"Spring and All" by William Carlos Williams

Selection Test

Critical Reading

In the blank, write the letter of the one best answer.

_____ 1. In "Fear," the speaker fears the loss of her
    a. child's life.
    b. child's happiness.
    c. closeness with her child.
    d. independence from her child.

_____ 2. In "Fear," the images of what the speaker longs for with her child are primarily related to the sense of _____.
    a. sight
    b. hearing
    c. smell
    d. touch

_____ 3. Which of the following words describes the tone of "Fear"?
    a. humble
    b. ironic
    c. anguished
    d. fierce

_____ 4. In "Fear," the image of the child in "tiny golden slippers" appeals primarily to the sense of _____.
    a. touch
    b. irony
    c. sight
    d. humor

_____ 5. The speaker in "Fear" doesn't want her daughter to grow up to be a queen because
    a. of the pressures rulers face.
    b. she is of humble origin.
    c. she fears the queen would be harmed.
    d. she could no longer see her daughter easily.

_____ 6. In "The street," the line "Everything dark and doorless" suggests that
    a. there are numerous people pursuing the speaker.
    b. there is nobody who can help the speaker.
    c. the speaker is describing things accurately.
    d. the speaker is running through the countryside.

_____ 7. What is the theme of Octavio Paz's "The street"?
    a. the terror of not knowing who or where you are
    b. the relief of turning from the hunted to the hunter
    c. the experience of directly confronting your worst fear
    d. the sadness of realizing you are a failure in life

____ 8. In which line from "The street" does the rhythm best convey a state of frenzied panic?
   a. "A long and silent street . . ."
   b. ". . . stepping on silent stones and dry leaves."
   c. ". . . if I run, he runs. I turn: nobody."
   d. ". . . where I pursue a man who stumbles . . ."

____ 9. What feeling do you get when the man the speaker pursues says "nobody" in the final line of "The street"?
   a. peaceful
   b. eerie
   c. humorous
   d. melancholy

____ 10. The dominant imagery of "Spring and All" is _____.
   a. pessimistic
   b. visual
   c. darkness
   d. bright and sunny

____ 11. The theme of "Spring and All" is
   a. the struggle of living things against disease.
   b. the hardiness of life in the bleakness of nature.
   c. the shock of explosive growth.
   d. the contrast between human life and plant development.

Vocabulary and Grammar

____ 12. Identify the coordinate adjectives in the following sentence.
   Along the road to the contagious hospital, we saw broad muddy fields, tall evergreen trees, dry autumn leaves, and patches of standing gray water.
   a. standing, gray
   b. tall, evergreen
   c. broad, muddy
   d. dry, autumn

____ 13. In which phrase is the comma unnecessary?
   a. dark, doorless road
   b. dry, prickly grass
   c. long, silent street
   d. bare, winter trees

____ 14. Something that is *contagious* is _____ .
   a. deadly
   b. spread by direct or indirect contact
   c. bound by a legal document
   d. the opposite of something else

____ 15. If your bedroom were *stark*, it would be _____ .
   a. cluttered
   b. dirty
   c. dimly lit
   d. bare

Essay Questions

16. In "Fear," the speaker uses adjectives sparingly, whereas the speaker in "Spring and All" makes frequent use of sensory adjectives, including many coordinate adjectives. Based on your understanding of the themes of each poem, write an essay comparing and contrasting the use of adjectives in each poem and explain how each style of writing is appropriate to the poem's theme.

17. Most of "Spring and All" focuses on the natural world as it prepares for spring. Yet Williams begins the poem on "the road to the contagious hospital." This clear image of human life does not occur again in the poem. In an essay, explain why you think Williams began the poem with this clear reference to human beings. Give examples from the rest of the poem that support your ideas.

18. The imagery, events, and ending of "The street" suggest an unrealistic world, a world of the speaker's imagination, taking place only in his mind. It seems unlikely that the pursuer in the poem is a real person. In an essay, discuss who or what is pursuing the speaker. Provide a reasonable explanation based on the imagined events depicted in the poem.

"Two Friends" by Guy de Maupassant
"Damon and Pythias" retold by William F. Russell

Selection Test

Critical Reading

In the blank, write the letter of the one best answer.

_____ 1. In "Two Friends," the author treats M. Morissot and M. Sauvage as
     a. gloriously heroic.
     b. quietly admirable.
     c. foolishly reckless.
     d. tragically comic.

_____ 2. Which of the following is a central theme in "Two Friends"?
     a. Even in wartime, people need a means of escape and diversion.
     b. Citizens defending their country must make heroic sacrifices.
     c. Political conflict can strain even the best of friendships.
     d. War does senseless damage to ordinary and innocent lives.

_____ 3. In "Two Friends," the image created by the phrase "a little blood remained on the surface" is most directly foreshadowed by which of the following lines from the story?
     a. "Paris was blockaded, starved, in its death agony."
     b. ". . . the sky . . . made the whole river crimson . . ."
     c. ". . . line in hand and feet dangling in the current."
     d. ". . . the two fish lines dropped from their hands . . ."

_____ 4. In "Two Friends," the author portrays the German officer as
     a. righteous and noble.
     b. patient and indulgent.
     c. sarcastic and callous.
     d. just and reasonable.

_____ 5. In "Two Friends," how does de Maupassant ensure that the reader understands his true feelings toward the Prussian officer?
     a. by portraying him as a rude and illiterate foreigner
     b. by describing him at first as a "kind of hairy giant"
     c. by having him use loud commands and coarse language
     d. by showing him ordering dinner and lighting his pipe

_____ 6. A significant detail about the friendship of Damon and Pythias is
     a. Pythias's neglect of his business affairs.
     b. Damon's dishonesty.
     c. the punishment Pythias receives from Dionysius.
     d. Damon's willingness to go to prison for Pythias.

_____ 7. Which of the following lines is taken from the climax of "Damon and Pythias"?
   a. "Damon and Pythias were two noble young men who lived on the island of Sicily in a city called Syracuse."
   b. "Presently the excitement grew more intense still as a swift runner could be seen approaching the palace courtyard . . ."
   c. "Now it happened that Syracuse was, at that time, ruled by a famous tyrant named Dionysius . . ."
   d. "They were such close companions and were so devoted to each other that all the people of the city admired them . . ."

_____ 8. What feeling(s) does Dionysius have toward the friendship of Damon and Pythias?
   a. envy and admiration
   b. disgust and anger
   c. indifference
   d. sympathy

_____ 9. At the climax of "Damon and Pythias,"
   a. readers are introduced to Dionysius.
   b. Damon is brought to prison.
   c. readers are told of the honesty of Damon and Pythias.
   d. Pythias rushes though the crowd sobbing with relief.

_____ 10. The climax of "Damon and Pythias" is different from the climax of "Two Friends" in that it
   a. is sad.
   b. stops abruptly.
   c. builds more slowly and is expected.
   d. is filled with violence.

_____ 11. Which of the following words best describes the mythical characters Damon and Pythias, as well as Morissot and Sauvage from "Two Friends"?
   a. selfish
   b. loyal
   c. cruel
   d. forgetful

Vocabulary and Grammar

_____ 12. In "Damon and Pythias," Pythias tried to return quickly, but various _____ stood in his way.
   a. hindrances
   b. annals
   c. amusements
   d. relatives

_____ 13. Which sentence uses the comparative form of an adjective?
   a. He could run faster than any other young man in Syracuse.
   b. Pythias was the swiftest runner the crowd had ever seen.
   c. There was no truer friendship than that of Damon and Pythias.
   d. His devotion touched the heart of the city's cruelest tyrant.

_____ 14. Damon agreed to help Pythias because his friend was in _____ need.
   a. ardent
   b. dire
   c. vernal
   d. quiet

____ 15. Which sentence uses the superlative form of an adverb?
   a. Of all Pythias's friends, Damon was the most loyal.
   b. Pythias had been unjustly accused of treason by Dionysius.
   c. He could think of no one more dependable than Damon to help him.
   d. Damon came more willingly than a lesser friend would have.

Essay Questions

16. In an essay, discuss the character of Dionysius and the reasons why he released both Damon and Pythias at the end of the myth. What is the one thing that he seems to want that he has not been able to attain? What does the ending of the story show about the character of Dionysius?

17. In "Damon and Pythias," Pythias is sentenced to die, but he is given the chance to leave prison to settle outstanding business and family matters. His friend Damon must wait in his place and agree to face execution if Pythias does not return on time. In an essay, answer the following questions: Why does Damon agree to such an arrangement, even though he is putting his own life in jeopardy? Why does Pythias return to the prison, even though his punishment is unfair, when he has the chance to escape and save his own life? What do these actions say about the characters of Damon and Pythias and the quality of their friendship?

18. Write an essay in which you describe the compelling circumstances featured in the story "Two Friends." What are some of the most significant background details of war? In what ways do these details hint at the story's outcome?

Unit Test: On the Edge

Critical Reading

In the blank, write the letter of the one best answer.

The questions below are based on the following selection.

In the following excerpt from Mark Twain's The Adventures of Tom Sawyer, *Tom Sawyer and Becky Thatcher find themselves on an adventure in a dark cave.*

They started through a corridor, and traversed it in silence a long way, glancing at each new opening, to see if there was anything familiar about the look of it; but they were all strange. Every time Tom made an examination, Becky would watch his face for an encouraging sign, and he would say cheerily:

"Oh, it's all right. This ain't the one, but we'll come to it right away!" But he felt less and less hopeful with each failure, and presently began to turn off into diverging avenues at sheer random, in the desperate hope of finding the one that was wanted. He still said it was "all right," but there was such a leaden dread at his heart, that the words had lost their ring, and sounded as if he had said, "All is lost!" . . . .

Tom shouted. The call went echoing down the empty aisles, and died out in the distance in a faint sound that resembled a ripple of mocking laughter . . . The children stood still and listened; but there was no result.

____ 1. What are Tom and Becky doing in the cave?
   a. They are fighting.
   b. They are running away from home.
   c. They are lost and trying to find their way out.
   d. They are searching for a lost friend.

____ 2. Why does Tom continue to tell Becky that everything is all right?
   a. so that she won't be afraid
   b. because he knows where he is going
   c. so that she won't leave without him
   d. because he has been in the cave many times before

____ 3. Which of the following lines from the excerpt best creates a feeling of suspense?
   a. They started through a corridor, and traversed it in silence a long way . . .
   b. Tom shouted.
   c. He still said it was "all right," but there was such a leaden dread at his heart, that the words had lost their ring, and sounded as if he had said, "All is lost!"
   d. Every time Tom made an examination, Becky would watch his face for an encouraging sign . . .

____ 4. Based on details in the excerpt, what mental image can you form of the cave?
   a. It is cold and damp.
   b. It is long and it trails off in many directions.
   c. It has a musty odor.
   d. It is narrow.

____ 5. Based on the excerpt, what can you infer about Tom's feelings for Becky?
   a. He is annoyed with her.
   b. He looks to her for encouragement.
   c. He is protective of her.
   d. He is afraid of her.

_____ 6. Which of the following phrases best emphasizes Tom's sense of frustration and defeat?
   a. The call went echoing down the empty aisles . . .
   b. . . . Becky would watch his face for an encouraging sign
   c. They started through a corridor . . .
   d. The call . . . died out . . . in a faint sound that resembled a ripple of mocking laughter.

_____ 7. Using context clues found in the excerpt, how would you define "diverging avenues"?
   a. branching paths
   b. dead-end paths
   c. familiar paths
   d. open areas

_____ 8. Which of the following images shows the length and depth of the caves by appealing to a reader's sense of hearing?
   a. They started through a corridor, and traversed it in silence a long way, glancing at each new opening, to see if there was anything familiar about the look of it; . . .
   b. But he felt less and less hopeful with each failure, and presently began to turn off into diverging avenues at sheer random . . .
   c. Every time Tom made an examination, Becky would watch his face for an encouraging sign . . .
   d. The call went echoing down the empty aisles, and died out in the distance in a faint sound that resembled a ripple of mocking laughter . . .

_____ 9. As the children wander through the cave, what is Tom's reason for shouting?
   a. to show that he is not afraid
   b. to listen to the echo of his voice
   c. to get someone's attention, so that they might be saved
   d. to express his anger with Becky

_____ 10. Which of the following words best describes how the children feel?
   a. frightened
   b. bored
   c. angry
   d. lonely

Vocabulary and Grammar

In the blank near the number, write the letter of the word that best completes each sentence.

_____ 11. He had a feeling that something bad was about to happen, and this sense of _____ kept him from answering the door.
   a. sadness
   b. foreboding
   c. excitement
   d. disapprobation

_____ 12. The _____ room, was _____ decorated.
   a. lavishly, stately
   b. colorful, vivid
   c. stately, lavishly
   d. colorfully, vividly

____ 13. Which pronoun cases are used in the following sentence?

The launch will take her out to sea; there she will board the ship.

    a. possessive and nominative
    b. objective and nominative
    c. nominative only
    d. possessive and objective

____ 14. Which sentence uses the comparative form of an adjective?
    a. Pythias had been unjustly accused of treason by Dionysius.
    b. There was no truer friendship than that of Damon and Pythias.
    c. Pythias was the swiftest runner the crowd had ever seen.
    d. His devotion touched the once bitter heart of Dionysius.

____ 15. In the word *interminable*, what is the meaning of the root *-term-*?
    a. slow
    b. think
    c. begin
    d. end

____ 16. Which of the choices is the best definition of the word *avaricious* as it is used in the following sentence?

We feared that wealth might turn him into an avaricious man.

    a. charitable
    b. greedy
    c. distant
    d. serious

The questions below consist of a related pair of words in CAPITAL LETTERS followed by four lettered pairs of words. Choose the pair that best expresses a relationship *similar* to that of the pair in capital letters.

____ 17. DEFTNESS : SKILLFULNESS ::
    a. bravery : courage
    b. icy : cold
    c. rapid : swiftness
    d. difficult : easy

____ 18. ARDENT : UNENTHUSIASTIC ::
    a. thrill : excitement
    b. orderly : organized
    c. busy : inactive
    d. boredom : eagerness

____ 19. Which of the following sentences contains a pronoun that uses the objective case?
    a. Annie was not interested in her father's talks with the night watchman.
    b. She had nothing to take her mind off her fear of slipping into the jetty.
    c. She would have liked them to talk about family life, or likes and dislikes.
    d. She had no choice but to ignore the men and let her thoughts roam.

_____ 20. Which of the following sentences contains a pronoun that uses the possessive case?
a. Miss Dulcie was a seamstress, and what a scornful woman was she!
b. She had me sweep the floor, which was always full of threads and pins and needles, and it was never clean enough for her.
c. She would send me to the store to buy her some buttons or thread.
d. When things went wrong, the fault was never hers.

Essay Questions

21. The selections in this unit present a variety of hair-raising scenarios. Choose the selection you find the most exciting, such as "Contents of the Dead Man's Pocket" or "The Masque of the Red Death." Write an essay in which you describe why the selection put you "on the edge of your seat." You might focus on the anxious thoughts of a character, the details of an unusual setting, or the images that helped you to appreciate the action of a particularly tense scene.

22. Choose a selection in the unit that features an intense moment of suspense, such as "Contents of the Dead Man's Pocket" or "The Masque of the Red Death." In an essay, describe the suspenseful moment and explain how the author creates tension in the scene.

23. Choose a selection in the unit that shows a character reassessing his or her life and values during or after a stressful situation, as happens in "View From the Summit" or in the excerpt from _A Walk to the Jetty._ In an essay, describe the character's experience and his or her thoughts during and after the experience.

24. From among the main characters presented in this unit, choose two characters from one selection that capture your interest the most. In an essay, cite the details in the selection that help you to make inferences about the characters. Explain how the characters' personality traits are revealed through their thoughts, actions, and interactions with others.

25. All of the selections in this unit explore the themes of danger and uncertainty. In an essay, compare and contrast two of the selections in the unit. How do both of these selections explore the idea of being "on the edge"? What similarities do the selections share? In what ways do they differ? Support your ideas with details from both selections.

Name_____ Date _____

from *In Commemoration: One Million Volumes* by Rudolfo A. Anaya

Selection Test

Critical Reading

In the blank, write the letter of the one best answer.

_____ 1. Who were the first *viejitos* in the author's life?
   a. the books he read
   b. the librarians he befriended
   c. the old people he knew
   d. the teachers he studied under

_____ 2. The author's first language was _____.
   a. English
   b. Navajo
   c. Spanish
   d. Creole

_____ 3. The first stories the author was exposed to were
   a. picture books.
   b. school story books.
   c. oral stories.
   d. math books.

_____ 4. The author's childhood library, the Santa Rosa library, was a
   a. fire station.
   b. dusty room.
   c. university building.
   d. schoolroom.

_____ 5. The author compares the pleasure of reading to the exhilaration of
   a. seeing a beautiful sunset.
   b. winning a contest.
   c. making money.
   d. being in love.

_____ 6. The author compares his first librarian, Miss Pansy, to a _____.
   a. pilot
   b. mother
   c. book character
   d. teacher

_____ 7. Which information is not given about the author's grandfather?
   a. He was a storyteller.
   b. He was wise.
   c. He studied at the university.
   d. He spoke many languages.

_____ 8. How did the author work his way through high school?
   a. He tutored students in writing.
   b. He worked as an assistant librarian.
   c. He wrote love poems.
   d. He wrote for a newspaper.

_____ 9. According to the author, one of the paradoxes of books is that
   a. you never learn from books as much as you knew when you were a child.
   b. there are more books than you could ever read in a lifetime.
   c. you can lose yourself in books without losing your identity.
   d. the more you read books, the more you want to learn.

_____ 10. This essay is mostly about
   a. how a library can affect people's lives.
   b. why the author writes books.
   c. how the author learned to love reading.
   d. why the author's favorite libraries were havens.

_____ 11. How would you summarize this passage from _In Commemoration: One Million Volumes?_
   In the summer evenings when I was a child, we, all the children of the neighborhood, sat outside under the stars and listened to the stories of the old ones, _los_
   viejitos. The stories of the old people taught us to wonder and imagine . . . I was
   fortunate to have had those old and wise _viejitos_ as guides into the world of nature
   and knowledge. They taught me with their stories; they taught me the magic of
   words. Now the words lie captured in ink, but the magic is still there, the power
   inherent in each volume.
   a. The stories told by _los viejitos_ inspired Anaya's love of words and books.
   b. Anaya listened to _los viejitos_ tell magical stories on summer evenings.
   c. _Los viejitos_ employed an oral tradition; now their stories are told in books.
   d. The stories _los viejitos_ told focused on nature and knowledge.

_____ 12. Which statement illustrates how important reading was to Anaya in his childhood?
   a. Can this library with its million volumes bestow that same inspiration?
   b. Words are a way, he said; they hold joy.
   c. Yes, I remember the _cuentos_ of my grandfather, the stories of the people.
   d. My tattered library card was my ticket into the same worlds my grandfather had
   known.

_____ 13. The most effective way to summarize a literary passage is to
   a. jot down the first sentence of every paragraph.
   b. use your own words to explain the main ideas.
   c. restate the first and last paragraphs in your own words.
   d. outline the specific details and examples presented.

_____ 14. How does summarizing a literary passage benefit the reader?
   a. It helps the reader create a detailed outline of the passage .
   b. It helps the reader clarify specific details within the passage.
   c. It helps the reader understand and remember the passage.
   d. It helps the reader interpret the significance of the passage.

_____ 15. Choose the statement that best captures Anaya's purpose for writing.
   a. He wrote to share his ideas about how children should be introduced to libraries.
   b. He wrote to share his ideas and to honor the existence of libraries.
   c. He wrote to inform his audience about the millionth volume.
   d. He wrote to inspire other Mexican Americans to strive for success.

Vocabulary and Grammar

_____ 16. When Anaya says that each volume has inherent power he means that
   a. he inherited the volumes from his grandfather.
   b. each book is capable of adding to a person's knowledge.
   c. the power of the words in the volumes comes from the authors' ancestors.
   d. each volume or book is naturally powerful or important.

____ 17. Anaya says that a library "liberates, informs, teaches, and enthralls." What does *enthralls* mean?
   a. keeps or retains
   b. captivates, fascinates
   c. educates
   d. trains

____ 18. In this passage, what does the word *labyrinth* mean?
   a. path
   b. map
   c. maze
   d. puzzle

____ 19. Which of the following sentences contains a linking verb?
   a. The stories of the old people taught us to wonder and imagine.
   b. Then he would whisper his favorite riddle.
   c. He could speak to the birds and the animals of the fields.
   d. It was only a dusty room in those days.

____ 20. Choose the item that correctly identifies the verbs in this sentence.
   > Anaya's boyhood sounds intriguing; it makes me want to learn more about his Mexican American heritage.

   a. *sounds*—linking verb; *makes*—linking verb
   b. *sounds*—action verb; *makes*—action verb
   c. *sounds*—linking verb; *makes*—action verb
   d. *sounds*—action verb; *makes*—linking verb

Essay Questions

21. Most of us think of the library as a place to research reports, as a warehouse for books, or maybe even a place to check out videos. In his essay "In Commemoration: One Million Volumes," Rudolfo Anaya articulates his personal vision of the library and what that has meant to him. How would you explain this essay to someone who has not read it? What is Anaya's vision of the library? In an essay, explain Anaya's perceptions as to the purposes of the library. Use examples from the selection to illustrate your points.

22. Anaya begins his essay with memories of his childhood and refers to "the old ones" in his native Spanish. Several times in the essay he uses the original Spanish term for something he's referring to, such as *adividanzas* for riddles and *oraciones en espanol* for the litany. How do these references contribute to "In Commemoration: One Million Volumes"? Write an essay in which you explain the effect of these ethnic references and reminiscences. Use examples from the essay to support your ideas.

23. With the advent of new technologies, the role of the library may change. CD-ROMs can hold entire encyclopedias, and there is almost no limit to the availability of information on line. Every book, newspaper, video, and almost all civic information can be obtained in one's home through the use of modern telecommunications devices. What do these changes mean to the library? Will libraries become extinct? Will they serve other purposes? Write an essay in which you assess the role of the library in the twenty-first century. Use principles from Anaya's essays as a guide for your discussion.

"How Much Land Does a Man Need?" by Leo Tolstoy

Selection Test

Critical Reading

In the blank, write the letter of the one best answer.

_____ 1. "How Much Land Does a Man Need?" is a parable because
   a. it is an uneventful story.
   b. it is a brief narrative that teaches a lesson.
   c. its language is complex and mysterious.
   d. there are few characters in the narrative.

_____ 2. "How Much Land Does a Man Need?" focuses on
   a. a land dispute between the peasants and landowners.
   b. Pahom's thirst for knowledge.
   c. the evil nature of the Devil.
   d. the problems of Pahom, a Russian peasant.

_____ 3. Pahom believes all his troubles would be solved if
   a. he had enough land.
   b. he had more money.
   c. he made a pact with the Devil.
   d. he and his wife moved to the steppe.

_____ 4. The parable "How Much Land Does a Man Need?" teaches the difference between
   a. acres and miles.
   b. urban and rural living.
   c. need and greed.
   d. wealth and poverty.

_____ 5. Which of the following quotations from the parable best predicts its lesson?
   a. "We may live roughly, but at least we're free from worry."
   b. ". . . though you often earn more than you need, you're very likely to lose all you have."
   c. "I can't go on overlooking it, or they'll destroy all I have. They must be taught a lesson."
   d. "Why should I suffer in this narrow hole, if one can live so well elsewhere?"

_____ 6. Which combination of Pahom's character traits hints at the outcome of Pahom's tussle with the Devil?
   a. laziness and greed
   b. greed and despair
   c. desire and envy
   d. boastfulness and greed

_____ 7. The Devil is happy to hear Pahom claim, "If I had plenty of land, I shouldn't fear the Devil himself!" because
   a. the boast reveals Pahom's fear of the Devil.
   b. the boast reveals to the Devil how he may put Pahom under his power.
   c. the boast reveals Pahom's foolish nature.
   d. the boast reveals Pahom's desire for rural living.

Unit 2: Striving for Success

_____ 8. Which quotation best predicts the effect of land ownership on Pahom?
   a. "Why should I suffer in this narrow hold, if one can live so well elsewhere?"
   b. "If you were honest folk yourselves you wouldn't let a thief go free."
   c. "The land is all being sold, and I'll get none of it."
   d. "Our only trouble is that we haven't land enough."

_____ 9. By describing how owning land affects Pahom, Tolstoy was probably hinting that he objected to private property because it led some people to
   a. become greedy and treat others badly.
   b. borrow money and make their children work.
   c. mistreat the land and leave it exhausted.
   d. labor too hard and damage their health.

_____ 10. What is the Bashkirs' attitude toward land ownership?
   a. They work hard to maintain their land.
   b. They take their fertile land for granted.
   c. They hope to sell their land as soon as possible.
   d. They do not worry about building wealth with land.

_____ 11. What was Tolstoy's purpose in using the Bashkirs in his story and in describing them as he does?
   a. He presented them as a symbol of a people under the influence of the Devil who was disguised as their chief.
   b. He used them as a bad example, because they did not farm the land and did not work in the summer.
   c. He held them up as an ideal, because they were carefree and did not worry about accumulating wealth.
   d. He presented them as model landowners because they had fertile soil and comfortable lives.

_____ 12. Tolstoy hints at the outcome of Pahom's agreement with the Bashkirs by having him
   a. walk in the direction of the rising sun.
   b. mark his way with holes in the ground.
   c. stop on the way for rest and refreshment.
   d. take the journey without his servant.

_____ 13. Which of the following details from Pahom's dream predicts what will happen?
   a. the appearance of the Devil with hoofs and horns
   b. the appearance of the peasant from the Volga
   c. the laughing Bashkir chief
   d. the sight of Pahom as a dead man

_____ 14. What is the outcome of the parable?
   a. Pahom and his wife live happily on a forty-acre farm.
   b. Pahom moves to the steppe.
   c. Pahom loses his life for just a little more land.
   d. Pahom tricks the Bashkirs into giving him more land.

_____ 15. Which Biblical verse would Tolstoy most likely have been alluding to when he devised the ending of his story?
   a. "Are there not twelve hours in a day? If any man walk in the day, he stumbleth not . . ."
   b. "Woe unto you, scribes and Pharisees, hypocrites! for ye are as graves which appear not . . ."
   c. "And he that reapeth receiveth wages, and gathereth fruit unto life eternal . . ."
   d. "And which of you with taking thought he can add to his stature one cubit?"

Vocabulary and Grammar

___ 16. Pahom's wife was _____ by her sister's boastful comments about the advantages of urban living.
   a. disparaged
   b. aggrieved
   c. piqued
   d. disappointed

___ 17. The word *forbore* means _____.
   a. refrained from
   b. ploughed, but not planted
   c. wronged
   d. offended

___ 18. The farmer had _____ wheat on his land the first year, so the following year it had to lie fallow.
   a. sow
   b. sown
   c. sewn
   d. sowed

___ 19. Before long Pahom _____ to search for even more land.
   a. begun
   b. began
   c. beginned
   d. beganned

___ 20. The word *sheaf* means a bundle of grain stalks. In a larger context, the word *sheaf* means
   a. a stack of paper.
   b. a gathered collection of things.
   c. strife or conflict.
   d. a plentiful harvest of grain.

Essay Questions

21. Pahom has certain character traits that help you predict the choices he will make and the outcome of the parable. What are his two strongest character traits? In an essay, fully describe Pahom's characteristics and explain how they help you predict how he will act in the story.

22. In an essay describe the lesson that Tolstoy's parable teaches. Explain the abstract ideas or moral qualities that are represented by the characters of Pahom and the Devil. Discuss the specific circumstances that motivate their actions.

23. In this parable, Tolstoy explores the question "How much land is enough land?" Given the lesson of the parable, what answer do you think Tolstoy would give to the question? Do you agree or disagree with Tolstoy's position on land ownership? Write an essay in which you support or refute Tolstoy's position. Use evidence from the parable to support your reply to Tolstoy's position on land ownership.

"Success is counted sweetest" and "I dwell in Possibility—" by Emily Dickinson
"Uncoiling" by Pat Mora
"Columbus Dying" by Vassar Miller

Selection Test

Critical Reading

In the blank, write the letter of the one best answer.

_____ 1. According to the speaker of "Success is counted sweetest," who most values success?
   a. soldiers
   b. unsuccessful people
   c. poets
   d. skilled fighters

_____ 2. What hardship afflicts Columbus's men in "Columbus Dying"?
   a. They must wear chains.
   b. They are lost at sea.
   c. They are starving and feverish.
   d. They have vertigo.

_____ 3. The speaker of "I dwell in Possibility—" describes the chambers "as the Cedars." Clues from the rest of the poem can help you infer that cedars are _____.
   a. massive
   b. unimpressive
   c. average
   d. as wide as the speaker's hands

_____ 4. An example of stated theme in poetry is
   a. "Success is counted sweetest."
   b. "I dwell in Possibility."
   c. "Columbus Dying."
   d. "Uncoiling."

_____ 5. In "I dwell in Possibility—," the lines "More numerous of Windows—/Superior—for Doors—" suggest that
   a. the house of prose is cramped and uninviting.
   b. imagination is better than real life.
   c. possibility includes entertaining a variety of views and opinions.
   d. the speaker despises people who lack imagination.

_____ 6. The "pale women" in "Uncoiling" react to the wind by
   a. running away in terror.
   b. hurriedly locking windows and doors.
   c. throwing back their heads and sighing.
   d. spinning themselves to sleep.

_____ 7. In "Columbus Dying," why does it make no difference to Columbus "whether they tumble off earth's edge or crawl/Till dropped dead in their tracks from vertigo"?
   a. No one believes his theory that the world is not flat.
   b. He is too modest to accept praise for his successes.
   c. He has become hopeless as he realizes death is near.
   d. In the face of death, his achievement seems insignificant.

_____ 8. What does "Prose" represent in "I dwell in Possibility—"?
   a. imagination
   b. nonfiction
   c. ordinary life
   d. confined quarters

_____ 9. For the dying man in "Success is counted sweetest," why do the "distant strains of triumph/Burst agonized and clear"?
   a. His senses are heightened in his final moments.
   b. He is most attuned to victory, the one thing he has longed for above all else.
   c. In death, he realizes his own personal triumph.
   d. He feels defeated and alone.

_____ 10. In "Columbus Dying," what can you infer from the lines, "No dragons gnawing on drowned sailors' brains,/He missed the angels guarding the four corners"?
   a. People in Columbus's time believed many myths about sea travel.
   b. Columbus was a superstitious person.
   c. Many sailors died on the transatlantic crossing.
   d. Columbus and his crew had an easy voyage.

_____ 11. From what evidence would you infer that the speaker of "Uncoiling" admires the power of the wind?
   a. "she scratches/on my window"
   b. "She spews gusts and thunder,/spooks pale women who scurry"
   c. "her tumbleweed skirt/starts its spin"
   d. "spins herself/to sleep"

_____ 12. The speaker's preference for possibility over prose implies that the theme of "I dwell in Possibility—" is
   a. everyday life is unbearable without imagination.
   b. poetry expresses deeper emotions than prose.
   c. imagination makes life richer.
   d. some people never realize their full potential.

_____ 13. What information can you infer from the images of thorns, lightning, cholla, hawks, tumbleweeds, and sand in "Uncoiling"?
   a. The wind is a powerful and awesome force.
   b. The poem is set in the southwestern United States.
   c. The pale women are easily frightened by nature.
   d. The speaker admires the wind's reckless energy.

Vocabulary and Grammar

_____ 14. In "Columbus Dying," Columbus is _thrall_ to "his vision of men creeping to and fro" because
   a. he can never escape his connection to his empty achievement.
   b. he feels free when it is time for him to die.
   c. he commands great power and respect.
   d. he is merely a servant to the king and queen.

_____ 15. Neither Columbus nor his _____ _____ illness.
   a. men; escapes
   b. sailors; escapes
   c. sailor; escapes
   d. men; escape

Success/Possibility/Uncoiling/Columbus Dying   **33**

_____ 16. Both lightning _____ hawks _____ in her dark hair.
   a. and; swarms
   b. and; swarm
   c. or; swarm
   d. nor; swarms

_____ 17. An *impregnable* building would
   a. catch fire.
   b. withstand attack.
   c. inspire imagination.
   d. make one feel dizzy.

_____ 18. A person suffering from *vertigo* might
   a. sleep heavily.
   b. feel hopeless.
   c. have scabs.
   d. fall down.

_____ 19. The antonym for *mature* is _____.
   a. inmature
   b. unmature
   c. immature
   d. imature

_____ 20. The women _____ while the wind _____.
   a. sings; roars
   b. sing; roar
   c. sing; roars
   d. sings; roars

Essay Questions

21. Although written by the same poet, "Success is counted sweetest" and "I dwell in Possibility—" have different themes. Which theme appeals to you more? Why? In an essay, give details from the poem to support your opinion.

22. Life is rarely all good or all bad but is instead a challenging mixture of the positive and negative. In an essay respond to this statement and support your opinion with details from the poems.

23. The speaker of "Uncoiling" uses women to represent different values. How does the speaker reinforce traditional or stereotypical female roles? How does the speaker create liberating images of women? In an essay, compare and contrast the different images that the poem presents.

from *My Left Foot* by Christy Brown

Selection Test

Critical Reading

In the blank, write the letter of the one best answer.

_____ 1. Christy Brown's mother sensed that there was something wrong when
   a. Christy was one year old.
   b. she noticed Christy couldn't hold his head up.
   c. she discovered he couldn't sit up by himself.
   d. she heard the doctors' opinions.

_____ 2. Identify Brown's purpose in writing the following paragraph.
   > Very worried by this, Mother told my father her fears, and they decided to seek medical advice without any further delay. I was a little over a year old when they began to take me to hospitals and clinics, convinced that there was something definitely wrong with me . . . .
   a. to demonstrate his parents' concerns and the corrective steps they took
   b. to show that his mother noticed something, but his father did not
   c. to show how old he was when the doctors decided he was "hopeless"
   d. to demonstrate how inexperienced his parents were

_____ 3. Which of the following describes Christy's life before he was able to show his family that he could communicate?
   a. He didn't like to be around his brothers and sisters because they were noisy.
   b. His mother arranged for friends and relatives to take care of Christy because she was too busy with the other children.
   c. He felt isolated from his family because he could neither communicate with them nor participate in their activities.
   d. He was fed and dressed each day and then just left on his own.

_____ 4. Christy remembers that as a child he felt
   I. lonely.   II. a part of a loving family.   III. rejected.   IV. useless.
   a. I and II   b. I and III   c. II and III   d. III and IV

_____ 5. Why does Christy write about the doctors' opinions?
   a. to show that his mother's faith is misplaced
   b. to provide medical information so readers understand his condition
   c. to emphasize his mother's strength and courage
   d. to show how little knowledge the doctors had about cerebral palsy in the 1930s

_____ 6. Which of the following best describes Christy's mother's reaction to the doctors?
   a. She yelled at them rudely and told them they were wrong.
   b. After hearing the first doctor's opinion, she refused to take Christy to any more doctors.
   c. She refused to listen to them.
   d. She refused to accept their belief that Christy was an imbecile.

_____ 7. Why does Christy's mother reject the doctors' advice?
   a. Her other children had similar symptoms and eventually grew out of them.
   b. She can't afford to put Christy in an institution.
   c. She doesn't understand his condition well enough to know that he won't get better.
   d. She simply believed that Christy's mind was not "crippled" like his body was.

____ 8. Christy's mother would *not* allow him to be hidden in a back room. This decision
  a. was of little consequence to Christy's life since he couldn't walk or talk.
  b. made a powerful impact on Christy's childhood.
  c. caused Christy to be paraded around whenever visitors came.
  d. depended on whether Christy's mother had time to care for him on any given day.

____ 9. After Christy's mother shows him pictures in a storybook and she asks him if he
  liked the pictures, he reaches up and grabs one of her curls. Why does Christy's
  mother then cry?
  a. She is tired from reading to Christy.
  b. She is in pain because he had pulled out some of her hair.
  c. She is frustrated because he doesn't respond to her.
  d. She wants him to be like her other children.

____ 10. Christy included the incident with the chalk in his autobiography because
  a. it showed his mother's patience.
  b. it was an important turning point in his life.
  c. it gave him an opportunity to describe the family's large kitchen.
  d. it gave him a chance to mention that Mona and Paddy could do sums.

____ 11. Which of the following does *not* add to the impact of Christy's significant moment?
  a. Christy tells us that he is the tenth child.
  b. Christy tells us that the doctors labeled him "hopeless."
  c. Christy's mother's faith leads readers to hope that she is right.
  d. Christy includes details about the appearance and mood in the room.

____ 12. Why was everything in Christy Brown's life changed by the incident with the chalk?
  a. Christy would no longer have to lie on his back in the kitchen.
  b. All of the doctors had to take back their opinions.
  c. Christy's display of intelligence was the first sign that his mind was not crippled.
  d. Learning the alphabet meant Christy could learn to talk.

____ 13. What is the "secret fear" Christy refers to in the following passage?
  > Then, suddenly, it happened! In a moment everything was changed, my future life
  > molded into a definite shape, my mother's faith in me rewarded and her secret fear
  > changed into open triumph.
  a. that Christy's mind really is crippled   c. that Christy's muscles are stiffening.
  b. that Christy's eyesight is failing   d. that Christy's health is failing

____ 14. Which of the following sentences from *My Left Foot* best demonstrates that one of
  Christy Brown's purposes for writing was to show that his mother was fair?
  a. But it wasn't easy for her because now the relatives and friends had decided oth-
     erwise.
  b. At this time she had the five other children to look after besides the "difficult
     one," though as yet it was not by any means a full house.
  c. No matter how dull and incapable I might grow up to be, she was determined to
     treat me on the same plane as the others, and not as the "queer one" in the back
     room who was never spoken of when there were visitors present.
  d. Her face was bent over mine hopefully.

Vocabulary and Grammar

____ 15. A verb in the past perfect tense indicates
  a. an action that began and ended in the past.
  b. an action that continued for some time in the past.
  c. a past action that ended before another past action took place.
  d. an action that began in the past and continues into the present.

_____ 16. Christy states that though he could not sit up or walk, he was by no means inert. What does he mean?
   a. He could sit up and walk if he wanted to, but did not have the desire to do so.
   b. He wasn't motionless because his family would carry him around.
   c. He couldn't move but his mind was extremely active.
   d. He had no control over the muscles in his arms and legs, which moved wildly.

_____ 17. When Christy writes that his left foot, "apparently by its own volition," reached out and took the chalk, it means
   a. he willed his left foot to reach out.
   b. his left foot moved as if it were detached.
   c. his left foot acted as if it had its own free will.
   d. his left foot moved but he couldn't feel it moving.

_____ 18. Mrs. Brown's so-called impertinence took the form of
   a. disagreeing with the doctors.
   b. maintaining round-the-clock care for Christy.
   c. not naming Christy until she was able to take him to church.
   d. allowing Christy to lie in the midst of the family's activities.

_____ 19. He remembered very clearly that he _____ out and grabbed the chalk.
   a. reaches
   b. reached
   c. has reached
   d. had reached

_____ 20. Choose the sentence that contains a verb in the past perfect tense.
   a. Knowing she was on his side gave him the strength to face his future.
   b. Although she spent many hours reading to him, he made no sign that he had understood her.
   c. His hands were clenched so tightly that his fingernails bit into his flesh.
   d. His mother was crying when he looked up at her.

Essay Questions

21. A writer's purpose shapes his or her choice of language and use of details. Study the following passage from *My Left Foot.* In an essay, state the author's purpose behind the paragraph. Use details from the passage to support your opinion.

   . . . I was lonely, imprisoned in a world of my own, unable to communicate with others, cut off, separated from them as though a glass wall stood between my existence and theirs, thrusting me beyond the sphere of their lives and activities. I longed to run about and play with the rest, but I was unable to break loose from my bondage.

22. From the very first paragraph of this excerpt from his autobiography, Christy Brown begins building toward a significant moment. In an essay, explain what this significant moment is and how Brown builds up to it in his writing. Cite details or pieces of information that contribute to the impact of this compelling time in Christy Brown's life.

23. In his autobiography, Christy Brown represents his mother's strength as one of the factors relating to his own success. In an essay, discuss some of Mrs. Brown's qualities. How does she strive for success? How does she keep going when faced with failure? Use details from the selection to support your opinions.

Name _____ Date _____

"A Visit to Grandmother" by William Melvin Kelley

Selection Test

Critical Reading

In the blank, write the letter of the one best answer.

_____ 1. What is the most important story in "A Visit to Grandmother"?
a. a teenager's first meeting with his father's family
b. a mother's reunion with her son
c. a man's attempt to face a childhood pain
d. a horse's misbehavior and its results

_____ 2. Which of the following lines from the story is an example of direct characterization?
a. ". . . he had spoken of GL with the kind of indulgence he would have shown a cute, but ill-behaved and potentially dangerous, five-year-old."
b. "'He'll be here though; he ain't as young and footloose as he used to be.'"
c. "And Chig had a suspicion now that the reunion had been only an excuse to drive south, that his father had been heading to this house all the time."
d. "She was a honey-colored woman, with long eyelashes."

_____ 3. Charles does not tell Chig right away about his plans to visit his family. What does this reveal about his feelings concerning the visit?
a. Charles is not looking forward to the visit.
b. Charles wants the visit to be a surprise for Chig.
c. Charles thinks Chig will be reluctant to go.
d. Charles didn't think he would have time to visit.

_____ 4. In "A Visit to Grandmother," Chig's father had never talked much about his family, with the exception of
a. Aunt Rose.   b. his brother GL.   c. Mae.   d. Uncle Hiram.

_____ 5. GL's character can best be described as
a. friendly and intelligent.
b. lazy and stupid.
c. sincere and persuasive.
d. charming and irresponsible.

_____ 6. Charles uses formal standard English at his mother's house because he
a. respects and admires the family.
b. wants Chig to be proud of him.
c. has serious professional ambitions.
d. sets himself apart from the family.

_____ 7. What detail is clarified, or made clear, in the following passage from the selection?
"Ten days before in New York, Chig's father had decided suddenly he wanted to go to Nashville to attend his college class reunion, twenty years out. . . . Chig was seventeen, had nothing to do that summer, and his father asked if he would like to go along."
a. The reason why Chig's father moved to New York when he was an adult.
b. The reason why Chig's father thinks of GL as a practical joker.
c. The reason why Chig and his father were traveling together, near Grandmother's home.
d. The reason Chig's father wanted to go to his college reunion.

____ 8. Which of the following lines from the story is an example of indirect characterization?

    a. "She smiled. She had all her teeth, but they were too perfect to be her own."

    b. "Uncle Hiram was somewhat smaller than Chig's father; his short-cropped kinky hair was half gray, half black."

    c. "She was standing now, her back and shoulders straight. She came only to Chig's chest."

    d. "They don't know nothing about old ladies. When I want help, I'll let you know. Only time I'll need help getting anywheres is when I dies and they lift me into the ground."

____ 9. For Charles, what does the story of GL and the horse represent?

    a. his mother's preference for GL

    b. GL's ignorance about horses

    c. his mother's stubborn pride

    d. GL's attractive personality

____ 10. When Mrs. Dunford says "GL could-a ended up swinging," she means he could have

    a. wasted his life at parties.

    b. lived a cheerful, carefree life.

    c. been hanged as a criminal.

    d. suffered emotional ups and downs.

____ 11. Which of the following passages clarifies the reason why Charles's mother spent more time with GL than with Charles?

    a. "You was more growed up than GL when you was five and he was ten, and I tried to show you that by letting you do what you wanted to do."

    b. "That's not true, Mama. You know it."

    c. "I said that if I had done it, if I had done just exactly what GL did, you would have beaten me good for it, Mama."

    d. "Don't ask me how I did that; I reckon it was that I was a mother and my baby asked me to do something, is all."

____ 12. How does Chig feel when he sees his father cry?

    a. He is angry that Mama has made his father cry.

    b. He is depressed that his father is so sad.

    c. He is alarmed that his father would show such emotion.

    d. He is impressed by his father's emotional honesty.

____ 13. What do Charles's words and actions surrounding his mother's treatment of him as a child reveal about his character?

    a. He is sensitive and full of anger.

    b. He is unable to express his feelings.

    c. He dislikes humorous stories.

    d. He views his mother as perfect.

____ 14. Why does GL refer to Charles as a "rascal"?

    a. GL suspects Charles is dishonest.

    b. GL is fond of Charles.

    c. GL resents Charles's intrusion.

    d. GL thinks Charles is mischievous.

____ 15. You can clarify the relationships among the characters in "A Visit to Grandmother" by

    a. rereading the story's final paragraph.

    b. reading the words of GL.

    c. making a family tree.

    d. defining the word *family*.

_____ 16. Which of the following statements best expresses the theme or message of "A Visit to Grandmother"?
  a. Brothers should be tolerant and forgiving of each other's faults.
  b. The pain of family misunderstandings can last a lifetime.
  c. Parents and adult children should resolve conflicts for the grandchildren's sake.
  d. Adults often resume childhood roles when they visit their parents.

Vocabulary and Grammar

_____ 17. As a doctor, Charles was always kind and friendly to frightened patients who _____ timidly into his office.
  a. ventured
  b. ran
  c. grimaced
  d. lacquered

_____ 18. Chig is surprised that he and his father _____ to visit his father's family the next day, because his father never talked about them.
  a. were going
  b. are going
  c. is going
  d. was going

_____ 19. Choose the sentence that contains a verb in the present progressive tense.
  a. I watched GL drag that poor animal up to the house.
  b. You must be crazy if you think that I am getting on that horse.
  c. I was watching that beast and it was boiling hotter all the time.
  d. This horse is as gentle as a rose petal.

_____ 20. I turned around to go back into the house because it _____ late, near dinner time.
  a. were getting
  b. are getting
  c. is getting
  d. was getting

Essay Questions

21. In an essay, clarify the problem Charles has with his mother and his brother. Explain the specific misunderstanding between Charles and his mother that is at the root of the problem. What is Charles's attitude toward GL? What is the true reason for this attitude?

22. When Charles bends down to kiss his mother, Chig notices that "something new and almost ugly had come into his (Charles's) eyes: fear, uncertainty, sadness, and perhaps even hatred." In an essay, explain why Chig sees each of these things in his father's eyes. Why does Charles have negative feelings toward his family? What is the purpose of his visit home? Why might his visit home cause him to feel fear, uncertainty, sadness, and hatred?

23. In an essay, discuss the techniques the author of "A Visit to Grandmother" uses to characterize Chig's grandmother, Charles, and GL. Describe at least two traits of each character and how you as a reader learn about these traits. What are some of each character's most revealing moments?

"Mowing" and "After Apple-Picking" by Robert Frost
"Style" and "At Harvesttime" by Maya Angelou

Selection Test

Critical Reading

In the blank, write the letter of the one best answer.

_____ 1. What is the main focus of Robert Frost's poem "Mowing"?
   a. admiring snakes and other wild creatures
   b. growing vegetables
   c. cutting grass with a scythe
   d. cutting grass with a gas-powered lawn mower

_____ 2. What is the tone of the following passage from "Mowing"?
   It was no dream of the gift of idle hours,/Or easy gold at the hand of fay or elf:
   Anything more than the truth would have seemed/too weak/To the earnest love
   that laid the swale in rows, . . .
   a. frightened   b. excited   c. annoyed   d. respectful

_____ 3. In "Mowing," what do the descriptions of the speaker's work reveal about the
   speaker?
   a. He values quiet, steady, outdoor work.
   b. He finds outdoor work draining and unsatisfying.
   c. He is looking forward to winter.
   d. He dislikes weeds and snakes.

_____ 4. Interpret the image of the lone, whispering scythe in "Mowing." What mood does this
   image create?
   a. desperation   b. suspense   c. sadness   d. tranquillity

_____ 5. In "After Apple-Picking," what images fill the speaker's mind as he tries to sleep?
   a. images of a vacation
   b. images of next year's crop of apples
   c. images of apples and the task he just completed
   d. images of profits from his apples

_____ 6. In "After Apple-Picking," how might you describe the speaker's condition as he tries
   to sleep?
   a. energized
   b. exhausted but unable to relax his mind
   c. angry that he failed at his task
   d. annoyed with his life

_____ 7. Interpret the image in "After Apple-Picking" of the woodchuck's long sleep. Why
   might the speaker compare himself to a woodchuck?
   a. Woodchucks eat apples.
   b. Woodchucks live in apple orchards.
   c. Woodchucks keep busy all summer and then hibernate for a long winter's rest.
   d. Woodchucks once destroyed his apple crop, and he hopes that they will hibernate
      soon.

© Prentice-Hall, Inc.

Unit 2: Striving for Success

_____ 8. According to "After Apple-Picking," how do extreme hard work and ambition sometimes affect people?
- a. People become exhausted and are unable to stop thinking about the job they've
just completed.
- b. People become wealthy and filled with greed.
- c. People decide to change completely the course of their lives.
- d. People look forward to winter.

_____ 9. What is the tone of the following line from Maya Angelou's "Style"?
> Content is of great importance, but we must not underrate the value of style.
- a. humorous
- b. angry
- c. timid and unsure
- d. firm and confident

_____ 10. Interpret the main idea of Angelou's piece "At Harvesttime." What message is she trying to convey to readers?
- a. Have confidence and develop a unique sense of style.
- b. Borrow ideas and mannerisms from other people.
- c. Walk away from difficult situations.
- d. Disarm rude people by uttering insults at them.

_____ 11. According to Angelou in "At Harvesttime," the "highest manifestations," or best displays, of style are
- a. cleverness and charm.
- b. good manners and tolerance.
- c. expensive clothing and jewelry.
- d. parties and other social events.

_____ 12. What is the tone of the following passage from "At Harvesttime"?
> Now, after years of observation and enough courage to admit what I have ob-
served, I try to plant peace if I want to avoid betrayal and lies. Of course, there is
no absolute assurance that those things I plant will always fall upon arable land . . .
- a. rude and arrogant
- b. sad
- c. serious and thoughtful
- d. light and humorous

_____ 13. How might you interpret the following passage from "At Harvesttime"?
> Of course, there is no absolute assurance that those things I plant will always fall
upon arable land and will take root and grow, nor can I know if another cultivator
did not leave contrary seeds before I arrived.
- a. Farming is difficult, time-consuming work that is not ideal for everyone.
- b. You should not trust other people, especially people with whom you are compet-
ing.
- c. Be careful where you plant seeds, because some soil is not arable.
- d. Even if you are thoughtful and careful, you cannot control everything in life.

_____ 14. Frost's poems "Mowing" and "After Apple-Picking," as well as Maya Angelou's poem
"At Harvesttime," convey ideas by using images of _____.
- a. apple orchards   b. wildlife   c. seeds   d. farming

Vocabulary and Grammar

____ 15. In the following sentence, what question does the underlined adverb answer?

Never try to take the manners of another as your own, for the theft will be immediately evident.

a. Where?
b. When?
c. In what way?
d. To what extent?

____ 16. The speaker of "After Apple-Picking" thinks about apples hanging from the _____ of a tree.

a. cider-heap   b. ladder   c. trough   d. bough

____ 17. Which sentence contains an adverb that modifies another adverb?

a. The pickers worked quickly to fill the large brown barrel.
b. Feeling the heat of the sun on their backs, the men worked very rapidly.
c. The apple-picker soon drifted into a deeply satisfying sleep.
d. There were ten thousand fruit to cherish in hand, lift down, and not let fall.

____ 18. According to the speaker in "Style," a person with style can respond calmly and confidently to an unfriendly _____.

a. manifestation   b. admonition   c. content   d. gibe

____ 19. How might you interpret the following line from Angelou's poem "At Harvesttime"?

. . . there are those who seem certain that if they plant tomato seeds, at harvesttime they can reap onions.

a. Some people do not know a great deal about farming.
b. Some people do not realize that they are responsible for their own actions and that they will often get what they deserve.
c. Some people quarrel too much and fail to find comfort in farming.
d. Some people have unrealistic expectations for their lives.

____ 20. The speaker in "At Harvesttime" lives according to a firm, _____ life principle.

a. disparaging   b. immutable   c. knowledgeable   d. quiet

Essay Questions

21. In a short essay, describe some of the advice Maya Angelou gives about dealing with other people in her poems "Style" and "At Harvesttime." What does Angelou mean when she says "Style allows the person to appear neither inferior in one location nor superior in the other. Good manners and tolerance can often transform disaster into good fortune"? In what way is this line similar to the following line from "At Harvesttime": "I try to plant peace if I want to avoid betrayal and lies"?

22. Write an essay in which you describe the two perspectives on work that are given in Robert Frost's poems "Mowing" and "After Apple-Picking." In your essay, answer the following questions: How does the speaker in "Mowing" feel about his work? How does the speaker in "After Apple-Picking" feel at the end of his day? What do the two speakers have in common? In what way do they differ?

23. In an essay, describe some of the images that Frost and Angelou use in their poems to depict the wonders of the natural world and the details and difficulties of the farmer's work. What do these images reveal about the different moods and the main ideas of the pieces?

© Prentice-Hall, Inc.

"The Apple Tree" by Katherine Mansfield

Selection Test

Critical Reading

In the blank, write the letter of the one best answer.

_____ 1. The narrator refers to this particular apple tree as the
   a. Untouchable Tree.
   b. English Tree.
   c. Forbidden Tree.
   d. Special Tree.

_____ 2. The friend from England tells Father that
   a. the tree is a particular variety of apple of which he is very fond.
   b. he's never seen an apple tree like this before.
   c. this kind of tree normally grows only in England.
   d. he will be surprised by the type of fruit the tree bears.

_____ 3. Why is Father's response in the following passage somewhat odd?
   "Great Scott!" said the friend, lighting upon it with every appearance of admiring astonishment: "Isn't that a—?" And a rich, splendid name settled like an unknown bird on the tree.
   "Yes, I believe it is," said Father lightly. He knew nothing whatever about the names of fruit trees.
   a. because the friend is so excited, but Father answers "lightly"
   b. because he knew very well that his friend was making up the name
   c. because he wasn't sure to what tree his friend was referring
   d. because Father knows nothing whatever about the names of fruit trees

_____ 4. Why does Father act as if he knows what kind of tree his friend has noticed?
   a. He wants to show off in front of his friend.
   b. He wants to appear to be knowledgeable about his own property.
   c. He really does know what kind of tree it is; his children just don't realize it.
   d. He just wants his friend to stop going on and on about it.

_____ 5. The friend says this type of apple tree is rare. What conclusion does Father then draw?
   a. The tree is really exceptional and worthy of special attention.
   b. The tree must be sent to a nursery to be properly cared for.
   c. He shouldn't have bought an orchard since he doesn't even know a rare apple tree when he sees one.
   d. Given the value of the tree, he should have paid a higher price for the orchard.

_____ 6. Which of the following best describes Father's behavior as he picks, cuts open, and examines the first apples from the tree?
   a. He selfishly keeps the surprises of the apples to himself.
   b. He acts as if he is very knowledgeable about apples.
   c. He reveals his expertise about the bouquet of apples.
   d. He is nervous and chatters about the apples as he slices them.

_____ 7. The apples that Father slices open are unusual because
   a. the skin is extremely tough.
   b. the flesh is pink.
   c. the insides are rotten.
   d. they have no seeds.

_____ 8. Why does Father never go near the apple tree again?
   a. because he learns that the tree isn't valuable after all
   b. because the children lied to him about the taste of the apple
   c. because he is so disappointed by the taste of the apple
   d. because he thinks the color of the apples is a bad sign

_____ 9. Three of the following questions are answered directly in "The Apple Tree." Choose the
   question that can be answered only by piecing together information from the story.
   a. What does Father know about the names of fruit trees?
   b. Why did Father go to look at the tree every Sunday morning?
   c. Why don't the children play in the "wild" orchard?
   d. What is unusual about the apples from the special tree?

_____ 10. Which of the following would be a useful question to ask—and answer—while you
   read "The Apple Tree"?
   a. Why does Father take a "new and lively interest" in the tree after his friend's com-
      ments?
   b. What is the narrator's name?
   c. Is the narrator a boy or a girl?
   d. What was the "rich, splendid name" that the friend gave the apple tree?

_____ 11. An allusion is
   a. a description of something that doesn't really exist.
   b. a reference to a well-known person, place, event, literary work, or art work.
   c. a quotation borrowed from another source.
   d. the mention of the name of another literary work within a story.

_____ 12. Which of the following general types of questions may be useful to ask yourself while
   reading in order to gain fuller understanding of a short story?
   I. Why does this character behave this way?
   II. Why does this character treat the other character in a certain way?
   III. How does the story end?
   IV. When does the story take place?
   a. I, II, and III
   b. I, II, III, and IV
   c. I, II, and IV
   d. II, III, and IV

_____ 13. Choose the sentence that contains an allusion.
   a. One, that we called the "wild" orchard, lay beyond the vegetable garden.
   b. "They're rare—they're very rare. Hardly ever see 'em in England nowadays," said
      the visitor.
   c. "Don't touch that tree! Do you hear me, children!" said he, bland and firm.
   d. If the house had burned to the ground at that time it would have meant less to
      him than the destruction of his tree.

_____ 14. Allusions can add meaning to a story by
   a. showing how familiar the author is with other literary works.
   b. forcing readers to read another literary work to understand the allusion.
   c. making readers guess to what literary work the author is referring.
   d. hinting at the underlying meaning of the story.

Vocabulary and Grammar

____ 15. When the children look for windfalls they are
   a. checking for any apple trees blown down by a storm.
   b. picking up branches blown down by the wind.
   c. searching for rotten apples with which to make apple cider.
   d. seeking edible apples that have fallen off the tree.

____ 16. Paddocks are best described as
   a. meadows surrounded by woods.   c. hillside orchards.
   b. large pastures.   d. small, enclosed fields.

____ 17. In which sentences are the words *lie* and *lay* used correctly?
   I. Bogey is lying beneath the tree, eating an apple.
   II. I think I'll lay my basket down and join him.
   III. After we had laid there for a while, we ran to catch up with father.
   IV. Father lay one apple down, opened the penknife, and cut the other in half.
   a. I and II   b. I and III
   c. II and III   d. III and IV

____ 18. Yesterday, we _____ under the tree all morning.
   a. lie   c. lay
   b. laid   d. lied

____ 19. Choose the sentence in which the adjective *exquisite* is used most accurately.
   a. As children, we viewed Grandmother's grape arbor as a magical and exquisite hiding place.
   b. The storm was exquisite, with its booming thunder and flickering lightning.
   c. The big stone house that stood high on the hill was exquisite.
   d. My neighbors chose the light, exquisite foliage of a cypress tree over that of the more traditional maple to shade their yard.

____ 20. The verb *to lay* is
   a. never followed by a direct object.
   b. rarely followed by a direct object.
   c. always followed by a direct object.
   d. usually followed by a direct object.

Essay Questions

21. In an essay, list three questions you had while reading "The Apple Tree." Cite information from the story that you used to answer the questions. Explain how asking and then answering the questions helped you to understand something about the story that was not directly stated.

22. Did you suspect that the apples might be a disappointment? What hints does the story contain that the apples would not meet anyone's expectations? In an essay, identify any hints, whether they are directly stated or implied in the text, that give you an indication as to the quality of the apples. Explain why these passages or events give clues about the coming disappointment.

23. Katherine Mansfield quite purposely wove an allusion into "The Apple Tree." The allusion is to the biblical story of Adam and Eve in the Garden of Eden that occurs in Genesis 3–4. In an essay, describe the allusion in the story and discuss the parts of Mansfield's story that are parallel to the story of Adam and Eve. In what ways does Mansfield's story differ from the biblical story? How does the allusion affect the reading of Mansfield's story?

"Africa" by David Diop
"Old Song" Traditional
"All" by Bei Dao
"Also All" by Shu Ting
from **The Analects** by Confucius

Selection Test

Critical Reading

In the blank, write the letter of the one best answer.

_____ 1. The speaker of "Africa" addresses his poem to
a. his grandmother beside her distant river.
b. the continent of Africa.
c. the holders of sjamboks.
d. an impetuous child.

_____ 2. How could one best summarize the question the speaker of "Africa" asks?
a. How can one return to a lost homeland?
b. What has happened to my aged grandmother?
c. Who caused the ancient bloodshed?
d. When will Africa rule itself?

_____ 3. The poem "Africa" compares Africa's political development to
a. a young and sturdy tree.
b. ancestral savannahs.
c. an impetuous child.
d. a solemn voice.

_____ 4. According to "Africa," which words summarize the continent's progress?
a. distance and blood
b. bending and trembling
c. patience and stubbornness
d. white and faded

_____ 5. According to "Africa," why will the fruits grow to have the "bitter taste of liberty"?
a. High hopes rarely come to pass.
b. Few people's ancestors were ever free.
c. Freedom has a high price.
d. The ends will not justify the means.

_____ 6. The message of "Old Song" might best be expressed as
a. fame is its own reward.
b. be proud but not prideful.
c. heroism is futile; heroes die.
d. the only victory is staying alive.

_____ 7. Which of the following words from "Old Song" is *not* a synonym for *aphorism*?
a. prediction
b. adage
c. saying
d. proverb

_____ 8. What do the following lines from "Old Song" express?

> Many heroes are not yet born, /many have already died.

  a. the striving required of heroes
  b. the permanence of heroism
  c. the need for heroes to appear
  d. the hopelessness of heroism

_____ 9. In "Also All" the line "Today is heavy with tomorrow" means

  a. tomorrow's cares cause us anxiety today.
  b. what happens today determines what happens tomorrow.
  c. both today and tomorrow are shrouded in doubt.
  d. today and tomorrow will be just the same.

_____ 10. Which of the following familiar modern proverbs is closest in meaning to a recurrent theme from *The Analects*?

  a. It's six of one and half a dozen of the other.
  b. A rolling stone gathers no moss.
  c. The early bird catches the worm.
  d. Actions speak louder than words.

_____ 11. According to *The Analects*, Confucius would approve most of someone who

  a. strives for self-improvement.
  b. studies a topic in detail.
  c. knows the faults of another.
  d. promises to take action.

_____ 12. According to Confucius, a worthy person is one who

  a. expects a lot from others.
  b. makes no promises.
  c. considers alternate views.
  d. governs many subjects.

_____ 13. The phrase "ritual performed without reverence, the forms of mourning observed without grief" is a judgment against people who are _____.

  a. simple
  b. happy
  c. fake
  d. biased

_____ 14. According to *The Analects*, a "small" person is a person of

  a. lowly office.
  b. rigid views.
  c. few words.
  d. sparse learning.

_____ 15. What does Confucius mean by "slow in word"?

  a. thoughtful
  b. lazy
  c. stingy
  d. dull-witted

_____ 16. Choose the best interpretation of the following sentence from *The Analects*.

> "He who will not worry about what is far off will soon find something worse than worry close at hand."

  a. If you spend too much time worrying, you won't recognize real problems.
  b. If you don't prevent problems, you will have to solve them.
  c. Don't waste time thinking about the future; concentrate on the present.
  d. Wherever you look, you can always find something to worry about.

Vocabulary and Grammar

_____ 17. The word *impetuous* means _____.
   a. unfortunate
   b. forsaken
   c. haughty
   d. impulsive

_____ 18. A verb is in the active voice when
   a. the subject comes immediately before the verb.
   b. it is a form of a linking verb.
   c. the subject of the sentence performs the action.
   d. it is preceded by a helping verb.

_____ 19. Choose the sentence that contains a verb in the passive voice.
   a. Not all is as you say.
   b. Not every seed finds barren soil.
   c. Not all flames consume themselves.
   d. Not all trees are felled by storms.

_____ 20. The word *lamentation* means _____.
   a. intention
   b. aphorism
   c. wailing in grief
   d. regret

Essay Questions

21. In *The Analects*, Confucius says " Yu, shall I teach you what knowledge is? When you know a thing, to recognize that you know it, and when you do not know a thing, to recognize that you do not know it. That is knowledge." Confucius does not refer to vast stores of learning, and even includes not knowing things in his definition of knowledge. Is this idea a conventional approach to knowledge? In an essay, explain Confucius' definition in your own terms. Use examples from life to illustrate how knowing and not knowing contribute to this concept of knowledge.

22. In many places and times, people have attempted to define qualities of good conduct and character. Two of these selections, *The Analects* and "Old Song," separated by place and time, concern themselves specifically with conduct. What might Confucius think of "Old Song"? Would the composer of "Old Song" agree with *The Analects*? How are these two works alike? In what ways do they differ? Write an essay in which you compare and contrast *The Analects* with "Old Song," noting similarities and differences. Give examples from the selections to support your ideas.

23. In "All," Bei Dao finds "every speech a repetition," and would probably agree with the ancient writer of the book of Ecclesiastes who said "there is no new thing under the sun." Yet we live in an age of constant change. New devices, images, ideas, and issues surround us. Do you agree with Bei Dao? Is "every speech a repetition"? Write an essay in which you assess his statement and explain whether or not you agree with it. Give specific reasons for your opinion.

Unit Test: Striving for Success

Critical Reading

In the blank, write the letter of the one best answer.

The questions below are based on the following selection.

In the following excerpt from "Paul's Case," a short story by Willa Cather, Paul makes a trip to a special place that lifts him from the obstacles of his life.

After supper was over, and he had helped to dry the dishes, Paul nervously asked his father whether he could go to George's to get some help in his geometry, and still more nervously asked for carfare. This latter request he had to repeat, as his father, on principle, did not like to hear requests for money, whether much or little. . . . He was not a poor man, but he had a worthy ambition to come up in the world. His only reason for allowing Paul to usher was that he thought a boy ought to be earning a little.

Paul bounded upstairs, scrubbed the greasy odor of the dishwater from his hands with the ill-smelling soap he hated, and then shook over his fingers a few drops of violet water from the bottle he kept hidden in his drawer. He left the house with his geometry conspicuously under his arm, and the moment he got out of Cordelia Street and boarded a downtown car, he . . . began to live again.

It was at the theater and at Carnegie Hall that Paul really lived. . . . The moment he inhaled the gassy, painty, dusty odor behind the scenes, he breathed like a prisoner set free, and felt within him the possibility of doing or saying splendid, brilliant things.

_____ 1. Why does Paul's father allow Paul to work as an usher?
   a. because Paul loves the theater
   b. because he feels Paul should be earning money
   c. because he feels it is a valuable experience for Paul
   d. because they need money

_____ 2. What can you infer from the fact that Paul "nervously" asks his father for money and permission to leave?
   a. Paul fears his father will say no to his requests.
   b. Paul does not really want to leave.
   c. Paul is worried about his geometry studies.
   d. Paul feels he did not clean the dishes well enough.

_____ 3. What is Paul's real reason for wanting to leave the house?
   a. He wants to ride the downtown car.
   b. He wants to escape to the theater.
   c. He wants to study geometry.
   d. He wants to explore the city.

_____ 4. How would you describe Paul's father?
   a. cold and bitter
   b. sensitive and understanding
   c. practical and conservative with money
   d. impractical and easygoing

_____ 5. What can you infer about Paul's relationship with his father, based on their interactions in the selection?
  a. They have a close relationship.
  b. They do not understand each other or communicate easily.
  c. They are always bitterly fighting with each other.
  d. They make an effort to spend quality time together.

_____ 6. Which of the following lines is an example of direct characterization, rather than indirect characterization?
  a. and the moment he got out of Cordelia Street and boarded a downtown car, he . . . began to live again.
  b. Paul bounded upstairs, scrubbed the greasy odor of the dishwater from his hands, . . . then shook over his fingers a few drops of violet water . . .
  c. Paul nervously asked his father whether he could go to George's to get some help in his geometry . . .
  d. He was not a poor man, but he had a worthy ambition to come up in the world.

_____ 7. How would you best interpret the image of Paul scrubbing the dishwater from his hands with soap he hates, and shaking drops of violet water over his fingers?
  a. He is leaving a place he considers unpleasant to go to a place of beauty.
  b. Cleanliness is important to Paul.
  c. Paul does not like doing chores at home.
  d. Paul is trying to delay his departure for as long as possible.

_____ 8. What do the sights, sounds, and smells of the theater represent to Paul?
  a. practical training for the future
  b. freedom and possibilities
  c. friendship
  d. pure entertainment

_____ 9. What does the description of Paul as "a prisoner set free" reveal about his feelings toward the world outside the theater?
  a. He enjoys the contrast between his life at the theater and his life in the world outside the theater.
  b. He feels he cannot control his behavior when he leaves home.
  c. He feels the world outside the theater is comfortably sheltered.
  d. He feels trapped and miserable in the world outside the theater.

_____ 10. How would you best describe the tone of the final paragraph in which Paul's feelings for the theater are described?
  a. cold and distant
  b. casual and carefree
  c. serious and passionate
  d. sad and wistful

Vocabulary and Grammar

The questions below consist of a related pair of words in CAPITAL LETTERS followed by four lettered pairs of words. Choose the pair that best expresses a relationship _similar_ to that of the pair in capital letters.

_____ 11. SATIATED : FULL ::
  a. tired : exhaustion
  b. open : closed
  c. speed : swiftness
  d. clear : transparent

___ 12. BOUQUET : NOSE::
    a. flower : petal
    b. observe : eyes
    c. flavor : mouth
    d. clasp : hands

Choose the word(s) that best completes each sentence.

___ 13. Choose the sentence that contains the present participle of an irregular verb.
    a. The younger sister is beginning to lose her patience.
    b. Let's offer the landowner a better price for the land.
    c. If you sow wheat on it the first year, it must lie fallow the next.
    d. I can't go on overlooking it, or they'll destroy all I have.

___ 14. Pahom _____ wheat on his land the first year he owned it.
    a. growed
    b. grew
    c. grown
    d. grow

___ 15. The wind _____, but people _____ lullabies so children will not hear the noise.
    a. howl . . . sing
    b. howls . . . sing
    c. howls . . . sings
    d. howl . . . sing

___ 16. She learned to think positively and ignore _____ remarks.
    a. immutable
    b. dilapidated
    c. disparaging
    d. interesting

___ 17. Despite what people told her, Christy Brown's mother held the _____ that her son would someday overcome his challenges.
    a. volition
    b. conviction
    c. indulgence
    d. potency

In the blank, write the letter of the one best answer.

___ 18. As they argued, each sister _____her own lifestyle.
    a. defends
    b. defending
    c. defended
    d. defend

_____ 19. Which of the following sentences contains a linking verb?

   a. Anaya feels amazed by the library's volumes of books.
   b. Through books, Anaya learns about different cultures.
   c. Books preserve ideas and cultural traditions.
   d. The library offers many opportunities.

_____ 20. Which choice is the best meaning of the word *judicious* as it is used in the following sentence:

People often asked her to solve problems because she was thoughtful and judicious.

   a. judgmental
   b. talkative
   c. slow
   d. wise

Essay Questions

21. This unit is filled with stories of people setting goals, striving for success, and overcoming obstacles. For example, think about "One Million Volumes," the selection from *My Left Foot*, "Mowing," "After Apple-Picking," "Style," and the writings of Confucius. Which selection do you find the most inspiring? In an essay, explain the main idea of the selection that most affected you. Why do you find the characters, message, or events so appealing?

22. Making important decisions and striving for success always involves some risk, and failure often helps people to learn, improve, and appreciate success when it is finally achieved. Some of the selections in this unit deal specifically with failure or disappointment, such as "How Much Land Does a Man Need?," "Success is counted sweetest," "Columbus Dying," "A Visit to Grandmother," "The Apple Tree," "Africa," and "Biko." In an essay, describe the ways in which the theme of failure or disappointment is explored in two of the selections. Explain what lessons can be learned. Support your answer with details from the text.

23. In creating characters, authors often use indirect characterization, revealing characters' personality traits through their thoughts, words, actions, and relationships with each other. From the selections in this unit, choose an interesting character such as Pahom in "How Much Land Does a Man Need?" or Charles Dunford from "A Visit to Grandmother." Write an essay in which you describe the character's personality and explain how that personality is revealed through methods of indirect characterization.

24. Often the paths people take in life are influenced by relatives, particularly older relatives such as parents and grandparents. Selections such as "One Million Volumes," *My Left Foot*, "A Visit to Grandmother," and "Africa" illustrate this idea. Write an essay describing how speakers' or authors' lives are shaped or changed in these selections, both positively and negatively, by the stories, actions, or beliefs of family members from other generations.

25. The attitude of a speaker or author toward his or her subject in a literary work is known as *tone*. A work might be serious, casual, sad, distant, instructive, or cheerful. In an essay, compare and contrast the tone in three selections in this unit. Which words and phrases help to express tone in these pieces? How does the tone relate to meaning?

"Through the Tunnel" by Doris Lessing

Selection Test

Critical Reading

In the blank, write the letter of the one best answer.

____ 1. What is the theme, or central idea, of "Through the Tunnel"?
a. a boy's rejection of his mother's opinions
b. an individual's struggle to achieve difficult goals
c. a mother's failure to guide her son
d. a child's vulnerability to destructive peer pressure

____ 2. Jerry's mother feels that it is important to
a. allow Jerry some independence.
b. monitor all of Jerry's activities.
c. spend a lot of time with Jerry.
d. preserve some time for herself.

____ 3. Which of the following quotations from the story best illustrates Jerry's internal conflict?
a. "He swam back to shore, relieved at being sure she was there, but all at once very lonely."
b. "They looked down gravely, frowning. He knew the frown."
c. "'I want some swimming goggles,' he panted, defiant and beseeching."
d. "All night the boy dreamed of the waterfilled cave in the rock, and as soon as breakfast was over he went to the bay."

____ 4. Which of the following is the best reading strategy to use as you read "Through the Tunnel"?
a. discussing events with a peer advisor
b. asking yourself questions as you read the story
c. scanning the story for key words and events
d. setting goals before reading the story

____ 5. What feelings motivate Jerry's resolution to swim through the tunnel?
a. delight in viewing the undersea world
b. rebellion against his mother's strictness
c. ambition to be a champion swimmer
d. shame at his childishness and fear

____ 6. An action that demonstrates Jerry's internal conflict is
a. diving off the rocks into the bay.
b. clowning for the local boys.
c. learning to hold his breath for two minutes.
d. obeying his mother's request that he not swim for the day.

7. Which of the following details would be most useful in answering questions about Jerry's motivation in "Through the Tunnel"?
   a. "And yet, as he ran, he looked back over his shoulder at the wild bay; and all morning, as he played on the safe beach, he was thinking of it."
   b. "The boys were gathering up their bits of clothing and running off along the shore to another promontory. They were leaving to get away from him."
   c. "He knew he must find his way through that cave, or hole, or tunnel, and out the other side."
   d. "He took the edges of the hole in his hands and drew himself into it, wriggling his shoulders in sidewise as he remembered he must, kicking himself along with his feet."

8. Jerry's preparations to swim the tunnel are
   a. determined and methodical.
   b. sloppy and careless.
   c. impulsive and irrational.
   d. timid and hesitant.

9. Before Jerry gets up the nerve to swim the tunnel, he
   a. swims halfway through the tunnel before turning around.
   b. asks the local boys for advice.
   c. trains himself to hold his breath for two minutes underwater.
   d. asks his mother for permission.

10. Which of the following would be a useful question to ask—and answer—while you read "Through the Tunnel"?
    a. Why does Jerry's mother prefer to spend time on the "safe" beach?
    b. How long have the local boys been able to swim through the barrier rock?
    c. Why is getting through the barrier rock so important to Jerry?
    d. How does Jerry stop his nose from bleeding after he holds his breath?

11. _____ will help you gain a fuller understanding of "Through the Tunnel."
    a. Reading other stories by Doris Lessing
    b. Picturing the dimensions of the barrier rock
    c. Predicting the outcome of Jerry's adventure
    d. Keeping questions in mind as you read

12. What question might you ask to increase your understanding of the following passage?
    Through his hot shame, feeling the pleading grin on his face like a scar that he could never remove, he looked up at the group of big brown boys on the rock and shouted, "Bonjour! Merci! Au revoir! Monsieur, monsieur!" while he hooked his fingers around his ears and waggled them.
    a. What kind of a face is Jerry making at the boys?
    b. What do the words *Bonjour! Merci! Au revoir! Monsieur, monsieur!* mean?
    c. Why is Jerry acting this way?
    d. Can the local boys see Jerry clearly from where they stand?

13. At the end of the story, Jerry feels
    a. disappointed and ashamed.
    b. proud and satisfied.
    c. excited and proud.
    d. defiant and sullen.

14. By the end of the story, Jerry has lost interest in the cave because he
    a. knows he has attained his goal.
    b. succumbs to his mother's pressure.
    c. understands his efforts were pointless.
    d. realizes how dangerous the tunnel is.

Vocabulary and Grammar

The following question consists of a related pair of words in CAPITAL LETTERS, followed by four lettered pairs of words. Choose the pair that best expresses a relationship similar to that expressed in the pair in capital letters.

____ 15. LUMINOUS : MOON ::
        a. astronomical : rocket
        b. ocean : lake
        c. sun : solar
        d. explosive : volcano

____ 16. Which emotion is most closely linked to *contrition?*
        a. happiness   b. guilt   c. fear   d. anger

____ 17. A complete subject consists of
        a. the essential noun that names the subject of a sentence
        b. the essential noun or pronoun that names the subject of a sentence
        c. the essential noun or pronoun that names the subject of a sentence and any
           words that modify the noun or pronoun
        d. any words that modify the subject of a sentence

____ 18. In "Through the Tunnel," the sight of a _____ near the tunnel's entrance frightens Jerry.
        a. contrition   b. frond   c. promontory   d. gout

____ 19. What is the complete subject in the following sentence?
        And then, at a hundred and sixty, the water beyond the rock was full of boys blowing like brown whales.
        a. a hundred and sixty   c. rock
        b. the water   d. the water beyond the rock

____ 20. In which sentence is the essential word or words of the subject underlined?
        a. The wildness of the <u>bay</u> appeals to him.
        b. <u>One</u> of the boys waves at him, giving him the encouragement he needs to join them.
        c. <u>The impact of the water</u> broke the rubber-enclosed vacuum.
        d. <u>His nose</u> bleeds so badly that he turns dizzy.

Essay Questions

21. In "Through the Tunnel," Jerry puts his own safety at risk to prove something to himself. Are personal challenges worth risking one's safety or health? State your opinion in a brief essay. Use details from the story to support your opinion.

22. Jerry struggles with conflicting feelings in "Through the Tunnel." What is Jerry's internal conflict? What actions represent both sides of this conflict? In a brief essay, describe and discuss Jerry's internal conflict and how he resolves it.

23. Jerry undergoes a change that may not be obvious to those around him but which has profound meaning for the boy. How does Jerry change from the beginning of the story to the end? What qualities does he gain? Which ones does he leave behind? Write a character sketch of Jerry, describing the changes he undergoes.

Name _____ Date _____

Selection Test

Critical Reading

In the blank, write the letter of the one best answer.

_____ 1. The author's primary purpose in "The Dog That Bit People" is to
a. persuade readers not to adopt dogs as house pets.
b. inform readers about animal behavior.
c. convince readers that he had good reason to dislike Muggs.
d. entertain readers with amusing anecdotes.

_____ 2. Thurber begins his essay with anecdotes about other dogs to
a. make fun of owners who take their relationships with dogs too seriously.
b. establish his fondness for dogs and set a humorous tone.
c. set a positive tone before describing the problems with Muggs.
d. tell an amusing story.

_____ 3. Which of the following would be the most appropriate replacement for the title of Thurber's essay?
a. "Why I Dislike Dogs"
b. "Man's Best Friend?"
c. "How Not to Train Dogs"
d. "A Most Unusual Pet"

_____ 4. Which of the following sentences best illustrates how Thurber uses odd juxtapositions to create a humorous effect?
a. "Muggs went up the backstairs and down the frontstairs and had me cornered in the living room."
b. "Muggs was afraid of only one thing, an electrical storm."
c. "Muggs would stand on the bench and eat."
d. "Muggs died quite suddenly one night."

_____ 5. Generally, Mother deals with conflicts involving Muggs by
a. punishing him.
b. making excuses for him.
c. training him.
d. sending him outside.

_____ 6. Which of the following sentences best illustrates how the author uses exaggeration to make the essay more humorous?
a. "They acted like pet mice, almost like mice somebody had trained."
b. "Nobody knew exactly what was the matter with him, but whatever it was made him irascible, especially in the mornings."
c. "Mother used to send a box of candy every Christmas to the people the Airedale bit."
d. "Lots of people reported our Airedale to the police but my father held a municipal office at the time and was on friendly terms with the police."

7. What does Thurber's mother hope to learn by attending the lecture on "Harmonious Vibrations"?
    a. how to get people to like the dog
    b. why the dog behaves as he does
    c. how to restore the dog's strength
    d. how to change the dog's behavior

8. Which line from the essay is the best example of a detail that can help you form a mental image?
    a. "He really wasn't my dog, as a matter of fact: I came home from a vacation one summer to find that my brother Roy had bought him while I was away."
    b. "Nobody could understand why we didn't get rid of the dog."
    c. "Muggs at his meals was an unusual sight."
    d. "He would rise slowly from the floor, growling low, and stalk stiff-legged and menacing toward nothing at all."

9. Thurber's anecdote about the thunder machine is intended to show
    a. how family members tried to adjust to the dog's behavior.
    b. how easily animals can be deceived by humans.
    c. how the author attempted to punish the dog for biting him.
    d. why neighbors wished the family would get rid of the dog.

10. Which element of a humorous essay does the following quotation best illustrate?
    Then he was all over it: he never bit anyone more than once at a time. Mother always mentioned that as an argument in his favor.
    a. exaggeration
    b. understatement
    c. irony
    d. anecdote

11. Forming mental images of the scenes Thurber describes is most helpful for
    a. appreciating the author's humor.
    b. understanding animal behavior.
    c. mapping the story.
    d. identifying conflict.

12. Which of the following quotations from the selection helps you create the most cartoon-like mental image?
    a. "He would rush into the house and hide under a bed or in a clothes closet."
    b. "Muggs' first free leap carried him all the way across the table and into a brass fire screen in front of the gas grate but he was back on his feet in a moment . . ."
    c. "I think that one or two people tried to poison Muggs—he acted poisoned once in a while . . ."
    d. "Still, in the years that we had him he bit everybody but Mother, and he made a pass at her once but missed."

13. Most people who'd been bitten by Muggs might describe Mother as
    a. an irresponsible dog owner.
    b. a generous woman.
    c. understanding and empathetic.
    d. mean spirited.

14. The author of "The Dog That Bit People" would most likely agree with which of the following statements?
    a. A bad experience with one dog is no reason to dislike all dogs.
    b. However badly dogs behave, one should try to please them.
    c. Most dogs are more trouble than they are worth.
    d. The more dogs one has, the easier it becomes to dislike them.

Vocabulary and Grammar

_____ 15. No one could predict when the _____ Muggs might bite someone.
   a. indignant   b. irascible   c. jangly   d. incredulity

_____ 16. A complete predicate consists of
   a. the essential verb that tells something about the subject of a sentence
   b. the essential verb or verb phrase that tells something about the subject of a sentence
   c. the essential verb or verb phrase that tells something about the subject of a sentence and any words that modify the verb or verb phrase or help it complete the sentence
   d. any words that modify the essential verb or verb phrase in a sentence

_____ 17. What is the complete predicate in the following sentence?
      The loud noise frightened Muggs so badly that he ran and hid for the rest of the day.
   a. The loud noise frightened Muggs
   b. frightened
   c. frightened Muggs so badly that he ran and hid
   d. frightened Muggs so badly that he ran and hid for the rest of the day

_____ 18. Mother seemed not to notice the _____ reactions of Muggs' victims.
   a. choleric   b. irascible   c. indignant   d. incredulity

The following question consists of a related pair of words in CAPITAL LETTERS, followed by four lettered pairs of words. Choose the lettered pair that best expresses a relationship similar to that expressed in the pair in capital letters.

_____ 19. INCREDULITY : DISBELIEF ::
   a. choleric ; patient
   b. irascible : relaxed
   c. epitaph : epilogue
   d. jangle : discord

_____ 20. In which sentence is only the essential word or words of the complete predicate underlined?
   a. Muggs stayed out in the pantry with the mice.
   b. He growled to himself about all the people in the next room that he would have liked to get at.
   c. One morning, when Muggs bit me slightly, I grabbed his tail.
   d. He took a different route and cornered me in the living room

Essay Questions

21. Thurber's lively tales of his wild dog Muggs create a highly entertaining story. What are some of the mental images that help you to envision the scenes Thurber describes? Choose two of your favorite anecdotes about Muggs, and in an essay analyze the details that help you to form mental images of the action.

22. As a comedic writer, Thurber expertly weaves different elements of humorous writing into "The Dog That Bit People." Which element do you find to be the most effective? Why? In a brief essay, state your opinion and support it with examples from Thurber's essay.

23. Although Thurber's essay treats Muggs' problems with humor, it also reveals much about how Thurber's family handles conflict. In an essay, explain what you learn about the interpersonal dynamic of the Thurber household. How does Mother's style of handling conflict differ from or reflect that of her sons? Support your conclusions with examples from the essay.

Unit 3: Clashing Forces

"Conscientious Objector" by Edna St. Vincent Millay
"A Man" by Nina Cassian
"The Weary Blues" by Langston Hughes
"Jazz Fantasia" by Carl Sandburg

Selection Test

Critical Reading

In the blank, write the letter of the one best answer.

_____ 1. The first response of the man who loses an arm in Nina Cassian's "A Man" is _____.
    a. anger
    b. sadness
    c. determination
    d. fear

_____ 2. Having lost an arm, the man in "A Man" thinks he
    a. must give up the piano.
    b. will be able to do half as much.
    c. will no longer attend shows where he must applaud.
    d. can no longer fight for his country.

_____ 3. The theme of "A Man" is
    a. the triumph of determination.
    b. the tragedy of war.
    c. the sacrifice required by patriotism.
    d. the difficulty of physical challenges.

_____ 4. The ending to "A Man"—"where the arm had been torn away/a wing grew"—means
    a. he recovered partially from his wound.
    b. he succeeded in spite of his loss.
    c. he learned skills with a single hand.
    d. his lover accepted him regardless of his injury.

_____ 5. In "Conscientious Objector," Edna St. Vincent Millay's adversary is _____.
    a. war
    b. slavery
    c. fear
    d. death

_____ 6. The tone of "Conscientious Objector" is _____.
    a. defiant
    b. respectful
    c. comic
    d. despairing

_____ 7. In "Conscientious Objector," why won't St. Vincent Millay reveal the whereabouts of her enemies?
    a. She cannot reliably know who her enemies might be.
    b. Her enemies are human and, like her, have a greater enemy.
    c. She has taken a vow of silence.
    d. She has not been promised enough to make the risk worthwhile.

_____ 8. Who is the "Brother" referred to at the end of "Conscientious Objector"?
   a. her adversary
   b. her actual brother
   c. the boy in the swamp
   d. her fellow man

_____ 9. The setting of "The Weary Blues" is
   a. a blues festival in New Orleans.
   b. a nightclub on Lenox Avenue.
   c. a steamboat on the Mississippi.
   d. a dark street lit by a gas lamp.

_____ 10. When the pianist in "The Weary Blues" made the piano "moan with melody," he
   a. played poorly though enthusiastically.
   b. hummed with the music.
   c. played sadly with feeling.
   d. banged violently on the keys.

_____ 11. The "blues" that the pianist sang were about _____.
   a. poverty
   b. labor
   c. racism
   d. loneliness

_____ 12. The theme expressed by the tone of "Jazz Fantasia" may be expressed as
   a. an imitation of music.
   b. an appreciation of the art form.
   c. the violence of the musicians.
   d. the role jazz played in history.

_____ 13. "Jazz Fantasia" creates its impression by
   a. using rhythms that sound like music.
   b. describing the troubles of the musicians.
   c. a series of images suggested by the music.
   d. listing various nontraditional instruments.

_____ 14. Images of love, a car chase, and a fight in "Jazz Fantasia" suggest
   a. the genuine feelings which jazz expresses.
   b. the negative reputation of the music.
   c. the failed personal lives of most musicians.
   d. specific sounds made by various instruments.

_____ 15. The tone of the section in "Jazz Fantasia" relating to the steamboat is _____.
   a. ironic
   b. gentle
   c. historic
   d. angry

Vocabulary and Grammar

_____ 16. The word _reap_ means
   a. fold
   b. attack
   c. gather
   d. deserve

____ 17. In which sentence is the usual subject-verb order reversed?
   a. I hear him leading his horse out of the stall.
   b. I will not tell him which way the fox ran.
   c. The plans of our city are safe with me.
   d. Never through me shall you be overcome.

____ 18. The word *pallor* means _____.
   a. flabbiness
   b. paleness
   c. meeting
   d. boredom

____ 19. The word *melancholy* means _____.
   a. depressed
   b. angry
   c. ill
   d. perplexed

____ 20. In sentences beginning with *here* or *there*
   a. the verb always follows the subject
   b. the verb is always a linking verb
   c. the subject usually follows the verb
   d. subject-verb order is never reversed

Essay Questions

21. A man loses his arm in Nina Cassian's poem, "A Man," and after considering his loss, tries to "do everything with twice as much enthusiasm." In some ways, understanding this resolve is easy to explain. He makes up for losing half his physical ability by doubling his effort. For those of us who are not physically challenged, however, there are other challenges which we must overcome with a change in attitude. How can a positive spirit like that of the man in Nina Cassian's poem help us to face such tasks? Write an essay in which you explain the role of attitude in overcoming obstacles. Give several specific examples from life, and show how one's state of mind is important in achieving goals.

22. A conscientious objector is one who, for reasons of ethical or religious belief, refuses to take part in warfare. Why would Edna St. Vincent Millay refer to herself as a conscientious objector in her poem about death? Is this title appropriate for the tone and images in the poem? Write an essay in which you discuss the title of "Conscientious Objector," and explain what Edna St. Vincent Millay objects to and how the poem shows her to be a conscientious objector. Use examples from the poem to illustrate your ideas.

23. Both Langston Hughes, in "The Weary Blues," and Carl Sandburg, in "Jazz Fantasia," write about unique forms of music. Each poet attempts to capture the essence of jazz and blues for the reader, yet each does so differently. Write an essay in which you consider the differing approaches of these two poets as they attempt a similar goal. Discuss setting, action, images, ideas, and tone as you assess the poets' perspectives on these distinct American art forms. Give specific examples from the poems to support your ideas.

"Like the Sun" by R. K. Narayan
"Tell all the Truth but tell it slant—" by Emily Dickinson

Selection Test

Critical Reading

In the blank, write the letter of the one best answer.

_____ 1. What is the nature of Sekhar's experiment in "Like the Sun"?
a. He wants to observe the different ways in which anger affects people.
b. He wants to find out if he can be completely truthful for one entire day.
c. He wants to learn more about the effects of sunlight on the Earth.
d. He wishes to study the effects of music on different people.

_____ 2. What is Sekhar's main reason for going through with the experiment?
a. He feels it will give everyone a good laugh.
b. He wants to please people.
c. He feels that without truth, life is meaningless.
d. He wants to get back at his enemies.

_____ 3. Why is Sekhar's negative response to his wife's "culinary masterpiece" an example of irony?
a. She spent hours preparing the meal.
b. He usually enjoys breakfast.
c. She knew he would not like the meal.
d. She was not expecting him to be so honest.

_____ 4. What is a consequence of Sekhar's truthfulness at his morning meal?
a. He leaves for work.
b. His wife prepares another meal.
c. His wife feels hurt and disappointed.
d. He is unable to finish his meal.

_____ 5. What does Sekhar's firm commitment to telling the truth at all costs say about his character?
a. He does not make friends easily.
b. He enjoys being rude.
c. He is kind and considerate.
d. He is sincerely interested in becoming an honest person.

_____ 6. How does Sekhar feel about being asked to the headmaster's home to critique the headmaster's singing?
a. excited
b. angry
c. pleased
d. uneasy

_____ 7. What becomes the most difficult test of Sekhar's vow to be truthful?
a. being honest with his co-workers
b. needing to tell the truth about his headmaster's singing
c. listening to music
d. making amends with his wife

Unit 3: Clashing Forces

____ 8. Why does Sekhar fear that losing his friends and his job might be a consequence of his decision to be honest?
    a. Honesty takes too much of his time.
    b. People do not want Sekhar to try to improve himself.
    c. People are against change.
    d. Hearing the truth often angers and hurts people.

____ 9. What seems ironic about the headmaster's response to Sekhar's criticism?
    a. The headmaster is openly angry with Sekhar.
    b. The headmaster refuses to speak to Sekhar.
    c. The headmaster seems to have accepted Sekhar's criticism.
    d. The headmaster seems hurt by the criticism.

____ 10. What is a consequence of Sekhar's decision to be brutally honest with the head-master?
    a. Sekhar has to spend his entire night correcting test papers.
    b. Sekhar has to find a new job.
    c. The headmaster spends more time practicing his music.
    d. Sekhar decides to stop teaching.

____ 11. What does Sekhar mean when he calls honesty a "luxury"?
    a. Being honest at all times is boring.
    b. Total honesty is a complete waste of time for most people.
    c. Total honesty can really only be practiced by people who do not need to succeed or get along with others.
    d. It is expensive to be honest.

____ 12. In "Tell all the Truth but tell it slant—," what does Dickinson mean when she says that truth must be told at a "slant"?
    a. People should lie.
    b. Truth should be at an angle.
    c. Truth should be told gently, not harshly.
    d. People should be brutally honest.

____ 13. To what does Dickinson compare truth?
    a. sunlight
    b. rainfall
    c. mountain slopes
    d. jewels

____ 14. According to Dickinson, what will happen if truth does not "dazzle gradually"?
    a. People will die.
    b. People will become blinded.
    c. Rain will fall.
    d. Truth will slant.

____ 15. What theme do "Like the Sun" and "Tell all the Truth but tell it slant—" share?
    a. It is impossible for people to be truthful.
    b. Achieving truth is a waste of time.
    c. People are dishonest.
    d. Truth is valuable but difficult to speak or hear.

Vocabulary and Grammar

____ 16. Sekhar is bothered by the fact that people are constantly _____ truth so that it might not shock.
    a. tempering
    b. ingratiating
    c. scrutinizing
    d. considering

____ 17. In the following sentence, which noun or pronoun is the direct object?
        He added half humorously, "I will give you a week's time."
    a. you   c. he
    b. time   d. week's

____ 18. Sekhar was _____ by the headmaster's singing.
    a. angered
    b. stupefied
    c. shirked
    d. scrutinized

____ 19. The headmaster reminds Sekhar that each paper must be carefully _____ .
    a. sorted
    b. tempered
    c. shirked
    d. scrutinized

____ 20. In the following sentence which noun or pronoun is an indirect object?
        No one would tell me the truth about my music all these days.
    a. me   c. music
    b. truth   d. days

Essay Questions

21. In a short essay, explain what Sekhar, the main character of "Like the Sun," means when he says that "Truth is like the sun." According to Sekhar, what characteristics do absolute truth and intense sunlight share? What has Sekhar observed about the way in which absolute truth's similarity to bright sunlight affects human behavior? Why does he feel his experiment is so crucial? Support your opinion with details from the selections.

22. In an essay, explain how "Like the Sun" makes use of the literary technique of irony of situation. Explain some of the events that violate the expectations of characters in the story. Why is Sekhar's statement at the end of the story—that "sitting up all night with a hundred test papers was a small price to pay for the luxury of practicing Truth"—particularly ironic?

23. In an essay, compare and contrast Sekhar's approach to expressing truth in "Like the Sun" to Emily Dickinson's approach to expressing truth in "Tell all the Truth but tell it slant—." In your essay, address the following questions: What specific details in each piece convey the idea that speaking and knowing truth is important? What does Dickinson mean when she says "Tell all the Truth but tell it slant—" and "The Truth must dazzle gradually . . ."? In what way does Sekhar's approach to introducing truth into his life seem to differ from Dickinson's approach? Does he express truth gradually, at a "slant"? Might he have had a more pleasant day had he read Dickinson's poem before he began his day of truth? Why, or why not?

"Hearts and Hands" by O. Henry
"The Fish" by Elizabeth Bishop

Selection Test

Critical Reading

In the blank, write the letter of the one best answer.

_____ 1. Based on this paragraph from "Hearts and Hands," choose a logical prediction.

> At Denver there was an influx of passengers into the coaches on the eastbound B. & M. express. In one coach there sat a very pretty young woman dressed in elegant taste and surrounded by all the luxurious comforts of an experienced traveler. Among the newcomers were two young men, one of handsome presence with a bold, frank countenance and manner; the other a ruffled, glum-faced person, heavily built and roughly dressed. The two were handcuffed together.

   a. The men will pose some threat to the young woman.
   b. The young woman is very haughty and will refuse to ride with a criminal.
   c. One man is a prisoner; the other is a law officer.
   d. The men will not be allowed to sit in the same coach with the young woman.

_____ 2. Of the following details from "Hearts and Hands," which might O. Henry have included to mislead readers as he builds toward his surprise ending?
   a. Passengers are boarding the train in Denver.
   b. The woman is described as an experienced traveler.
   c. One man is "handsome" and "bold"; the other is "glum-faced" and "roughly dressed."
   d. The two men are handcuffed together.

_____ 3. Suppose you are beginning to read "Hearts and Hands" for the first time. Which of the following conclusions about the young woman are logical based on the second sentence of the paragraph above?
   I. The young woman's servants will wait on her during the train ride.
   II. The young woman is wealthy.
   III. The young woman is traveling with her parents.
   IV. The young woman will play an important part in this story.
   a. I and II   b. I and IV   c. II and III   d. II and IV

_____ 4. When Miss Fairchild speaks to Mr. Easton, the narrator tells us he "roused himself sharply." Why is this a clue that he might not be a marshal?
   a. If he were a marshal, he would be acting "bold" and "frank."
   b. If he were a marshal escorting a criminal, he would be alert and watchful.
   c. If he were a marshal, he would have already greeted the young woman out of courtesy.
   d. If he were a marshal, he would have kept his prisoner away from a respectable-looking young woman.

_____ 5. In "Hearts and Hands," how is the presence of the handcuffs explained?
   a. Mr. Easton just raises his right hand and laughs.
   b. Mr. Easton says he needed money to keep up with the Washington crowd and tried counterfeiting.
   c. The glum-faced man speaks up and says Mr. Easton is taking him to Leavenworth for counterfeiting.
   d. The glum-faced man is a former train robber and must be guarded.

_____ 6. In "Hearts and Hands," why does the real marshal deceive Miss Fairchild?
  a. He doesn't want Miss Fairchild to worry about having a dangerous criminal on board.
  b. He enjoys fooling or teasing strangers.
  c. He is compassionate and wants to spare Mr. Easton some embarrassment.
  d. He wants to have a chance to get acquainted with Miss Fairchild because she is pretty.

_____ 7. Which of the following details hints that Mr. Easton is concerned about money, and that he might logically be a counterfeiter?
  a. " . . . well, a marshalship isn't quite as high a position as that of ambassador, . . . "
  b. "Money has a way of taking wings unto itself . . . ."
  c. "My butterfly days are over, I fear."
  d. "Duty calls, you know."

_____ 8. Why do the two men leave their seat across from Miss Fairchild?
  a. They have to go to another coach where criminals are supposed to travel.
  b. The train arrives at their destination.
  c. Mr. Easton's conversation with Miss Fairchild is over.
  d. They move into the smoker.

_____ 9. What evidence does the passenger at the end of the story use to figure out who the marshal is?
  a. The passenger knew that officers usually handcuff prisoners to their left hand.
  b. The passenger was slightly acquainted with Mr. Easton.
  c. The passenger noticed the "keen, shrewd eyes" of the older man and guessed he was the marshal.
  d. The passenger knew Mr. Easton was too young to be a marshal and guessed the older man was the marshal.

_____ 10. Which line from "Hearts and Hands" would logically lead a reader to conclude that Miss Fairchild admires Mr. Easton?
  a. "Well, Mr. Easton, if you _will_ make me speak first, I suppose I must."
  b. "And so now you are one of these dashing Western heroes . . . .'"
  c. "But you must go on to Leavenworth, I suppose?'"
  d. "The glad look in the girl's eyes slowly changed to a bewildered horror."

_____ 11. Based on the following passage from "The Fish," what is the most logical assumption a reader could make?

  I thought of the coarse white flesh / packed in like feathers, / the big bones and the little bones,

  a. The speaker is looking forward to eating the fish.
  b. The speaker thinks the old fish's meat will be tough and unappealing.
  c. The fish has been wounded so that the speaker can see the flesh and bones.
  d. The speaker thinks the meat will have too many bones in it.

_____ 12. Which of the following lines from "The Fish" is a clue to the surprise ending?
  a. "He hadn't fought at all."
  b. "While his gills were breathing in/the terrible oxygen . . ."
  c. "They shifted a little, but not/to return my stare."
  d. ". . . a five-haired beard of wisdom/trailing from his aching jaw."

_____ 13. What does the speaker in "The Fish" discover in the fish's mouth?
  a. five old fish hooks   b. green weeds   c. barnacles   d. a small fish

_____ 14. For some readers of "The Fish," the ending might not be a surprise because
  a. the speaker thinks the fish looks sad.
  b. the speaker indicates the fish is old and will therefore not be good to eat.

c. the boat is only rented, so they know that the speaker is not a serious fisherman.

d. the speaker spends so much time describing and admiring the fish.

_____ 15. What do the following lines from "The Fish" mean?
> and victory filled up / the little rented boat,

a. After seeing that this fish had gotten away from other fishermen, the speaker is especially pleased.

b. The idea of eating such a sought-after fish makes the catch even more valuable.

c. The speaker added the fish to a pile of other fish, nearly filling the little boat.

d. The speaker feels it is a good omen to have caught *this* fish on the first attempt.

Vocabulary and Grammar

_____ 16. The glum-faced man in "Hearts and Hands" forestalls Mr. Easton by

a. nudging him.

b. interrupting him.

c. speaking before Mr. Easton has a chance to.

d. begging Miss Fairchild to convince the marshal to be merciful.

_____ 17. The fish is described as infested with tiny white sea-lice because it

a. once had sea-lice but is now rid of them.   c. is crawling with sea-lice.

b. has a few sea-lice on its body.   d. has scars from having had sea-lice.

_____ 18. What are the parts of the compound predicate in the following sentence?
> When I arrived, the fisherwoman was sitting in her boat, reeling in her line, and hauling up the hugest fish I had ever seen.

a. arrived, had seen   c. reeling, hauling, had seen

b. arrived, was sitting, reeling   d. was sitting, reeling, hauling

_____ 19. Where would someone be most likely to sidle?

a. on a bus   c. on an escalator

b. in a hallway at the airport   d. in a check-out line at the grocery store

_____ 20. When a compound predicate consists of two or more verb phrases with the same helping verb

a. the helping verb is dropped.

b. the helping verb is often used only with the first verb.

c. the helping verb is always repeated before each verb.

d. the helping verb is often used only with the last verb.

Essay Questions

21. In an essay, explain how the speaker in "The Fish" and the marshal in "Hearts and Hands" show compassion. Then explain why compassion is important in our everyday lives. Cite examples of compassionate behavior you have seen or experienced.

22. "Hearts and Hands" contains a number of clues that foreshadow the ending. Having finished the story, use your knowledge of the outcome to identify, in an essay, as many clues or hints as you can. Explain how each is tied to the outcome.

23. O. Henry's story depends to some extent upon appearance and assumptions. Miss Fairchild, just like the rest of us, makes assumptions based on the appearance of the two men. In an essay, discuss how the description of the two men directs your own assumptions. What are the stereotypes that O. Henry is playing against? Consider the stereotyping you see in our own culture as depicted on television and in movies. Explain whether you think it is acceptable for television and movie producers to use stereotypes to convey certain attributes of their characters.

from *Desert Exile* by Yoshiko Uchida

"Speech on Japanese American Internment" by Gerald Ford

Selection Test

Critical Reading

In the blank, write the letter of the one best answer.

_____ 1. In *Desert Exile*, where were Uchida and her family assigned to live at Tanforan?
   a. in a former horse stable
   b. under the grandstand
   c. in a black tarpapered shack
   d. in a gloomy, cavernous hall

_____ 2. What was the writer's purpose for including the following detail in *Desert Exile*?
   The space, while perhaps a good source of ventilation for the horses, deprived us of all but visual privacy, and we couldn't even be sure of that because of the crevices and knotholes in the dividing walls.
   a. to inform readers that the family was living in a stall
   b. to emphasize the lack of privacy the family had to endure
   c. to tell readers that the walls of the stall were not very solid
   d. to describe how hot and stuffy the stalls were

_____ 3. Identify Uchida's purpose for including the following detail in *Desert Exile*.
   When I reached the serving table and held out my plate, a cook reached into a dishpan full of canned sausages and dropped two onto my plate with his fingers. Another man gave me a boiled potato and a piece of butterless bread.
   a. to point out the unsanitary serving habits and the unappealing food
   b. to call attention to the cook's lack of culinary talent
   c. to emphasize that there was only one serving table
   d. to note that the diet, though plain, was relatively balanced

_____ 4. What had the Uchidas packed in their camp bundle?
   a. coats and a tea kettle
   b. sleeping cots and bedding
   c. bedding, a tea kettle, and a hot plate
   d. coats and light bulbs

_____ 5. What does the following sentence from *Desert Exile* reveal about Uchida's attitude?
   I wondered how much the nation's security would have been threatened had the army permitted us to remain in our homes a few more days until the camps were adequately prepared for occupancy by families.
   a. She resents not having been allowed to pack more belongings since the camp wasn't ready anyway.
   b. She feels humiliated by having to live in such conditions.
   c. She recognizes a certain irony in being viewed as a threat to national security.
   d. She is angry that the camp was so poorly prepared.

_____ 6. Why does Uchida conclude that the army was "ill-equipped to build living quarters for women and children"?
   a. There were no women's latrines.
   b. There were no play areas for children.
   c. There were separate quarters for women and children.
   d. Basic civilities, such as shower curtains, were not provided.

_____ 7. Why would walking a mile for a hot shower boost the morale of Yoshiko and her sister?
   a. It got them out of the stall and away from their annoying neighbors.
   b. It was a small luxury that made them feel good.

c. It was the only chance they had to exercise.

d. They were allowed only one shower a week.

_____ 8. What reason does Uchida give for the fact that "there was little inclination for anyone to feel responsible for anyone else" in the early days at Tanforan?

a. the natural reserve and self-reliance of the Japanese

b. the lack of availability of basic necessities on top of the shock of the evacuation

c. the living conditions that kept people isolated from each other.

d. the close proximity with strangers who had no desire to get acquainted.

_____ 9. What kind of prior knowledge or experience would help a reader relate to the following detail from *Desert Exile*?

> We sat huddled on our cots, bundled in our coats, too cold and miserable even to talk.

a. having sat on an army cot

b. having nothing to say to one's family

c. having been cold and uncomfortable

d. having worn a coat

_____ 10. What is the occasion of Gerald Ford's "Remarks . . ."?

a. the signing of a proclamation

b. the celebration of the anniversary of an historical event

c. the repeal of Executive Order 9066

d. the official recognition that Japanese Americans were interned

_____ 11. What piece of prior knowledge would most help a reader understand Gerald Ford's "Remarks . . ."?

a. More than 100,000 Japanese Americans were interned.

b. The actual number of interned Japanese Americans is disputed by some members of the Japanese American Citizen League.

c. Some Japanese Americans were not interned, because they volunteered to serve in the military.

d. After World War II, Executive Order 9066 stopped being enforced but it was never officially terminated.

_____ 12. Why does Ford close with the reminder that Americans must "treasure liberty and justice for each individual American"?

a. He is reminding Japanese Americans how they should act.

b. He is recalling former enemies of the United States and how they threatened our nation.

c. He is encouraging people to fight for our country should it ever be threatened again.

d. He is acknowledging that the Japanese Americans had their liberty taken away from them.

_____ 13. Choose the statement that best describes Gerald Ford's purpose in writing his speech.

a. Ford commemorates the anniversary of the issuing of Executive Order 9066.

b. Ford restores lost property to Japanese Americans who experienced internment.

c. Ford acknowledges contributions made by Japanese Americans to the nation.

d. Ford officially acknowledges that Japanese Americans were treated unjustly during World War II.

_____ 14. What kind of concerns might Japanese Americans have had with regard to Executive Order 9066?

a. Since it was never officially terminated, it could have been used to intern Japanese Americans again.

b. They didn't want it to be used to intern any other immigrant groups.

c. The existence of the order prevented them from becoming full U.S. citizens.

d. They wanted it terminated to prove their loyalty to the United States.

_____ 15. You can use your prior knowledge
 a. so that you don't have to read material so carefully.
 b. to help summarize material you have read.
 c. to help you understand what you are reading.
 d. to understand characters' behaviors.

Vocabulary and Grammar

_____ 16. In *Desert Exile*, Yoshiko Uchida calls "apartments" a euphemism for "stalls" because
 a. "apartments" is a nicer word than the less-appealing "stalls."
 b. the apartments were shared by all.
 c. the apartments were far from the mess hall.
 d. "apartments" was what the camp administrator called them.

_____ 17. Yoshiko's mother placed signs in conspicuous places because
 a. she didn't want to get in trouble with the camp administrators.
 b. she wanted to be sure people saw and read them.
 c. she wanted only the women to see them.
 d. the signs were in Japanese.

_____ 18. In which sentence are the parts of the compound subject correctly underlined?
 a. An elderly <u>man</u> and a young <u>family</u> with two crying <u>babies</u> shared our table.
 b. Twenty-five <u>stalls</u> facing north and an <u>equal number</u> facing <u>south</u> comprised our stable.
 c. <u>Shelves</u>, a crude <u>table</u>, and two <u>benches</u> filled our makeshift livingroom.
 d. <u>Mama</u> and <u>Kay</u> made up the army <u>cots</u> with our <u>bedding</u>.

_____ 19. What joins the subjects in a compound subject?
 a. a preposition   c. a linking verb
 b. a conjunction   d. a predicate

_____ 20. To be *adept* is to be _____.
 a. clumsy   b. fast   c. unfamiliar with   d. highly skilled

Essay Questions

21. In an essay, draw conclusions about the American government's attitudes toward Japanese Americans in 1942. Give specific details from Uchida's account to support your conclusions. Discuss how appearances or stereotypes played a part in the attitudes and actions of American citizens and government officials.

22. If you read the excerpt from *Desert Exile* before you read Gerald Ford's speech, information you acquired from *Desert Exile* became prior knowledge that you were able to apply to the speech. Explain how details and attitudes you encountered in the excerpt from Uchida's *Desert Exile* affected how you responded to Ford's speech. Cite specific facts or ideas from *Desert Exile* that helped you understand or form an opinion about something in Ford's speech.

23. The U.S. Constitution guarantees all U.S. citizens certain civil liberties. These rights or liberties include freedom of speech, freedom of the press, freedom of petition and assembly, freedom of religion, the right to a trial by jury, and the right to have counsel. Explain in an essay how Executive Order 9066 resulted in the suspension of civil liberties for Japanese Americans. Discuss whether it is ever acceptable to suspend a U.S. citizen's civil liberties, either temporarily or permanently.

"The Cabuliwallah" by Rabindranath Tagore

Selection Test

Critical Reading

In the blank, write the letter of the one best answer.

_____ 1. What word best describes the relationship between Mini and her father at the beginning of the story?
a. distant
b. silly
c. loving
d. uncommunicative

_____ 2. How does Mini respond at first to the Cabuliwallah?
a. She squeals with delight.
b. She flees in fear.
c. She is surprised by his offer of nuts and raisins.
d. She approaches him with caution.

_____ 3. Which of the following images appeals to your sense of hearing?
a. He put his hand inside his big loose robe and brought out a small dirty piece of paper.
b. He wore the loose, soiled clothing of his people, and a tall turban.
c. He would reply in the nasal accents of a mountaineer: "An elephant!"
d. After the rains, there was a sense of cleanness in the air, and the rays of the sun looked like pure gold.

_____ 4. What do Mini's father and the Cabuliwallah have in common?
a. They share an interest in writing.
b. They share similar political views.
c. They both were born in Afghanistan.
d. They both are fathers.

_____ 5. How does Mini's relationship with her father change?
a. As Mini matures, she and her father grow apart.
b. As Mini matures, she and her father enjoy quiet talks in his study.
c. As Mini matures, she relies upon her father for advice.
d. Mini's relationship with her father remains lively and fun-loving.

_____ 6. Select the two best reasons why Mini and the Cabuliwallah develop such a close relationship.
I. Mini reminds the Cabuliwallah of his own daughter.
II. Mini is lonely.
III. The Cabuliwallah is a patient listener to Mini's chatter.
IV. Mini understands the Cabuliwallah's funny jokes.
a. I & II
b. I & III
c. II & III
d. II & IV

_____ 7. Which of the following statements is false?
   a. The narrator, Mini's father, is devoted to his writing.
   b. The Cabuliwallah is a lower-class fruit seller from Afghanistan.
   c. While in prison, the Cabuliwallah receives from Mini small gifts of raisins and nuts.
   d. Mini and the Cabuliwallah meet again briefly on her wedding day.

_____ 8. Which of the following images engages your sense of touch?
   a. . . . I would fall to weaving a network of dreams: the mountains, the glens, the forests of his distant homeland with a cottage in its setting. . .
   b. All at once I heard an uproar in the street.
   c. . . . looking with all her tiny dignity on his gigantic frame, Mini would ripple her face with laughter.
   d. With great care he unfolded this [dirty piece of paper] and smoothed it out with both hands on my table.

_____ 9. How does Mini's mother show her love for Mini?
   a. She is overprotective of Mini's safety and well-being.
   b. She gives Mini lavish clothes.
   c. She invites Mini's friends for frequent visits.
   d. She encourages Mini's friendship with the Cabuliwallah.

_____ 10. What does the Cabuliwallah gain from his relationship with Mini?
   a. a chance to meet Mini's father
   b. a chance to think of his own daughter while spending time with Mini
   c. a loving place in Mini's family
   d. a more privileged status in Indian society

_____ 11. What change in Mini's response to the Cabuliwallah most clearly shows that she has grown up?
   a. She treats the Cabuliwallah with disdain.
   b. She understands the double meaning of "father-in-law's house" and blushes.
   c. She does not want to meet the Cabuliwallah again.
   d. She no longer wants to hear the elephant joke.

_____ 12. To what sense does the imagery in the following sentence appeal?
   Clad in the red silk of her wedding day, with the sandal paste on her forehead, and adorned as a young bride, Mini came and stood bashfully before me.
   a. sight
   b. hearing
   c. touch
   d. smell

_____ 13. What is Mini's father's final act of kindness and justice toward Rahmun, the Cabuliwallah?
   a. He invites the Cabuliwallah to Mini's wedding.
   b. He allows Mini and the Cabuliwallah to revive their old friendship.
   c. He gives the Cabuliwallah money to return home to his daughter.
   d. He tells the Cabuliwallah that his arrest was unjust.

_____ 14. What does the Cabuliwallah sadly realize at the end of the story, when he sees Mini dressed in her red silk wedding sari?
   a. that Mini is a beautiful young bride
   b. that he has intruded upon Mini's wedding day
   c. that his own daughter, too, has grown up while he was in prison
   d. that he is no longer welcome in Mini's house

Vocabulary and Grammar

_____ 15. The word *judicious* means
   a. making judgments without facts or knowledge.
   b. exhibiting sound judgment.
   c. dangerously lacking in security.
   d. exhibiting unstable characteristics.

_____ 16. Which word in the following sentence is the predicate nominative?
   Mini and the Cabuliwallah were now great friends, and their quaint jokes afforded them a great deal of amusement.
   a. Mini
   b. Cabuliwallah
   c. friends
   d. them

_____ 17. The phrase "father-in-law's house" is a(n) _____ for jail.
   a. antecedent
   b. antonym
   c. euphemism
   d. sensory detail

_____ 18. On the day of Mini's wedding, noise and great excitement _____ the house.
   a. implored
   b. pervaded
   c. fettered
   d. preceded

_____ 19. A subject and a predicate nominative are two different words
   a. that describe the subject of a sentence.
   b. for the same person, place, or thing.
   c. with different meanings.
   d. commonly joined by a conjunction.

_____ 20. Which word in the following sentence is the predicate adjective?
   To Tangore's wary wife, the Cabuliwallah's unusual friendship with her outgoing daughter was suspicious.
   a. wary
   b. unusual
   c. outgoing
   d. suspicious

Essay Questions

21. Tagore's story "The Cabuliwallah" includes many details that engage the senses of sight, hearing, taste, touch, and smell. Choose three sensory details from the story that evoke an image of Mini, Mini's father or mother, or of the Cabuliwallah. In an essay, fully explain how the details engage your senses and how they form a picture of the character in your mind.

22. The Cabuliwallah's arrest and eight-year imprisonment are the turning point in his relationship with Mini. In an essay, compare and contrast their relationship before and after his arrest.

23. In an essay, explain the probable series of events leading to the Cabuliwallah's arrest. In connection with these events, also consider the following questions: Who caused the trouble between Rahmun, the Cabuliwallah, and the "certain neighbor"? Who is the owner of the knife? Is the arrest of the Cabuliwallah justified? What can be inferred about the caste system in India at the time of this story? Use details from the story to support your ideas.

Name _____ Date _____

Unit Test: Clashing Forces

Critical Reading

In the blank, write the letter of the one best answer.

The questions below are based on the following selection.

In the following excerpt from Anton Chekhov's short story "Gooseberries," a narrator describes a difficult visit he has with his brother, who spent years saving and planning for an estate that has servants and his own gooseberry bushes.

In the evening when we were having tea, the cook served a plateful of gooseberries. They were not bought, they were his own gooseberries, the first ones picked since the bushes were planted. . . . he put one berry in his mouth, glanced at me with the triumph of a child who has at last been given a toy he was longing for and said: "How tasty!" And he ate the gooseberries greedily, and kept repeating: "Ah, how delicious! Do taste them!" They were hard and sour . . .

I saw a happy man, one whose cherished dream had so obviously come true, who had attained his goal in life, who had got what he wanted . . . Behind the door of every contented, happy man there ought to be someone standing with a little hammer and continually reminding him with a knock that there are unhappy people, that however happy he may be, life will sooner or later show him its claws, and trouble will come to him—illness, poverty, losses, and then no one will see or hear him, just as now he neither sees nor hears others. But there is no man with a hammer. The happy man lives at his ease, faintly fluttered by small daily cares, like an aspen in the wind . . .

_____ 1. Which of the following images engages the reader's sense of taste?
   a. I saw a happy man, one whose cherished dream had so obviously come true
   b. "Ah, how delicious! Do taste them!" They were hard and sour . . .
   c. Behind the door of every contented, happy man there ought to be someone standing with a little hammer and continually reminding him with a knock that there are unhappy people.
   d. The happy man lives at his ease, faintly fluttered by small daily cares, like an aspen in the wind.

_____ 2. The image of the narrator's brother as "a child who has at last been given a toy he was longing for" conveys the idea that
   a. the brother is content because his own needs have been fulfilled
   b. the brother is much younger than the narrator
   c. the brother enjoys playing with toys and having fun
   d. the brother appreciates what he has

_____ 3. Why doesn't the brother seem to notice the sour taste of the gooseberries?
   a. He is distracted by the idea that his brother has come to visit him.
   b. He does not want the narrator to know the gooseberries he grew are sour.
   c. He is caught up in his own greed and self-satisfaction.
   d. He has never had gooseberries before.

_____ 4. How does the narrator feel about his brother's happiness and success?
   a. content
   b. uneasy
   c. jealous
   d. surprised

_____ 5. According to the narrator, what does every happy man forget?
a. that there is suffering in the world
b. to visit relatives
c. that he must continue to work hard
d. that he should reward himself with servants

_____ 6. According to the narrator, what will happen to the happy man who eventually experiences suffering?
a. He will get help from his community.
b. Nobody will see him or hear him.
c. He will have the strength to help himself.
d. People will laugh at him.

_____ 7. Which of the following images best expresses the narrator's view of life?
a. . . . life will sooner or later show him its claws . . .
b. I saw a happy man, one whose cherished dream had so obviously come true, who had attained his goal in life
c. . . . And he ate the gooseberries greedily, and kept repeating: "Ah, how delicious!"
d. The happy man lives at his ease . . .

_____ 8. The narrator uses the image of the happy man "faintly fluttered by small daily cares, like an aspen in the wind" to emphasize the idea that
a. nature is beautiful and peaceful.
b. happy people often do not look beyond themselves and the present.
c. people should use their wealth to plant trees.
d. people are never truly happy.

_____ 9. What creates internal conflict within the narrator?
a. the fact that he cannot tell his brother that the gooseberries are sour
b. the idea that his brother has achieved happiness but he has not
c. the idea that achieving happiness leads to selfishness and ignorance of reality
d. the wish to see his brother more often

_____ 10. How would you describe the tone of the last paragraph of the selection?
a. enthusiastic
b. casual
c. serious
d. humorous

Vocabulary and Grammar

Choose the word(s) that best completes each sentence.

_____ 11. The musician played a slow and _____ blues tune on his piano.
a. melancholy
b. complicated
c. infested
d. stupefied

_____ 12. What is the complete predicate in the following sentence?
I grabbed Muggs's tail one morning when he bit me.
a. when he bit me   c. grabbed Muggs's tail one morning when he bit me
b. I grabbed Muggs's tail   d. grabbed

In the blank, write the letter of the one best answer.

____ 13. In the following sentence, what is the essential word or words in the complete subject?
       The bluish green water beyond the big dark barrier rock was full of triumphant
       boys blowing like brown whales.

    a. barrier rock   c. boys
    b. water   d. whales

____ 14. What are the parts of the compound subject in the following sentence?
       An elderly man and a young family with two crying babies shared our table.

    a. man, family   c. man, family, babies, table
    b. man, family, babies   d. babies, table

____ 15. Which of the following is the best meaning of the word *incessantly* as it is used in the
following sentence?

Sekhar's boss chatted incessantly about music.

    a. calmly
    b. quietly
    c. angrily
    d. endlessly

The questions below consist of a related pair of words in CAPITAL LETTERS followed by four
lettered pairs of words. Choose the pair that best expresses a relationship similar to that of the
pair in capital letters.

____ 16. LUMINOUS : SUN ::
    a. darkness : night
    b. light : lamp
    c. fragrant : rose
    d. sky : overcast

____ 17. SHIRKED : RESPONSIBILITY ::
    a. neglected : duty
    b. honor : promises
    c. avoid : escape
    d. move : slowly

____ 18. ASSUAGE : UPSET ::
    a. thrill : excite
    b. organize : arrange
    c. flatter : insult
    d. pleased : furious

Questions 19 and 20 are based on the sentence below.
       Emily Dickinson gives her readers useful advice about the need to "dazzle gradually."

____ 19. Which word is the direct object?
    a. her   c. advice
    b. need   d. readers

____ 20. Which word is the indirect object?
    a. her   c. advice
    b. need   d. readers

Essay Questions

21. Life often presents many struggles and battles of will, both large and small. People often have to make choices about how they will deal with these battles. The selections in this unit present a variety of characters experiencing struggle, such as the excerpts from *Desert Exile* and "Hearts and Hands." With which character's experience did you most identify? Write an essay in which you identify the struggle of one character in the unit and then explain what you liked or didn't like about how the character handled the struggle.

22. Selections such as "Hearts and Hands," "The Fish," from *Desert Exile,* and "Remarks Upon Signing a Proclamation" deal specifically with struggles for different types of justice. In an essay, describe how the issue of justice is addressed in one of these selections. What type of justice is in danger? Does justice win by the end of the selection? Explain.

23. When you think of "clashing forces," you may think of arguments between people, wars between countries, or the battles between man and nature. Some struggles, however, are internal struggles that take place inside a single person such as the speaker in "The Fish" and Jerry in "Through the Tunnel." In an essay, describe the opposing forces within a character of your choice and explain how he or she deals with this struggle. Support your ideas with details from the selection.

24. In stories or poems, writers present vivid details that can help you to form mental images of their characters and scenes. In an essay, name two selections in the unit that were most vivid for you. Describe the specific words and phrases that helped you to create mental images, and explain how these mental images helped you to appreciate the selections.

25. When a writer creates an essay, he or she often has a specific purpose. Sometimes an author's purpose is to entertain, and sometimes his or her purpose is to inform or persuade. In an essay, compare the nonfiction pieces "The Dog that Bit People," the excerpt from *Desert Exile,* and Ford's "Remarks Upon Signing a Proclamation." What is each writer's purpose? What specific details reveal the writer's purpose in each selection?

from *Speak, Memory* by Vladimir Nabokov

Selection Test

Critical Reading

In the blank, write the letter of the one best answer.

_____ 1. The selection from Nabokov's *Speak, Memory* is a personal narrative because
I. it is a true story drawn from his own life.
II. it is a fictional account of his own life.
III. it is told from the first-person point of view.
IV. it is told from the third-person point of view.
   a. I and II   b. I and III   c. II and III   d. III and IV

_____ 2. In his personal narrative, Nabokov describes
   a. memories of an upper-class Russian life.
   b. memories of his childhood reading experiences.
   c. the tumultuous Russian Revolution of 1917.
   d. his relationship with his beloved parents.

_____ 3. In *Speak, Memory*, who are Ben, Dan, Sam, Ned, Meg, Weg, Sarah Jane, and Midget?
   a. Nabokov's childhood friends   c. characters in Nabokov's novels
   b. Nabokov's brothers and sisters   d. characters in children's books

_____ 4. What do you think is Nabokov's purpose for including the following passage from "Speak, Memory"?

> Summer *soomerki*—the lovely Russian word for dusk. . . . The day would take hours to fade, and everything—sky, tall flowers, still water—would be kept in a state of infinite vesperal suspense, deepened rather than resolved by the doleful moo of a cow in a distant meadow or by the still more moving cry that came from some bird beyond the lower course of the river, where the vast expanse of a misty-blue sphagnum bog, because of its mystery and remoteness, the Rukavishnikov children had baptized America.

   a. to honor this childhood memory and let readers know what a peaceful, satisfying time of day this was
   b. to persuade readers that summertime is more beautiful in Russia than anywhere else
   c. to entertain readers by recounting this boisterous, playful time of day
   d. to let readers know what a sad, mournful time of day this was

_____ 5. Which of the following statements most accurately explains the way in which writers develop a particular bias?
   a. A writer's mood at the time of writing influences his or her point of view.
   b. The particular audience that a writer has in mind influences his or her point of view.
   c. A writer's upbringing and lifelong experiences influence his or her point of view.
   d. A writer's purpose for writing influences his or her point of view.

_____ 6. What was Nabokov's purpose in writing this personal narrative?
   a. to describe aristocratic life in pre-revolutionary Russia
   b. to emphasize the effect learning to read had upon him as a child
   c. to compare and contrast a number of characters from a variety of children's books
   d. to emphasize the importance of learning more than one language

© Prentice-Hall, Inc.

Unit 4: Turning Points

_____ 7. From what kind of background does Nabokov come?

    a. peasant   b. Bolshevik   c. middle class   d. aristocratic

_____ 8. Which of the following statements most accurately describes the effect of Nabokov's childhood reading experience?

    a. Reading helped Nabokov fill many lonely hours of his childhood.

    b. Reading had a profound effect upon Nabokov's childhood as well as upon his adult life.

    c. Reading helped Nabokov develop his formidable memory skills.

    d. Reading helped Nabokov learn how to empathize with the "simple souls" described in his childhood books.

_____ 9. How does Nabokov's background influence his attitude toward Ben, Dan, Sam, and Ned?

    a. Nabokov's peasant heritage enables him to feel great empathy toward them.

    b. Nabokov's aristocratic background causes him to feel smug and superior toward them.

    c. Nabokov's aristocratic background influences him to see them as "four simple souls."

    d. Nabokov's liberal training causes him to identify with them.

_____ 10. Why does Nabokov include such a detailed description of his mother's ruby and diamond ring?

    a. because he wants the reader to know that it later paid for many years of émigré life

    b. because he wants the reader to see its beauty

    c. because he wants the reader to understand how wealthy the Nabokovs are

    d. because he wants the reader to understand its worth

_____ 11. What is Nabokov's response to Midget's experience in the following passage?

> And, yes—the airship. Yards and yards of yellow silk went to make it, and an additional tiny balloon was provided for the sole use of the fortunate Midget. At the immense altitude to which the ship reached, the aeronauts huddled together for warmth while the lost little soloist, still the object of my intense envy notwithstanding his plight, drifted into an abyss of frost and stars—alone.

    a. He wants to ride in an airship, too.

    b. He decides to become an aeronaut.

    c. He empathizes, envies, and identifies with Midget's solo experience.

    d. He is intensely envious of Midget's flight experience.

_____ 12. To which senses do the details in the following passage appeal?

> Pears' Soap, tar black when dry, topaz-like when held to the light between wet fingers, took care of one's morning bath.

    a. sight and sound   b. sight and touch   c. sight and taste   d. sight and smell

_____ 13. Why does Nabokov describe his family as the kind "now extinct"?

    a. because he is the only surviving member of his family

    b. because it is no longer fashionable to be a member of the aristocracy

    c. because he is now a member of the middle class

    d. because the Russian Revolution destroyed, or forced into exile, Russia's aristocracy

_____ 14. What is so memorable about the way in which Nabokov describes his childhood reading experience?

    a. His quotations from the stories make the characters come alive.

    b. He makes the reader think about his or her own childhood reading experience.

    c. He engages the reader with vivid descriptions and details that appeal to the senses.

    d. He clearly states to the reader the importance of his early reading experience.

Vocabulary and Grammar

_____ 15. The prefix *pro-* means
a. a number of things moving forward.   c. before in place or time, or moving forward.
b. an expertise or knowledge.   d. ominous.

_____ 16. The word *proficiency* means
a. an expertise.   b. with great difficulty.   c. professional.   d. perfectly clear.

_____ 17. From the English Shop on Nevski Avenue came a _____ of "snug, mellow things . . . : fruitcakes, smelling salts, playing cards, picture puzzles, striped blazers, talcum-white tennis balls."
a. prologue   b. proficiency   c. procession   d. purpose

_____ 18. Which statement describes the use of clauses in the following sentence?
Her voice would slow down, and her words would be spaced portentously.
a. An independent clause is followed by a subordinate clause.
b. An independent clause is followed by an independent clause.
c. A subordinate clause is followed by an independent clause.
d. A subordinate clause is followed by a subordinate clause.

_____ 19. Which of the following statements combine to define a subordinate clause?
I. It has a subject and a verb.
II. It cannot stand alone as a sentence.
III. It can appear before or after an independent clause.
IV. It can appear in the middle of an independent clause.
a. I and II   c. II, III and IV
b. I, II and III   d. I, II, III and IV

_____ 20. What is the subordinate clause in the following sentence?
The magic has endured, and whenever a grammar book comes my way, I instantly turn to the last page to enjoy a forbidden glimpse of the laborious student's future. . . .
a. The magic has endured
b. whenever a grammar book comes my way
c. I instantly turn to the last page
d. to enjoy a forbidden glimpse

Essay Questions

21. Explain in an essay how Nabokov's first reading experiences influenced his later life. Support your answer with details from the selection.

22. One of the ways in which Nabokov engages the reader in his personal narrative is through the use of sensory details. In an essay, identify a passage that makes effective use of sensory details. How does Nabokov appeal to the reader's senses?

23. In an essay, consider the point of view Nabokov takes toward the Russian Revolution. Describe his experiences and how they might have influenced his attitude. Support your answer with details from the narrative.

© Prentice-Hall, Inc.

Speak, Memory **81**

Unit 4: Turning Points

Name _____ Date _____

"**Games at Twilight**" by Anita Desai

Selection Test

Critical Reading

In the blank, write the letter of the one best answer.

_____ 1. Why are the children too eager to go outdoors and play at the start of "Games at Twilight"?
a. They are beginning to bicker and feel they need their own space.
b. Their faces are turning red and they are having trouble breathing.
c. They have been in the house all day and they are feeling restless.
d. It will be a refreshing change from the heat of the house.

_____ 2. What does the narrator mean by "worthier prey" in the following passage from "Games at Twilight"?
"You're dead," he said with satisfaction, licking the beads of perspiration off his upper lip, and then stalked off in search of worthier prey, whistling spiritedly so that the hiders should hear and tremble.
a. children he dislikes
b. children who will not be easily caught
c. children who have chosen poor hiding places
d. children he will be able to find quickly

_____ 3. In the following passage from "Games at Twilight," what do Mira's actions reveal about her personality?
The motherly Mira intervened. She pulled the boys roughly apart. . . "Make a circle, make a circle!" she shouted, firmly pulling and pushing till a kind of vague circle was formed.
a. She is a natural leader.   c. She is rough and uncaring.
b. She is reluctant to take charge.   d. She is gentle, but stern.

_____ 4. In "Games at Twilight," why does Ravi charge at the other children, crying, "I won, I won, I won!"?
a. He is pleased with the children's reaction to his victory.
b. He is upset at being forgotten and wants their attention.
c. He is angry that his brother Raghu is claiming to have known where Ravi had hidden.
d. He is furious that he was chosen to be "It" in the next game.

_____ 5. What initially motivates Ravi to enter the shed in "Games at Twilight"?
a. his certainty that he will win the game if he hides in there
b. knowing that he can easily slip back out and find another hiding place
c. his amusement that he would consider something so bold
d. his fear that his brother Raghu will find him on the flower pot

_____ 6. When evaluating a character's decision, it is important to consider
a. how things might have been different if the character had made a different decision.
b. the character's problem, motivation, and the final outcome of the decision.
c. the character's other options and the pros and cons of each option.
d. how the decision affected other characters in the story.

_____ 7. In "Games at Twilight," why would the children's games "become legitimate" in the evening?
    a. Their parents would sit on the lawn and watch them.
    b. They would play games that their parents chose for them.
    c. The gardener would moisten the ground, making it easier to run.
    d. The weather would cool down, making it safe to play outdoors.

_____ 8. Which of the following statements accurately evaluates Ravi's decision to remain in the shed?
    a. Ravi made a poor decision, given the other options he had and the disappointing outcome.
    b. Ravi's decision was the best he could have made considering his age and ability.
    c. Ravi made a pretty good decision, considering the other options available to him.
    d. Ravi made a poor decision, given the affect of his behavior on the other children.

_____ 9. Which of the following statements reflects Ravi's feeling toward Raghu?
    a. He admires Raghu's gentle and compassionate nature.
    b. He is intimidated by Raghu but also admires him.
    c. He thinks Raghu is a bully and has no respect for him.
    d. He thinks Raghu is weak and cowardly.

_____ 10. What is it about the shed that makes Ravi apprehensive?
    a. It is filled with broken furniture, spiders, and rats.
    b. It is old and rickety, and he is afraid it might fall apart.
    c. He is afraid that once he gets inside he will not be able to get back out.
    d. It is not a very good hiding place; Raghu could easily find him.

_____ 11. How do the other children feel about Ravi after he charges at them?
    a. They feel bad that they have forgotten about him, and they want to make it up to him.
    b. They are angry at him for interfering with their game.
    c. They don't remember who he is at first and are not sure what he's carrying on about.
    d. They are happy to see him because they were worried about him and wondered where he was.

_____ 12. Why is Ravi so determined to win the game of hide-and-seek in "Games at Twilight"?
    a. Raghu always wins, and Ravi wants to show that he can win, too.
    b. He wants to prove something to the other children because they always tease him about his size.
    c. He believes that defeating the older, bigger children would be thrilling beyond imagination.
    d. He feels that the other children do not take him seriously.

_____ 13. What causes Ravi to finally leave the shed in "Games at Twilight"?
    a. He hears the other children calling for him to join them.
    b. He remembers that he must touch the "den" in order to win.
    c. He is feeling confined and overheated in the stuffy shed.
    d. He wants to smell the "intoxicating scent of water on dry earth."

_____ 14. At the end of "Games at Twilight," the other children invite Ravi to
    a. play a funeral game.
    b. play another game of hide-and-seek.
    c. sit on the veranda and "share a loot of mulberries."
    d. run through the water falling from the hosepipe.

© Prentice-Hall, Inc.

Vocabulary and Grammar

____ 15. What is the subordinating conjunction that introduces the less important idea in the following sentence.

> Ravi had once gotten locked in the linen cupboard and sat there weeping for half an hour before he was rescued.

    a. for   c. into
    b. before   d. and

____ 16. In "Games at Twilight," another way of saying that Ravi "*sidled* away" is to say that he _____.

    a. crawled on his hands and knees
    b. walked slowly backwards
    c. jumped forward in an awkward manner
    d. moved slowly to the side

____ 17. The word *defunct* means

    a. dirty   c. dead
    b. thriving   d. empty

____ 18. Choose the sentence in which the less important idea is italicized.

    a. Only small Manu reappeared, *as if he had dropped out of an invisible cloud*, and stood for a moment in the center of the yellow lawn.
    b. Ravi sat dejectedly *on the flower pot* which was cut to his own size.
    c. The parents would sit out on the lawn on cane basket chairs and *watch the children* as they tore around the garden.
    d. *It then occurred to him* that he could have slipped out long ago, dashed across the yard to the veranda and touched the "den."

____ 19. If someone is "dogged" he or she

    a. is rude and obnoxious.   c. likes to be in control.
    b. does not give in easily.   d. is easily swayed.

____ 20. Writers use subordination when they

    a. connect equal but unrelated ideas in a complex sentence.
    b. connect two subordinate clauses to form a sentence.
    c. connect unequal but related ideas in a complex sentence.
    d. connect equal ideas with a subordinating conjunction.

Essay Questions

21. In an essay, explain what motivates Ravi to win the game of hide-and-seek in "Games at Twilight." Why is winning so important to him? Does his plan work out the way he hopes? Why or why not?

22. Write an essay explaining how the use of dialogue in "Games at Twilight" contributes to the development of the story. How does it affect the plot? What does it reveal about Ravi's personality? his motivation? What does it reveal about Mira and Raghu?

23. Write an essay evaluating the decision Ravi made in "Games at Twilight." Consider all the factors that went into it: the problem itself, Ravi's motivation, his options, the pros and cons of each option, and the final outcome of his decision. Was it the best decision Ravi could have made? Why or why not?

"The Bridge" by Leopold Staff
"The Old Stoic" by Emily Brontë
"I Am Not One of Those Who Left the Land" by Anna Akhmatova
"Speech During the Invasion of Constantinople" by Empress Theodora

Selection Test

Critical Reading

In the blank, write the letter of the one best answer.

____ 1. In Brontë's "The Old Stoic," the speaker's most important value is _____.
   a. prayer
   b. liberty
   c. love
   d. art

____ 2. In "The Old Stoic," when Brontë seeks a "chainless soul," she means
   a. she wishes to find someone her equal.
   b. she wishes to be free of the cares of money.
   c. she wishes to be free from her family.
   d. she wishes her thoughts to be unrestricted.

____ 3. "The Old Stoic" seems dramatic because
   a. the speaker has experienced considerable personal stress.
   b. the audience will object to its themes.
   c. its tone and its message are self-reliant.
   d. a stoic makes emotional statements.

____ 4. The word that best characterizes Brontë's perspective in "The Old Stoic" is _____.
   a. loneliness
   b. independence
   c. hostility
   d. isolation

____ 5. In "The Bridge," by Leopold Staff, the speaker doesn't believe he has the ability to cross the bridge
   a. without help.
   b. until he crosses.
   c. because the bridge is too fragile.
   d. before or after he crosses.

____ 6. When the speaker in "The Bridge" says he walked "delicately as a butterfly/And heavily as an elephant" he is describing
   a. his hope and determination.
   b. his caution and anxiety.
   c. his body and his mind.
   d. his past and the present.

____ 7. The setting of "The Bridge" refers to
   a. moving into the future.
   b. a bridge destroyed in World War II.
   c. a formidable challenge.
   d. the power of memory.

8. In "The Bridge," the speaker suggests his success in crossing is
    a. hard to explain.
    b. a result of courage.
    c. certain from the first.
    d. a miracle.

9. In "Speech During the Invasion of Constantinople," Theodora rises to speak because
    a. the rebellion has failed.
    b. Justinian is about to abandon his empire.
    c. the emperor has been killed by Hypatius.
    d. she has been asked to do so by advisors.

10. Theodora's opinion in "Speech During the Invasion of Constantinople" is that
    a. women should speak in council during grave situations.
    b. those who are in extreme danger should follow conventional behavior.
    c. the right course is to pursue safety.
    d. it is better to die as a ruler than live as a fugitive.

11. In "Speech During the Invasion of Constantinople," Theodora is motivated by
    a. her royal pride.
    b. her love for her husband.
    c. her contempt for the rebels.
    d. her disgust with the advisors.

12. What is the dramatic situation of "I Am Not One of Those Who Left the Land" by Anna Akhmatova?
    a. War has broken out.
    b. Her homeland has been occupied by foreigners.
    c. Her family and friends have all left their homeland.
    d. Her village is under attack.

13. In "I Am Not One of Those Who Left the Land," Akhmatova writes "their flattery leaves me cold." To whom is she referring?
    a. survivors who do not flinch
    b. enemies who show mercy
    c. absent ones who praise her work
    d. people who have no tears

14. In "I Am Not One of Those Who Left the Land," what is Akhmatova's attitude toward those who left?
    a. contempt
    b. pity
    c. apathy
    d. vindictiveness

15. Why are the survivors "people without tears" at the end of "I Am Not One of Those Who Left the Land"?
    a. They have no reason to regret their conduct.
    b. Their sufferings have destroyed their emotions.
    c. They have cared for nothing but survival.
    d. They will eventually seek vengeance.

Vocabulary and Grammar

____ 16. The word *implore* means _____.
   a. plead
   b. hope
   c. expect
   d. discover

____ 17. Choose the sentence in which the adjective clause is italicized.
   a. Anna Akhmatova, *who survived the most tumultuous events of modern times*, published her first poetry at the age of seventeen.
   b. The Brontë sisters, who grew up in Yorkshire England, *in a landscape of bleak windswept hills*, were all successful novelists.
   c. The present occasion is too serious *to allow me to follow the convention* that a woman should not speak in a man's council.
   d. *The speaker did not think he could cross the bridge*, which was plaited from fragile reeds.

____ 18. The word *timorous* means _____.
   a. insinuating
   b. timid
   c. devious
   d. ambitious

____ 19. What does the word root *-dom-* mean?
   a. to help
   b. to forget
   c. to explore
   d. to rule

____ 20. Which word is modified by the adjective clause in the following sentence?
   Empress Theodora delivered a brief speech that convinced her husband to defend their palace in Constantinople, rather than try to escape.
   a. Empress Theodora   c. husband
   b. speech   d. palace

Essay Questions

21. Choose one of the selections and write an essay that explains the choice the author is making and the values he or she is using to make that decision. Use examples from the selection you choose to support your ideas.

22. Write an essay comparing and contrasting Brontë's and Staff's ideas of courage as expressed in "The Old Stoic" and "The Bridge." Use specific examples from the two poems to support your ideas.

23. These selections consider choices made in dramatic situations. Write an essay that explains why dramatic situations are the basis of many works of art. Use examples from the selections to illustrate your points.

"The Good Deed" by Pearl S. Buck

Selection Test

Critical Reading

In the blank, write the letter of the one best answer.

_____ 1. Why is Mr. Pan worried about his mother at the beginning of "The Good Deed"?
a. She bothers the neighbors.
b. She is desperately unhappy in New York.
c. She is ill.
d. She does not get along with his wife.

_____ 2. What is the reason old Mrs. Pan is unable to appreciate the fact that she is safe?
a. She is an unpleasant person.
b. She dislikes her family.
c. She was never in danger.
d. She is frightened by the city and felt safer in her village.

_____ 3. Based on his thoughts and actions, what inferences can you make about Mr. Pan's feelings for his mother?
a. He believes she should return to China.
b. He is afraid of her.
c. He loves and respects her.
d. He is usually annoyed with her.

_____ 4. How does old Mrs. Pan's loneliness affect her behavior at the beginning of "The Good Deed"?
a. She sits in her room and refuses to eat.
b. She shouts at her grandchildren.
c. She wanders the streets of New York.
d. She visits the china shop every day.

_____ 5. What can you infer about young Mrs. Pan based on her relationship with old Mrs. Pan?
a. She is impatient.
b. She is patient and kind.
c. She is resentful of her husband's relationship with his mother.
d. She wants nothing to do with Chinese culture.

_____ 6. What upsets old Mrs. Pan the most about her grandchildren?
a. They do not eat properly.
b. They watch too much television.
c. They do not respect their elders.
d. They attend an American school.

_____ 7. Why do Mr. Pan and young Mrs. Pan invite Lili Yang to their home?
a. to discipline the children
b. to cook
c. to provide old Mrs. Pan with company
d. so that she can show old Mrs. Pan around New York

_____ 8. What can you deduce about the character of Lili, based on her treatment of old Mrs. Pan?

    a. She is uncomfortable talking about Chinese culture.

    b. She is kind and knows how to help Mrs. Pan.

    c. She enjoys children.

    d. She is impatient.

_____ 9. What shocks old Mrs. Pan most about Lili?

    a. She speaks Chinese.

    b. She is unmarried at the age of twenty-seven.

    c. She works full time.

    d. She has never been to China.

_____ 10. What "wound" in Lili's heart does old Mrs Pan touch upon?

    a. the fact that she is unmarried and childless

    b. the fact that her parents have passed away

    c. the fact that she will never visit China

    d. the fact that she dislikes her job

_____ 11. What can you deduce about the way Lili's visit begins to change the character of old Mrs. Pan?

    a. She takes a greater interest in American culture.

    b. For the first time since she left her village she forgets her own troubles.

    c. She will no longer tolerate living in a big city like New York.

    d. She tries again to communicate with her grandchildren.

_____ 12. In what way does old Mrs. Pan's character actively change as she tries to find Lili a husband?

    a. She begins to learn English.

    b. She becomes less patient.

    c. She begins to take an interest in her life.

    d. She helps young Mrs. Pan with housework.

_____ 13. What is the main reason why old Mrs. Pan enjoys talking with old Mr. Lim and his son?

    a. They are kind to her.

    b. She believes young Mr. Lim might be a suitable match for Lili.

    c. They sell her fine china.

    d. They enjoy her stories of China.

_____ 14. What is the reason for the change in the character of old Mrs. Pan at the end of the story?

    a. She was tired of sitting in her room.

    b. She begins to appreciate America.

    c. She wants to please her son.

    d. She finally feels needed and comfortable.

_____ 15. What can you deduce about the feelings Lili and young Mr. Lim have for each other?

    a. They seem to like each other.

    b. They seem indifferent.

    c. They are only trying to make Mrs. Pan think they like each other.

    d. They dislike each other.

Vocabulary and Grammar

____ 16. When Lili Yang looked *abashed*, you might say that she looked _____.
  a. embarrassed
  b. repressed
  c. conferred
  d. annoyed

____ 17. When old Mrs. Pan watched her grandchildren *contemplatively*, she was looking at them
  a. in a loving manner.
  b. coldly.
  c. indignantly.
  d. in a thoughtful manner.

____ 18. Identify the complete adverb clause in the sentence *Mrs. Pan wondered why the children did not obey.*
  a. why the children did not obey
  b. did not obey
  c. Mrs. Pan wondered
  d. Mrs. Pan wondered why

____ 19. Identify the word that is modified by an adverb clause in the sentence *Mrs. Pan listened when Lili described American customs.*
  a. Mrs. Pan
  b. Lili
  c. customs
  d. listened

____ 20. Mr. Pan _____ his urge to tell his mother he was too busy to talk.
  a. conferred
  b. repressed
  c. rewrote
  d. compelled

Essay Questions

21. In a short essay, explain the title of the story "The Good Deed." What good deed may be described as central to the story? What other good deeds are performed or mentioned in the story? What different reasons do characters have for performing their good deeds?

22. In an essay, analyze the character of Mrs. Pan. How does she fit the definition of a dynamic character? Describe how her attitudes about life in America change and the effect these changes have on her character.

23. In an essay, describe the differences between American and Chinese marriage customs presented in "The Good Deed." According to the story, what problems exist in both traditions? At what point in the story do both sets of traditions come together?

"Thoughts of Hanoi" by Nguyen Thi Vinh
"Pride" by Dahlia Ravikovitch
"Auto Wreck" by Karl Shapiro
"Before the Law" by Franz Kafka

Selection Test

Critical Reading

In the blank, write the letter of the one best answer.

_____ 1. How does the man in "Before the Law" try to persuade the doorkeeper to let him in?
   a. He keeps asking the doorkeeper, hoping to wear him down.
   b. He tries to sneak in when the doorkeeper steps to one side.
   c. He distracts the doorkeeper with stories about his home and many other things.
   d. He gives all of his belongings to the doorkeeper in an attempt to bribe him.

_____ 2. In "Before the Law," if the gate was made only for this man, why isn't he allowed to go through and gain access to the Law?
   a. He didn't try hard enough or in the right way.
   b. People don't actually have the access to the Law that the man thinks they should.
   c. The doorkeeper must keep him out because the man is a criminal.
   d. The man is only curious and doesn't really need access to the Law.

_____ 3. What is the turning point in "Before the Law"?
   a. the moment the man approaches the doorkeeper
   b. the moment the doorkeeper denies access
   c. the moment the man decides to wait and get permission
   d. the moment the man asks about why others have not come to the gate

_____ 4. How does Shapiro use the following lines from "Auto Wreck" to support his message?
   Its quick soft silver bell beating, beating,
   And down the dark one ruby flare
   Pulsing out red light like an artery,
   The ambulance at top speed floating down
   Past beacons and illuminated clocks
   Wings in a heavy curve, dips down,
   And brakes speed, entering the crowd.
   The doors leap open, emptying light;
   Stretchers are laid out, the mangled lifted
   And stowed into the little hospital.
   a. The lines describe the panic and chaos that follows an accident.
   b. The lines emphasize the prompt response of emergency personnel.
   c. The lines establish the setting of the poem as the scene of an accident.
   d. The lines create an otherworldly scene that suggests a lack of reality or sense.

_____ 5. What point about dying in an auto accident does Shapiro make in "Auto Wreck"?
   a. It defies explanation and appears to be caused by evil.
   b. It is a natural occurrence, like other deaths.
   c. It can be understood only by common sense.
   d. It can be explained only through logic.

Unit 4: Turning Points

_____ 6. Which of the following lines best expresses the theme of "Auto Wreck"?
   a. Wings in a heavy curve, dips down,/And brakes speed, entering the crowd.
   b. But this invites the occult mind,/Cancels our physics with a sneer,/And spatters all we knew of denouement Across the expedient and wicked stones.
   c. One hangs lanterns on the wrecks that cling,/Empty husks of locusts, to iron poles.
   d. Already old, the question Who shall die?/Becomes unspoken Who is innocent?

_____ 7. What does the speaker of "Thoughts of Hanoi" expect dawn to bring?
   a. an end to insomnia   c. peace to Vietnam
   b. an end to the nightmare of separation   d. a springtime of hope

_____ 8. The stanza describing the girls and boys in "Thoughts of Hanoi" emphasizes
   a. the theme of youthful exuberance and accomplishment.
   b. the proverb that only the good die young.
   c. the restrictions imposed by a repressive culture.
   d. the innocence of children.

_____ 9. The speaker in "Thoughts of Hanoi" recalls the past. How does this support the writer's message?
   a. The writer purposely dwells on the past and ignores present difficulties.
   b. Recalling the past points out whose side won.
   c. Recalling the past brings out strong emotions or anger about the past.
   d. Recalling the past brings to mind a time when a relationship was stronger than political differences.

_____ 10. In the final stanza of "Thoughts of Hanoi," the speaker
   a. resolves his dilemma.
   b. distances himself from his "Brother."
   c. remains unable to understand his current predicament.
   d. rationalizes his own behavior and attitudes.

_____ 11. The theme of "Thoughts of Hanoi" is
   a. the past can never be recaptured.
   b. war makes brothers into enemies.
   c. ties of blood endure despite political division.
   d. political affiliation is stronger than kinship.

_____ 12. In the poem "Pride," what do the cracks in the rocks stand for?
   a. faults or weaknesses that everyone has
   b. unkind thoughts or wrongdoings of people
   c. Troubles or hurts that people suppress because of pride
   d. Pride itself, which can cause damage when someone has too much of it

_____ 13. Why does the speaker in "Pride" say "it almost seems peaceful" when describing how the rocks lie on their backs for so many years?
   a. Because the rocks lie there, the speaker describes them as if they were alive.
   b. The rocks lie still, but the cracks have already begun to form.
   c. The rocks would be peaceful except that they are lying in the heat and the cold.
   d. The speaker is referring to how peaceful it is to see rocks lying on the seashore.

_____ 14. Which of the following lines from "Pride" looks ahead to the seal's visit?
   a. For years they lie on their backs/in the heat and the cold,
   b. Years pass over them, waiting.
   c. Whoever is going to shatter them/hasn't come yet.
   d. the sea pushes through and rolls back—/the rocks seem motionless.

_____ 15. How does Ravikovitch support her message in "Pride"?
   a. She gives many examples of how a rock—or a person—is treated in ways that eventually cause it to break.
   b. She applies the whole poem to people in the last line.
   c. She explains how the natural motion of the sea causes particular damage.
   d. She makes the rocks seem just like people with phrases such as "they lie on their backs."

Vocabulary and Grammar

_____ 16. What is the noun clause in the following sentence?
   American poet Karl Shapiro, who has been a college professor, a critic, and an editor, as well as a Pulitzer Prize-winning poet, said that he would like to see the elimination "of the line between poetry and prose."
   a. that he would like to see the elimination of the line between poetry and prose
   b. who has been a college professor, a critic, and an editor as well as a Pulitzer Prize-winning poet
   c. American poet Karl Shapiro
   d. of the line between poetry and prose

_____ 17. When the Doorkeeper describes the man in "Before the Law" as *insatiable* he means that the man
   a. constantly wants more.   c. thinks too much.
   b. demonstrates pride.   d. appears weak and ill.

_____ 18. If the onlookers of the auto wreck are *deranged*, they are _____.
   a. depressed   b. desperate   c. unsettled   d. frightened

_____ 19. How does the noun clause function in the following sentence?
   Nguyen Thi Vinh fears that her friend will forget their shared past and look at her with hatred.
   a. direct object   c. predicate noun
   b. indirect object   d. object of a preposition

_____ 20. The speaker in "Auto Wreck" mentions the "banal resolution" that the onlookers make. What does *banal* mean here?
   a. The resolutions are renewed fervently.
   b. The resolutions are meaningless because they have been repeated too often.
   c. The resolutions are humorous.
   d. The resolutions are like those made by people recovering from illnesses.

Essay Questions

21. At the end of Karl Shapiro's "Auto Wreck," the poet's opinions about death come through clearly. In an essay, state those opinions, and explain why you agree or disagree. Use examples from the poem to support your answer.

22. In an essay, analyze the message of either "Thoughts of Hanoi" or "Pride." First, state the message you believe the writer is communicating through the poem. Then explain how the writer supports that message. Does the poet succeed in convincing readers of the message?

23. In an essay, examine Kafka's allegory "Before the Law." Remember that in an allegory, everything is symbolic. Explain what "the Law," the man, and the doorkeeper each stand for, and why the man is unable to gain access to the Law.

Unit 4: Turning Points

Unit Test: Turning Points

Critical Reading

In the blank, write the letter of the one best answer.

The questions below are based on the following selection.

In the following excerpt from A Separate Peace *by John Knowles, the narrator and his classmates are looking for diversion during the summer session at a New England boarding school. The story takes place during World War II.*

We went outside into the cordial afternoon sunshine. The playing fields were optimistically green and empty before us. The tennis courts were full. The softball diamond was busy. A pattern of badminton nets swayed sensually in the breeze. Finny eyed them with quiet astonishment. Far down the fields toward the river there was a wooden tower about ten feet high where the instructor had stood to direct the senior calisthenics. It was empty now. The seniors had been trotted off to the improvised obstacle course in the woods, or to have their blood pressure taken again, or to undergo an insidious exercise in The Cage which consisted in stepping up on a box and down again in rapid rhythm for five minutes. They were off somewhere, shaping up for the war. All of the fields were ours.

Finny began to walk slowly in the direction of the tower. Perhaps he was thinking that we might carry it the rest of the way to the river and throw it in; perhaps he was just interested in looking at it, as he was in everything. Whatever he thought, he forgot it when we reached the tower. Beside it someone had left a large and heavy leather-covered ball, a medicine ball.

He picked it up. "Now this, you see, is everything in the world you need for sports. When they discovered the circle they created sports. As for this thing," embracing the medicine ball in his left arm he held up the shuttlecock, contaminated, in his outstretched right, "this idiot tickler, the only thing it's good for is eeny-meeny-miney-mo." He dropped the ball and proceeded to pick the feathers out of the shuttlecock, distastefully, as though removing ticks from a dog. The remaining rubber plug he then threw out of sight down the field, with a single lunge ending in a powerful downward thrust of his wrist. Badminton was gone.

He stood balancing the medicine ball, enjoying the feel of it. "All you really need is a round ball."

_____ 1. Which of the following most profoundly informs the dramatic situation of *A Separate Peace?*
   a. competitive sports
   b. World War II
   c. an academic school year
   d. Finny's quiet astonishment

_____ 2. From the description of activities involving the seniors, what would you say is the author's perspective on training young people and sending them to war?
   a. indifference
   b. loathing
   c. respect
   d. skepticism

_____ 3. Based on what you know from reading *A Separate Peace*, what motivates Finny to pull apart the shuttlecock?
   a. disgust
   c. boredom
   b. admiration
   d. fascination

_____ 4. Which of the following characters is most likely to be an example of a static character?
   a. Finny
   b. the seniors
   c. the narrator
   d. the calisthenics instructor

_____ 5. From Finny's behavior as he walks "slowly in the direction of the tower," what can you infer about his character?
   a. He is prone to violence.
   b. He can be inscrutable.
   c. He does not value physical exercise highly.
   d. He is a profound thinker.

_____ 6. Which of the following sentences seems most likely to suggest one of the themes in *A Separate Peace*?
   a. The playing fields were optimistically green and empty before us.
   b. Beside it someone had left a large and heavy leather-covered ball, a medicine ball.
   c. He stood balancing the medicine ball.
   d. The tennis courts were full.

_____ 7. What is Finny's opinion of badminton?
   a. He has no opinion about it.
   b. He prefers playing to watching the game.
   c. He abhors it.
   d. He finds it exciting and enjoyable.

_____ 8. Which of the following words or phrases best describes the atmosphere created by the sentence, "We went outside into the cordial afternoon sunshine"?
   a. inhospitable
   b. jovial
   c. informal
   d. pleasant

_____ 9. What does Finny mean when he says "when they discovered the circle they created sports"?
   a. The best playing fields are round.
   b. Sports can be played with just a ball.
   c. Mathematicians are responsible for the earliest competitive games.
   d. Most sports involve measurement of one kind or another.

_____ 10. Why do you think Finny takes apart the shuttlecock?
   a. He wants to learn how it is constructed.
   b. He knows it will be easier to throw without feathers.
   c. He feels contempt for the object.
   d. He wants to demonstrate his dexterity to the narrator.

Vocabulary and Grammar

In the blank, write the letter of the one best answer.

____ 11. Which of the following sentences contains an adjective clause?
   a. Anna Akhmatova is a poet who survived two world wars, the Russian Revolution, and Stalin's "reign of terror."
   b. Empress Theodora told her husband that he should defend their palace in Constantinople, rather than try to escape.
   c. In his poetry, Leopold Staff kept true to the themes of history and nature despite the chaos of two World Wars.
   d. Yet reflect for a moment whether, when you have once escaped to a place of security, you would not gladly exchange such safety for death.

____ 12. In which of the following sentences does the noun clause function as an indirect object?
   a. Franz Kafka's allegory, "Before the Law," offers whoever reads it a cautionary message.
   b. In his will, Kafka asked that all his unpublished literary works be burned.
   c. That the past can be buried is the speaker's hope in "Thoughts of Hanoi."
   d. In "Auto Wreck," the speaker suggests that some forms of death seem to have a purpose.

____ 13. Which of the following sentences does not contain an adverb clause?
   a. When her son was away, she could not say to her daughter-in-law, "Do you remember how the willows grew over the gate?"
   b. She knew that the village had fallen into the hands of their enemies and that strangers lived in the house, but she hoped even so that the land was tilled.
   c. He became impassioned when she said this.
   d. Many people depended upon her and she had left them, because her son compelled her, and she was not used to this idleness that was killing her day by day.

____ 14. Which of the following sentences does not contain a subordinate clause?
   a. The house, which was not cool, was at least protection from the sun.
   b. After they were confined in the house all day, the children strained to get out.
   c. Their faces were red and bloated with the effort, but their mother would not open the door.
   d. They felt that their lungs were stuffed with cotton wood.

Choose the word closest in meaning to the word in italics.

____ 15. "I know I have to, idiot," Raghu said, *superciliously* kicking him with his toe.
   a. angrily   c. disdainfully
   b. respectfully   d. excitedly

____ 16. "I have a friend," she said at last, "a schoolmate whose family *compelled* her to speak Chinese."
   a. encouraged
   b. forbid
   c. allowed
   d. forced

____ 17. "What do you want to know now?" asks the doorkeeper; "you are *insatiable.*"
   a. annoying
   b. greedy
   c. niggardly
   d. boring

In the blank, write the letter of the one best answer.

_____ 18. Which of the following words most nearly means the opposite of *indomitable?*
    a. unyielding
    b. placid
    c. indescribable
    d. vulnerable

_____ 19. The word *banal* means _____.
    a. awkward
    b. filthy
    c. stale due to overuse
    d. fresh, untested

_____ 20. Which of the following words is the best synonym for *implore?*
    a. insist
    b. plead
    c. increase
    d. delay

Essay Questions

21. In "Games at Twilight" Anita Desai describes how a character arrives at a decision that ultimately leaves him humiliated. Write an essay in which you discuss Ravi's personality and behavior, especially in relation to his decision to remain inside the shed for so long. What would you say are his most dominant personality traits? Why do you believe he failed to think through his decision more carefully? What might have distracted him?

22. Turning points in people's lives are often sparked by important decisions. Choose a selection—such as "I Am Not One of Those Who Left the Land" or "Speech During the Invasion of Constantinople"—that illuminates a person's life-changing decision. In an essay, describe the possible consequences of each course of action relating to that person's decision. After presenting each side of the decision thoroughly and honestly, judge the wisdom of that decision.

23. In some cases, a turning point in one's life appears suddenly, and a person has little influence or control over the situation. Choose a selection from this unit—such as "The Old Stoic," "Auto Wreck," or "Before the Law"—and write an essay in which you explain how the dramatic situation changes the lives of one or more characters.

24. The turning points in "Games at Twilight" and "Before the Law" both revolve around a realization that occurred too late to benefit the main character. Write an essay in which you compare and contrast the distinct but similar experiences of Ravi and the man from the country.

25. Sometimes an individual embraces or attempts something completely new, and this experience takes on symbolic meaning and becomes a turning point in his or her life. For instance, in "The Bridge," the speaker executes a simple action—crossing a bridge—that has important implications for his future. Choose a selection from this unit that features a symbolic act, and write an essay in which you analyze the action and its symbolic meaning, and speculate on the action's implications for the future of the character.

Unit 4: Turning Points

"The Widow and the Parrot" by Virginia Woolf

Selection Test

Critical Reading

In the blank, write the letter of the one best answer.

_____ 1. The author's primary purpose in writing "The Widow and the Parrot" is to
   a. inform readers of parrot behavior.
   b. entertain readers with an engaging story.
   c. persuade readers of animal intelligence.
   d. criticize miserly behavior.

_____ 2. Which word best describes Mrs. Gage's lifestyle at the beginning of "The Widow and the Parrot"?
   a. modest   c. extravagant
   b. mysterious   d. unfulfilling

_____ 3. In "The Widow and the Parrot," what does the parrot's phrase "Not at home!" reveal about Joseph Brand, the parrot's owner?
   a. He had a good sense of humor.
   b. He appreciated the parrot's intelligence.
   c. He did not like the company of others.
   d. He was a miser.

_____ 4. What can be inferred from the details about the house that Mrs. Gage inherits in "The Widow and the Parrot"?
   a. The parrot liked Joseph Brand.
   b. Mrs. Ford disapproved of Joseph Brand.
   c. Mrs. Gage has expensive tastes.
   d. Joseph Brand was an eccentric miser.

_____ 5. In "The Widow and the Parrot," how does Mrs. Gage's treatment of her dog hint at her motives for showing kindness to the parrot?
   a. It reveals that Mrs. Gage cares deeply for animals.
   b. It shows that she prefers dogs to birds.
   c. It demonstrates that she is a lonely, old woman.
   d. It indicates that she thinks animals are better than people.

_____ 6. What can you infer about Mrs. Gage's attitude toward the parrot based on her initial treatment of the it in "The Widow and the Parrot"?
   a. She thinks the parrot is ill-tempered and doesn't want to take responsibility for it.
   b. She is concerned about the parrot and wants to make it happy.
   c. She thinks it is an unattractive bird with sadly neglected feathers.
   d. She is appalled by the parrot's foul language and obnoxious screeching.

_____ 7. In "The Widow and the Parrot," the farmer tells Mrs. Gage terrible tales of young people drowning while crossing the river at high tide. What effect does this detail have on the story?
   a. It foreshadows events.
   b. It creates suspense.
   c. It shows Mrs. Gage's motivation.
   d. It helps readers identify with Mrs. Gage.

_____ 8. In "The Widow and the Parrot," Mrs. Gage is disappointed with the inheritance from her brother because
  a. she must share the money with another relative.
  b. she doesn't want to keep the parrot.
  c. the house is in bad shape and the money cannot be found.
  d. the solicitors inform her that there is nothing to inherit.

_____ 9. As Mrs. Gage walks along the river bank in "The Widow and the Parrot," what conclusion does she draw about her brother's reason for leaving her an inheritance?
  a. He was being deliberately cruel.
  b. He felt guilty.
  c. He wanted to express his love for her.
  d. He was repaying her kindness to him.

_____ 10. In "The Widow and the Parrot," why does Mrs. Gage despair as she returns from the solicitors' offices?
  a. She worries about having to pay back the money for her trip.
  b. She wishes she had spent more time with her brother.
  c. She is concerned about the parrot's health.
  d. She cannot remember her way back to the town.

_____ 11. When you draw inferences you
  a. respond to the story.
  b. identify with a character or situation.
  c. make assumptions about a character or situation.
  d. envision the setting.

_____ 12. In "The Widow and the Parrot," what motivates Mrs. Gage to follow the parrot to the burned house?
  a. amusement
  b. greed
  c. belief in animal intelligence
  d. desperation

_____ 13. In "The Widow and the Parrot," what is the parrot's motive for leading Mrs. Gage to the gold?
  a. fear   c. wisdom
  b. revenge   d. gratitude

_____ 14. Which sentence best summarizes the theme of "The Widow and the Parrot"?
  a. Some people have a special way with animals.
  b. Never give up hope.
  c. Family ties are important.
  d. Kindness to others is eventually rewarded.

Vocabulary and Grammar

_____ 15. In "The Widow and the Parrot," which detail best reveals that the house Mrs. Gage inherits is _dilapidated_?
  a. Mrs. Gage must light a lantern to see her way inside.
  b. The kitchen floor is overgrown with toadstools.
  c. A kitchen range hides the spot where gold is buried.
  d. The furniture is worth very little.

_____ 16. What is the appositive in the following sentence?

"Be thankful you're not inside yourself, Madam," said the Rev. James Hawkesford, the clergyman.

a. yourself

c. the Rev. James Hawkesford

b. Madam

d. the clergyman

_____ 17. Which sentence uses an appositive to combine the following two sentences?

Mrs. Ford was an old village woman. Mrs. Ford took Mrs. Gage by the hand and led her off to her own cottage, where she was to sleep the night.

a. An old village woman named Mrs. Ford took Mrs. Gage by the hand and led her off to her own cottage, where she was to sleep the night.

b. Mrs. Ford was an old village woman who took Mrs. Gage by the hand and led her off to her own cottage, where she was to sleep the night.

c. Mrs. Ford, who was an old village woman, took Mrs. Gage by the hand and led her off to her own cottage, where she was to sleep the night.

d. Mrs. Ford, an old village woman, took Mrs. Gage by the hand and led her off to her own cottage, where she was to sleep the night.

_____ 18. An appositive is a noun or noun phrase

a. that renames the subject of the sentence.

b. that modifies another noun or pronoun by telling _what kind or which one._

c. that is placed near another noun or pronoun to explain it.

d. that functions as the object of a preposition.

_____ 19. The parrot demonstrates his _sagacity_ by

a. leading Mrs. Gage to the gold.

b. shrieking "Not at home!"

c. perching on Mrs. Gage's head.

d. falling over dead.

_____ 20. Why would carrying an apronful of _sovereigns_ slow Mrs. Gage's progress?

a. The paper bills flutter out of the apron.

b. The coins are very heavy.

c. The oddly shaped objects are difficult to balance.

d. The slippery creatures try to escape.

Essay Questions

21. In a brief essay, describe the reading strategy you applied while reading "The Widow and the Parrot," and explain how it helped you understand the story. Provide examples from the selection to support your main points.

22. In "The Widow and the Parrot," characters' motivations drive the story's action, or plot. What crucial results arise from these actions? Write a cause-and-effect essay in which you describe how character motivations affect three different story events.

23. In "The Widow and the Parrot," Mrs. Gage interacts with humans and with animals. Write an essay in which you compare and contrast these interactions and conclude how they reveal the story's theme.

"Civil Peace" by Chinua Achebe

Selection Test

Critical Reading

In the blank, write the letter of the one best answer.

_____ 1. In "Civil Peace," what does Jonathan appear to value most?
a. the security of his savings
b. the precepts of his religion
c. the preservation of his home
d. the safety of his family

_____ 2. In "Civil Peace," when the soldier attempts to commandeer Jonathan's bicycle, we learn that Jonathan is
a. a shrewd observer of human behavior.
b. a cynical agent of social corruption.
c. an innocent victim of postwar crime.
d. an earnest believer in God's mercy.

_____ 3. Used as a greeting, what does the phrase "happy survival" mean?
a. Put on a happy face.
b. Beware of further violence.
c. Congratulations on surviving the war.
d. Survival does not ensure happiness.

_____ 4. Applying prior knowledge while reading "Civil Peace" is useful because most readers
a. believe war is wrong.
b. are not familiar with proverbs.
c. have not lived through a civil war.
d. do not speak the dialect spoken by the thieves.

_____ 5. In Achebe's story the hard work of Jonathan and Maria connotes
a. tragic ignorance.
b. personal courage.
c. religious miracles.
d. financial ruin.

_____ 6. Jonathan's reliance on the proverb "Nothing puzzles God" shows his
a. faith in the divine plan.
b. refusal to confront reality.
c. lack of faith in himself.
d. desire to acquire more education.

_____ 7. Which bit of prior knowledge would best help a reader relate to Jonathan's feelings upon finding his house intact?
a. winning a valuable prize
b. losing personal belongings in a flood
c. returning home from a long trip
d. talking to an old friend on the phone

Unit 5: Unit Title

8. The experience of waiting in a long line to sign up for a class might help a reader relate to Jonathan's experience of
   a. having his bicycle commandeered.
   b. being robbed in the middle of the night.
   c. clutching his money tightly in his hand.
   d. standing for hours outside the treasury building.

9. Jonathan's everyday actions after the war demonstrate that
   a. most people did not want to work.
   b. people had to be resourceful to make money.
   c. the government provided jobs.
   d. many people became very rich.

10. The principal conflict in "Civil Peace" occurs when
    a. Jonathan bribes the ragged soldier.
    b. the thieves steal Jonathan's "egg-rasher."
    c. Jonathan angrily rejects public sympathy.
    d. the thieves argue among themselves.

11. Which recurring word supports the meaning of the statement "Nothing puzzles God"?
    a. "egg-rasher"   b. miracle   c. "tief-man"   d. bicycle

12. Which passage illustrates the climax of Achebe's story?
    a. " . . . if you come inside and find one hundred pounds, take it and shoot me. . . ."
    b. "It was like Christmas for him and for many others like him. . . ."
    c. " . . . no sooner had he got his twenty pounds than some heartless ruffian picked it off him."
    d. "It was unbelievable. He rubbed his eyes and looked again. . . . "

13. Jonathan's reaction to the theft of his twenty pounds is _____.
    a. despair   b. bitterness   c. outrage   d. resignation

14. What is the theme of "Civil Peace"?
    a. Poverty breeds crime and despair.
    b. War ruins the lives of survivors.
    c. Where there is life there is hope.
    d. God protects the faithful believer.

Vocabulary and Grammar

15. Which miracle does Jonathan consider *inestimable*?
    a. his house
    b. the five heads of his family
    c. the egg-rasher
    d. his bicycle

16. Which sentence contains a present participial phrase?
    a. Greeting old friends with the words "Happy survival" was the current fashion in the first hazy days of peace.
    b. Jonathan was riding his bicycle when it was commandeered "for urgent military action."
    c. The officer who stopped him wore disreputable rags and his toes were peeping out of his shoes.
    d. That night he buried the bicycle in the little clearing in the bush where the dead of the camp, including his own youngest son, were buried.

____ 17. The word *amenable* means _____.
   a. shameful
   b. acceptable
   c. responsive
   d. powerful

____ 18. What noun or pronoun does the present participial phrase modify in the following sentence?

   Jonathan, suspecting he might be amenable to influence, rummaged in his raffia bag and produced the two pounds with which he had been going to buy firewood.

   a. he   c. pounds
   b. Jonathan   d. raffia bag

____ 19. In which sentence is the present participial phrase underlined.
   a. The second time <u>the knocking</u> came it was so loud that the rickety old door, shaking with every vibration, could have fallen down.
   b. The second time <u>the knocking came it was so loud</u> that the rickety old door, shaking with every vibration, could have fallen down.
   c. The second time the knocking came it was so loud that the rickety old door, <u>shaking with every vibration</u>, could have fallen down.
   d. The second time the knocking came it was so loud that the rickety old door, <u>shaking with every vibration, could have fallen down.</u>

____ 20. The _____ thief forces Jonathan to hand over his money.
   a. commiserate
   b. edifice
   c. amenable
   d. imperious

Essay Questions

21. "Civil Peace" relates one man's struggles in the aftermath of Nigeria's civil war. How does prior knowledge help you relate to Jonathan's experiences? In a brief essay, compare and contrast three of Jonathan's experiences with three of your own.

22. In "Civil Peace," Jonathan Iwegbu relies on the proverb "Nothing puzzles God." What significance does the proverb hold for him? Does it provide an easy explanation for events, or is its meaning more complex? Write a brief essay in which you analyze the key statement's meaning.

23. Jonathan Iwegbu possesses a positive outlook on an arguably bleak life. In an essay, compare and contrast Jonathan's optimism with the reality of his life, naming at least three incidents from the story. Draw a conclusion about the reason for Jonathan's optimism—does it arise because of the incidents, or for some reason unrelated to the incidents?

"The Bean Eaters" by Gwendolyn Brooks
"How to React to Familiar Faces" by Umberto Eco

Selection Test

Critical Reading

In the blank, write the letter of the one best answer.

_____ 1. What are the connotations of the title of Brooks's poem, "The Bean Eaters"?
    a. old age
    b. the cultural background of the characters
    c. simplicity
    d. the clutter of the characters' lives

_____ 2. What is the setting of Brooks's poem?
    a. a ramshackle shelter
    b. a rented back room containing a wooden table
    c. a park bench
    d. a dingy diner with old tables and tin plates

_____ 3. In the following stanza from "The Bean Eaters," which phrase expresses the poet's respect for the subjects of her poem?
    Two who are Mostly Good.
    Two who have lived their day,
    But keep on putting on their clothes
    And putting things away.
    a. Mostly Good
    b. have lived their day
    c. keep on putting on their clothes
    d. putting things away

_____ 4. What is the overall message of the preceding stanza from "The Bean Eaters"?
    a. Bad things can happen to good people.
    b. The two people live in utter despair.
    c. The two people putter endlessly, putting things away compulsively.
    d. The people are old, but they carry out their simple routine each day.

_____ 5. What mental picture would most logically result from reading the preceding stanza from "The Bean Eaters"?
    a. two quiet elderly people following a quiet routine
    b. two old people living in a cluttered, messy house
    c. two very elderly people who require assistance in caring for themselves
    d. two active senior citizens who keep busy with various activities

_____ 6. What does the poet mean when she writes that the people remember "with twinklings and twinges"?
    a. They remember the past, but are absorbed now with the twinges and pain of old age.
    b. They always remember to put things away.
    c. They fondly remember their lives when they were younger and lived in happier circumstances.
    d. The beads and other objects in the room twinkle as they sit and remember the past.

7. In "How to React to Familiar Faces," in what way does Eco create an image in the first few sentences to which *all* readers can relate?
   a. He mentions a famous movie star whose name everyone recognizes.
   b. He tells about being recognized by someone who talks about him as if he weren't there.
   c. He tells about a celebrity being mobbed by fans.
   d. He relates the very common experience of walking along the sidewalk and seeing someone he recognizes.

8. In "How to React to Familiar Faces," what does the author do when he realizes the person he's looking at is Anthony Quinn?
   a. He walks past without making eye contact.
   b. He smiles broadly at him, but does not speak.
   c. He nods and waves.
   d. He goes over and introduces himself.

9. In "How to React to Familiar Faces," the author relates his personal experiences with reacting to familiar faces. How does this affect the tone of the essay?
   a. It makes the essay friendly and easy to relate to.
   b. It makes the essay seem silly because Eco relates insignificant incidents.
   c. It adds excitement because his experiences involved movie stars.
   d. His experiences were so personal that they are hard for readers to relate to.

10. According to "How to React to Familiar Faces," what do people normally do when they see someone they don't know personally?
    a. They simply pay no attention to the person.
    b. They neither stare nor point nor speak loudly about the person.
    c. They may comment on the person's clothing or make other remarks.
    d. They greet the person amiably.

11. What is the tone of the following paragraph from "How to React to Familiar Faces"?
    I might as well have grabbed Anthony Quinn by the lapel, dragged him to a phone booth, and called a friend to say, "Talk about coincidence! I've run into Anthony Quinn. And you know something? He seems real!" (After which I would throw Quinn aside and go on about my business.)
    a. angry
    b. ridiculing
    c. humorous
    d. regretful

12. Why does the author include the preceding paragraph in his essay?
    a. to let readers know what he really wanted to do when he met Quinn
    b. to point out the absurdity of people's behavior
    c. to give evidence by telling what someone once did to him
    d. to relate an incident that he witnessed

13. Which of the following best states the theme of "How to React to Familiar Faces"?
    a. People are very rude when they meet celebrities.
    b. Celebrities resent the treatment they get at the hands of the general public.
    c. The mass media create a mask of mystery around the celebrities, which causes them to behave strangely in public.
    d. People get confused when they see a face out of context, particularly when it is a face they know from the media.

_____ 14. A word's *connotations* are
       a. the feelings and emotions associated with the word.
       b. the various meanings of the word.
       c. the words from which the English word originates.
       d. the different contexts in which the word can be used.

Vocabulary and Grammar

_____ 15. The author of "How to React to Familiar Faces" says that people meeting a celebrity, are likely to "continue their conversation amiably." *Amiably* means _____.
       a. rudely   b. cheerfully   c. loudly   d. enviously

_____ 16. Which sentence contains a participle acting as an adjective?
       a. As I was strolling down the crowded street, I saw a man I knew well.
       b. He was still looking at the opposite side of the street, but now he was beginning to turn his eyes toward me.
       c. I was just about to break into a broad, radiant smile, when suddenly I recognized him.
       d. I might as well have grabbed him by the lapel and dragged him into a phone booth.

_____ 17. In writing or in conversation, if you *expound*, you
       a. ignore the topic.   c. express distaste.
       b. explain in detail.   d. ignore the facts.

_____ 18. In the following sentence, the word _____ functions as a participle.
       I realized that he valued his privacy, so I followed the recommended course of action and minded my own business.
       a. valued   b. followed   c. recommended   d. minded

_____ 19. In which sentences does the word *creaking* function as a verb?
       I. I hear the door creaking as it swings open and closed in the wind.
       II. The creaking stairs announce our approach to the rented back room.
       III. She tells me that her muscles are aching and her bones are creaking.
       IV. The table is creaking because you are leaning on it.
       a. I and II   b. I and III   c. II and III   d. III and IV

_____ 20. A *syndrome* is
       a. an event that is the cause of other events.
       b. a disease.
       c. a series of events that occur simultaneously.
       d. a group of signs that occur together, forming a pattern.

Essay Questions

21. In "The Bean Eaters," Brooks conveys a tone that is intimate, sad, and respectful. In an essay, analyze how she does this. Support your answer with specific words, lines, or images from the poem.

22. In an essay, analyze how the author conveys the informal tone of "How to React to Familiar Faces." What attitudes do you think are behind the tone? Consider the word choice, sentence structure, and personal details in your explanation.

23. In an essay, discuss the views of the author of "How to React to Familiar Faces" on how the media contribute to our confusion between the real and the imaginary. Analyze the point the author is making about a society in which this happens. What could result from blending the real and the imaginary?

"A Picture From the Past: Emily Dickinson" by Reynolds Price
"What Makes a Degas a Degas?" by Richard Mühlberger

Selection Test

Critical Reading

In the blank, write the letter of the one best answer.

_____ 1. In "A Picture From the Past: Emily Dickinson," to what does the author compare an old picture?
a. an anonymous calling card
b. a pebble from Mars
c. an old secret
d. an ancient maiden aunt

_____ 2. In "A Picture From the Past: Emily Dickinson," what kind of life does the author think Dickinson lived?
a. intellectual   b. lively   c. lonely   d. pleasant

_____ 3. What personality trait in "A Picture From the Past: Emily Dickinson" does Price attribute to Dickinson's "rough-knuckled hands"?
a. sensibility   b. silliness   c. intelligence   d. loneliness

_____ 4. Why does the author in "A Picture From the Past: Emily Dickinson" describe Dickinson as "our own Cassandra"?
a. because she wasted her poetic talent
b. because her great gift went unrecognized during her lifetime
c. because she made the most of her average talent
d. because she kept her writings secret

_____ 5. Which of the following details appear in the photograph of Emily Dickinson as well as in the essay, "A Picture From the Past: Emily Dickinson"?
  I. the ribbon around her neck
 II. an open book of poems
III. rough-knuckled hands
IV. her tall strong neck
a. I   b. I and II   c. I, II, and III   d. I, III, and IV

_____ 6. What conclusion does the author of "A Picture From the Past: Emily Dickinson" draw about Dickinson, based upon the following details in the photograph?
> A lopsided face, bigger on her right; a skewed part in the dark horsehair above the high forehead, unmatched eyebrows, a fleshy nose, unpainted bruised lips, an ample chin and a tall strong neck.
a. She is a shy, lonely girl.
b. She is a homely girl.
c. She is a sensible cook.
d. She is a gifted poet.

_____ 7. According to "What Makes a Degas a Degas?" what theme recurs in hundreds and hundreds of Degas' drawings, prints, pastels, and oil paintings?
a. horse racing   b. opera   c. ballet   d. mother and child

_____ 8. What kind of effect did Degas strive to convey with oil paint?
a. surprising   b. moody   c. spontaneous   d. composed

_____ 9. According to "What Makes a Degas a Degas?" which of the following words best describes Degas?
   a. traditionalist   b. amateur   c. follower   d. innovator

_____ 10. According to "What Makes a Degas a Degas?" which of the following details supports the feeling of movement in Degas' work?
   a. patches of brilliant color
   b. imitation charcoal pencil lines
   c. cut-off figures
   d. large open spaces

_____ 11. In "What Makes a Degas a Degas?" what characteristic in Degas' paintings shows the influence of photography and Japanese prints?
   a. the simulated matte finish
   b. the cut-off figures and forms
   c. the sketchy charcoal outlines of figures
   d. the large areas of brilliant color

_____ 12. What is the purpose of an analytical essay?
   a. to break down a large idea into its smaller parts
   b. to convey the author's feelings toward his or her subject
   c. to entertain and inform
   d. to narrate the story of the subject's life

_____ 13. According to "What Makes a Degas a Degas?" which of the following techniques did Degas innovate?
   a. pastel painting
   b. impressionistic painting
   c. simulated matte finish of pastels with oils
   d. painting from photographs

_____ 14. From reading "What Makes a Degas a Degas?" what would you say might be a viewer's first impression of the composition of a Degas painting?
   a. balanced   b. stark   c. busy   d. lopsided

_____ 15. According to "What Makes a Degas a Degas?" what qualities in a Degas painting suggest the influence of photography?
   I. immediate
   II. intimate
   III. studied
   IV. realistic
      a. I   b. I and II   c. I, II, and III   d. I, II, and IV

Vocabulary and Grammar

_____ 16. A _____ is a person who is at least one hundred years old.
   a. centaur   b. centurion   c. centennial   d. centenarian

_____ 17. A person with severe or stern characteristics may be described as _____.
   a. laconic   b. titanic   c. austere   d. jocular

_____ 18. In the following sentence, the infinitive "to admire" functions as an _____ to modify the word _____.

Price presents his characterizations as "photographs" for readers to admire.

a. adjective; readers
b. adjective; "photographs"
c. adverb; presents
d. adjective; characterizations

_____ 19. The _____, or varnished, surface of Degas' paintings enhanced the contrast among elements within the paintings.

a. covered   b. lacquered   c. oiled   d. relinquished

_____ 20. In which sentence is the infinitive phrase italicized?

a. Degas wanted *to make* the painting look as though it had been executed quickly.
b. Degas used patches of brilliant color *to increase the feeling* of movement.
c. Degas tipped the stage upward *to keep figures from blocking one another*.
d. Degas used large, open spaces *to move the eye deep* into the picture.

Essay Questions

21. The author of "A Picture From the Past: Emily Dickinson" uses details in the daguerreotype of Emily Dickinson to interpret her personality and the kind of life she lived. In an essay, explain the author's interpretation of Dickinson and why you agree or disagree.

22. In "What Makes a Degas a Degas?" the author states that part of Degas' lifelong quest was "to make viewers feel that they were right there beside him." In an essay, identify elements in Degas' paintings that illustrate his lifelong quest. Explain how these elements create a sense of immediacy for the viewer. Use details from the essay and from Degas' paintings to support your answer.

23. In an essay, answer the question: What makes a Degas a Degas? Cite details from Degas' paintings and Mühlberger's essay to support your interpretation.

Name _____ Date _____

"The Orphan Boy and the Elk Dog," a Blackfeet Myth

Selection Test

Critical Reading

In the blank, write the letter of the one best answer.

_____ 1. Why do the villagers reject Long Arrow at the beginning of the story?
   a. They believe he is cruel and dangerous.
   b. They believe he is foolish and dull-witted.
   c. He is caught stealing food from people.
   d. He mistreats his sister.

_____ 2. How would you interpret the following passage from "The Orphan Boy and the Elk Dog"?

   Good Running said, "They called you a stupid, crazy boy, but now that I think of it, the name you were given at birth is Long Arrow. I'll see that people call you by your right name. Now come along."

   a. Good Running feels that even though Long Arrow is dimwitted, he still should be called by his given name.
   b. Good Running wants Long Arrow to change his name.
   c. Good Running feels that Long Arrow is worthy of respect and he wants the villagers to respect him, too.
   d. Good Running feels that Long Arrow should have been given a different name at birth.

_____ 3. Why does Good Running decide to adopt Long Arrow?
   a. Good Running begins to like Long Arrow, who seems alert and capable of becoming a good hunter and warrior.
   b. Good Running is no longer able to hunt, and he needs Long Arrow's help.
   c. Good Running is pressured by his wife, who feels abandoning the boy is wrong.
   d. Good Running is lonely and has always wanted a son.

_____ 4. What sets Good Running apart from other people in his village?
   a. He is a skilled hunter and warrior.
   b. He has a strong sense of compassion and is willing to look beyond people's prejudices against Long Arrow.
   c. He is slow-witted and people take advantage of his kindness.
   d. He enjoys the company of children.

_____ 5. Judging from details provided in the myth, what qualities in young men did the Blackfeet most value?
   a. sensitivity and compassion
   b. planting, cleaning, and cooking abilities
   c. a sense of humor and the ability to tell stories
   d. strength, knowledge, and hunting skills

_____ 6. Why is Good Running at first reluctant to suggest that Long Arrow search for Elk Dogs?
   a. Good Running wants to find the Elk Dogs himself.
   b. He loves Long Arrow and does not want to lose him.
   c. He feels Long Arrow is not really strong or brave enough to search for Elk Dogs.
   d. He does not believe Elk Dogs really exist.

_____ 7. What is the significance of Long Arrow's journey to find the Elk Dogs in "The Orphan Boy and the Elk Dog"?
   a. It is a chance for him to add some excitement to his life.
   b. It is an opportunity for him to prove to the villagers that Elk Dogs do not really exist.
   c. It is a chance for him to bring relief to the hardworking village dogs who were his only friends during the time he was an outcast.
   d. It is an opportunity for him to prove his worth to his fellow villagers and to make Good Running proud.

_____ 8. Where does Long Arrow have to go to find the mysterious Elk Dogs and the holy man who controls them?
   a. to the bottom of a deep canyon
   b. to a castle in the sky
   c. to the bottom of a lake
   d. to the top of a mountain

_____ 9. Which quality helps Long Arrow most as he faces each obstacle on his journey?
   a. his gentleness
   b. his bravery
   c. his physical strength
   d. his knowledge of animals

_____ 10. Which passage best shows Long Arrow as a "larger than life," mythical character?
   a. Following Good Running's advice, Long Arrow wandered southward. On the fourth day of his journey he came to a small pond, where a strange man was standing as if waiting for him.
   b. The beautiful boy took Long Arrow to a meadow on which some strange animals, unlike any the young man had ever seen, were galloping and gamboling, neighing and nickering.
   c. Long Arrow wandered on, walking for long hours and taking little time for rest. Through deep canyons and over high mountains he went, wearing out his moccasins and enduring cold and heat, hunger and thirst.
   d. Long Arrow thanked him and vowed to follow his advice. For four days the young man stayed in the spirit chief's lodge, where he ate well and often went out riding on the Elk Dogs.

_____ 11. What is the chief's attitude when Long Arrow catches a glimpse of his leg and hoof?
   a. He is angry and orders Long Arrow to leave the lodge immediately.
   b. He feels depressed that he has been unable to hide his embarrassing secret.
   c. He feels Long Arrow must have been fated to see it.
   d. He wants Long Arrow to become the new chief.

_____ 12. Which words best describe Long Arrow's state of mind as he leaves the land of the spirit people?
   a. bold and proud
   b. timid and humble
   c. sad and disappointed
   d. angry and vengeful

_____ 13. What does Long Arrow's decision to share his Elk Dogs with Good Running reveal about his character?
   a. He is fearful that Good Running will reject him.
   b. He is considerate and generous as well as strong and brave.
   c. The Elk Dogs are not important to him.
   d. His main concern is making the other villagers feel envious.

_____ 14. What is the most beneficial aspect of the journey for Long Arrow?
   a. It gives Long Arrow a chance to ride his own Elk Dogs.
   b. It proves once and for all Long Arrow's worth to people in the camp.
   c. It gives Long Arrow a chance to offer his adopted grandparents a gift.
   d. It gives Long Arrow a chance to explore the countryside.

____ 15. The main purpose of "The Orphan Boy and the Elk Dog" is to explain
        a. how the Blackfeet came to have horses.
        b. how the Blackfeet treated orphans.
        c. the importance of bravery and determination.
        d. the activities of young Blackfeet boys.

Vocabulary and Grammar

____ 16. Which of the following sentences contains an error in its use of *accept* or *except*?
        a. People continued to except Long Arrow from the community.
        b. Long Arrow excepted a difficult challenge.
        c. Good Running was willing to accept Long Arrow into his home.
        d. Everyone except Good Running doubted the boy's abilities.

____ 17. Which of the following is the best meaning of the word *surpassed* as it is used in the following sentence?

        Long Arrow was a fast learner and soon *surpassed* other boys his age in knowledge and skills.

        a. enjoyed   b. taught   c. went beyond   d. fell behind

____ 18. Long Arrow noticed that power seemed to be _____ from the holy man.
        a. emanating   b. stifling   c. relishing   d. surpassing

____ 19. The holy man _____ Long Arrow into his lodge. The holy man looked like a normal human, _____ for the fact that he had the leg and hoof of an Elk Dog.
        a. excepted; except
        b. accepted; except
        c. excepted; accept
        d. accepted; accept

____ 20. Which of the following is the best meaning of the word *stifle* as it is used in the following sentence?

        Long Arrow tried to stifle his cry of surprise.

        a. sing
        b. shout
        c. exaggerate
        d. hold back

Essay Questions

21. In an essay, explain why the journey to find Elk Dogs becomes so important to Long Arrow. What prompts him to go on the journey? What, in addition to Elk Dogs, is he hoping to find? How does he feel as he returns to the village with the Elk Dogs? Why does he feel this way?

22. In an essay, explain the character of Long Arrow. What personality traits does he exhibit in the story? In what way do some of these traits help him to find a place in the home of Good Running? In what way do some of these traits make completing his difficult task possible? How has his personality been shaped by the early events of his life?

23. In an essay, analyze "The Orphan Boy and the Elk Dog" as an example of myth. What is a myth? What characteristics of myth does this story have? Answer these questions using examples from the story.

"The Street of the Cañon" from *Mexican Village* by Josephina Niggli

Selection Test

Critical Reading

In the blank, write the letter of the one best answer.

_____ 1. What might readers logically predict about the stranger after reading the details presented in the opening lines of the story?
   a. He plans to dance at the party with a certain person.
   b. He is deliberately going where he will be unwelcome, where his presence could cause a commotion.
   c. He is carrying cheese to a party.
   d. He is on a casual walk through a neighboring town.

_____ 2. Why is the stranger drawn to the young girl at the party with "laughing black eyes"?
   a. She is his relative.
   b. She seems frightened and unsure of herself.
   c. He recognizes her and plans to dance with her.
   d. She is the only person at the party who seems friendly.

_____ 3. When the stranger asks the orchestra to play the *Virgencita*, the favorite song of Hidalgo, Sarita thinks the stranger is
   a. making a foolish and tasteless joke.
   b. unaware of the significance of the song.
   c. a man from the village of Hidalgo.
   d. trying to embarrass and upset her.

_____ 4. What is the stranger, Pepe Gonzalez, hiding from the young woman as the two dance?
   a. that he is enjoying her company
   b. that he has never been to San Juan Iglesias before
   c. that he is from Hidalgo
   d. that he is not enjoying the party

_____ 5. What is the most recent cause of tension between Hidalgo and San Juan Iglesias?
   a. It is a land dispute.
   b. Both claim ownership of a chest full of gold that was found.
   c. Both claim ownership of the bones of a famous historian.
   d. Both want to be leaders in cheese production.

_____ 6. Based on what Sarita says as she dances with Pepe, what logical prediction can a reader make about what her reaction will be when she learns she has danced with a person from Hidalgo?
   a. She will want to meet other Hidalgo people.
   b. She will be pleasantly surprised.
   c. She will be shocked and confused.
   d. She will leave the party.

_____ 7. Why does the author include the following passage, written from Pepe's point of view?
   The Hidalgo man twisted his mouth remembering how Rubén the candymaker had
   ridden across the whitewashed line high on the cañon trail that marked the division
   between the Three Marys' and the Sabinas' sides of the mountains, and then had

fallen in a faint from his saddle because his left arm was broken. There was no candy in Hidalgo for six weeks.

    a. to discount Sarita's perspective on the situation

    b. to introduce Rubén as a character

    c. to show the brutality of the fight

    d. to present Pepe's perspective on the events described by Sarita

_____ 8. What do Pepe Gonzalez's actions reveal about his personality?

    a. He is gentle and kind.

    b. He is bold and manipulative.

    c. He is a coward.

    d. He is interested only in parties.

_____ 9. What is Sarita's attitude as she describes Pepe's reputation for "doing the impossible"?

    a. contempt for his escapades

    b. fear of his wildness

    c. amusement at the rumors

    d. admiration for his courage

_____ 10. At the end of the story, what causes an uproar among the guests?

    a. They realize Pepe is dancing at the party.

    b. Pepe makes his identity known to Don Roméo.

    c. The goat cheese brought by Pepe is spoiled.

    d. The goat cheese brought by Pepe is found.

_____ 11. Which of the following is a logical deduction as to why Pepe leaves the party?

    a. He needs to get home.

    b. He knows the crowd will figure out that he and the cheese are from Hildago.

    c. He feels Sarita will think he likes her if he stays.

    d. He feels guilty for being at a party at San Juan Iglesias.

_____ 12. Why does the author reveal Pepe's identity through the thoughts of Sarita?

    a. to show that Sarita is not angry but intrigued with the idea that she danced with Pepe

    b. to show Sarita's rage over the incident

    c. to show she is the only one left at the party

    d. to show the reaction of Don Roméo to the incident

_____ 13. Which of the following creates suspense in the story?

    a. the package of cheese

    b. the historian's remains

    c. the birthday party

    d. the song *Virgencita*

_____ 14. Which of the following lines from the story best explains Pepe's motivation for crashing the party?

    a. " . . . Don Rómolo Balderas was the greatest historian in the entire Republic."

    b. "When all the world says a thing cannot be done, he does it to prove the world wrong."

    c. "But most of all there were cheeses, for the Three Marys was a cheese-eating valley."

    d. "Such fine manners were not common to the town of San Juan Iglesias."

_____ 15. At the end of the story, the reader does not know if the young stranger really is

    a. interested in marrying Sarita.

    b. able to do the impossible.

    c. from the village of Hidalgo.

    d. the son of Don Timotéo.

_____ 16. Which of the following statements best expresses the theme, or central idea, of "The Street of the Cañon"?

    a. A man clever enough to pat the lamb has a right to play with the sheep.

    b. An excessive preoccupation with the dead spoils the lives of the living.

    c. A girl who is overly friendly with strangers risks damage to her reputation.

    d. The feelings of the young will always challenge the prejudices of their elders.

Vocabulary and Grammar

_____ 17. Which of the following is the best meaning of the word *nonchalantly*?

    a. timidly

    b. arrogantly

    c. slowly

    d. casually

_____ 18. Which of the following sentences does not contain a prepositional phrase?

    a. As the music began to play, the stranger slipped his arm around Sarita's waist.

    b. Little by little the stranger edged Sarita closer to the door.

    c. Before the stranger could answer, the chattering in the patio swelled to louder proportions.

    d. She realized to her own amazement that she was more apprehensive than angry.

_____ 19. Which of the following is the best meaning of the word *audaciously*?

    a. calmly

    b. angrily

    c. boldly

    d. nervously

_____ 20. An infinitive always ends with a _____, and a prepositional phrase always ends with a _____.

    a. verb; noun or pronoun   c. noun; pronoun

    b. verb or adverb; preposition   d. noun or pronoun; verb

Essay Questions

21. In an essay, explain how the author uses third-person omniscient point of view in "The Street of the Cañon." What does she accomplish by using this point of view? Support your response with details from the story.

22. In an essay, explain the following quotation from "The Street of the Cañon": "When all the world says a thing cannot be done, he does it to prove the world wrong." What is the thing Pepe is trying to do? How does this relate to the theme of the story?

23. In an essay, analyze the character of Sarita and her feelings toward Pepe Gonzalez. How do her feelings relate to the theme of the story? In what way is the ending of the story unexpected?

"A Storm in the Mountains" by Alexander Solzhenitsyn
"In the Orchard" by Henrik Ibsen
"A Tree Telling of Orpheus" by Denise Levertov

Selection Test

Critical Reading

In the blank, write the letter of the one best answer.

_____ 1. In "A Storm in the Mountains," the most powerful effect on those caught in the storm is
    a. the danger of avalanche.
    b. the volume of rain.
    c. the destruction of the wind.
    d. the contrast between light and dark.

_____ 2. In "A Storm in the Mountains," why are the pine trees "springing back" in the same place?
    a. They are bending in the ferocious wind.
    b. The travelers lose sight of them between lightning flashes.
    c. The travelers are lost and keep circling.
    d. All pine trees look the same in the dark.

_____ 3. The speaker in "A Storm in the Mountains" is
    a. a solitary traveler alone in the mountains.
    b. one of the pine trees.
    c. one of a group caught in the storm.
    d. a soldier.

_____ 4. Why does the speaker in "A Storm in the Mountains" compare the lightning flashes to the arrows of Biblical armies?
    a. The image illustrates the danger they are in.
    b. These mountains are the site of historic events.
    c. The power of the storm seems godlike in its wrath.
    d. The image suggests the faith that made them fearless.

_____ 5. Why aren't the travelers in "A Storm in the Mountains" afraid of the storm?
    a. They know they are safe in a protected spot in the mountain pass.
    b. They don't fully appreciate the danger at the time.
    c. They left their tents for shelter at the beginning of the storm.
    d. They forget their fear amid the spectacular sights and sounds.

_____ 6. At the end of "A Storm in the Mountains," those caught in the storm feel "insignificant yet grateful" because
    a. they feel a part of nature's creative force at work.
    b. their lives have been miraculously spared.
    c. such a powerful storm is unusual in these mountains.
    d. they are not subject to the world's primal forces.

_____ 7. The speaker of "In the Orchard" celebrates
    a. the reward promised in the fruitage of autumn.
    b. the physical beauty of a spring moment.
    c. the acceptance of time passing.
    d. the virtues of farm work.

_____ 8. The speaker of "In the Orchard"
a. speaks in the first person.
b. is depicted as a Scandinavian farmer.
c. addresses warblers and thrushes.
d. addresses only other workers.

_____ 9. The message of "In the Orchard" is to
a. recognize the deception of spring beauty.
b. pay close attention to the passing of time.
c. pay the price to get one's work done.
d. appreciate the loveliness of the moment.

_____ 10. The images in "In the Orchard" are intended to
a. illustrate how easy it is to forget one's duty.
b. make spring seem less attractive than autumn.
c. create the rich sights and sounds of spring.
d. celebrate the virtues of farm work.

_____ 11. According to the speaker of "In the Orchard," what will finally "shut the garden gate"?
a. passing time
b. labor and effort
c. the speaker himself
d. the other workers

_____ 12. In "In the Orchard," why will you "win the bargain" if you heed the poet?
a. The fruit may be late but there will be plenty to spare.
b. The cattle and sheep graze better in the orchard.
c. You will trade prosperity for joy.
d. You will be prepared for the unpredictability of weather.

_____ 13. In "A Tree Telling of Orpheus," Denise Levertov tells, from the point of view of a tree,
a. a fable with a moral about passing time.
b. an imaginative re-creation of a true story.
c. a classical myth of a powerful musician.
d. an account of the birth of music and fire.

_____ 14. What do the following lines from "A Tree Telling of Orpheus" describe?

in anguish, in haste
wrenched from the earth root after root,
the soil heaving and cracking, the moss tearing asunder—
a. what a tree might feel if it tried to move
b. the effect of fire on a tree
c. the effect of drought
d. the grief of the tree for the death of Orpheus

_____ 15. In "A Tree Telling of Orpheus," having a tree as the speaker of the poem
a. causes us to find the story of Orpheus more believable.
b. makes the poem lighter because of its impossibility.
c. allows us to imagine Orpheus' power more vividly.
d. explains the unusual arrangement of line breaks.

Vocabulary and Grammar

___ 16. Which of the following sentences contains a gerund that functions as a direct object?
   a. There was no word he sang but I knew its meaning.
   b. The breaking was painful but necessary.
   c. We did not lose the sound of the singing.
   d. The greatest gift he gave us was his singing.

___ 17. *Terra firma* means
   a. awe of the heavens.
   b. solid earth.
   c. fear of height.
   d. mountainous land.

___ 18. The word *sultry* means _____.
   a. sweltering
   b. mild
   c. moody
   d. changeable

___ 19. A gerund is a verb form ending in *-ing* that acts as
   a. an adjective   c. an adverb
   b. a noun   d. a verb

___ 20. The word *asunder* means _____.
   a. below
   b. loudly
   c. rapidly
   d. apart

Essay Questions

21. The word *primal* means first in time, original, or primitive. In "A Storm in the Mountains," Alexander Solzhenitsyn says he became part of this "primal world in creation before our eyes." Write an essay in which you explain why storms create such dramatic feelings in observers, using "A Storm in the Mountains" to support your ideas.

22. Write an essay in which you explain the theme of Ibsen's "In the Orchard." Discuss how and why nature is such a powerful setting for the theme. Use examples from the poem to support your ideas.

23. Denise Levertov's "A Tree Telling of Orpheus" starts with an ancient myth and expands it dramatically. Why does she choose to write in the first person? In an essay, analyze the benefits of writing from the first-person point of view. Support your ideas with examples from the poem.

Unit Test: Expanding Horizons

Critical Reading

In the blank, write the letter of the one best answer.

The questions below are based on the following selection.

The Sonnet-Ballad by Gwendolyn Brooks

Oh mother, mother, where is happiness?
They took my lover's tallness off to war,
Left me lamenting. Now I cannot guess
What I can use an empty heart-cup for.
He won't be coming back here any more.
Some day the war will end, but, oh, I knew
When he went walking grandly out that door
That my sweet love would have to be untrue.
Would have to be untrue. Would have to court
Coquettish death, whose impudent and strange
Possessive arms and beauty (of a sort)
Can make a hard man hesitate—and change.
And he will be the one to stammer, "Yes."
Oh mother, mother, where is happiness?

_____ 1. A poem's speaker is its _____.
a. tone
b. character
c. meter
d. voice

_____ 2. Which of the following is an unlikely connotation of the word *coquettish*?
a. female
b. insistent
c. persuasive in attitude and behavior
d. attractive and sensual

_____ 3. What two subjects does Brooks's speaker integrate in lines 8–11?
a. infidelity and death
b. war and motherhood
c. love and poetry
d. war and peace

_____ 4. Which of the following is *not* emphasized by Brooks's use of repetition in lines 8 and 9?
a. the soldier's tallness
b. the speaker's sadness
c. the speaker's shock and bitterness
d. the soldier's death

_____ 5. Which is the most accurate description of the speaker's tone?
   a. lighthearted
   b. angry and confused
   c. serious, sad, and somewhat bitter
   d. ironic

_____ 6. What three senses are engaged by Brooks's use of language in this poem?
   a. sight, hearing, and taste
   b. sight, hearing, and smell
   c. hearing, taste, and touch
   d. sight, taste, and touch

_____ 7. Your understanding of this poem will be deeper if you apply prior knowledge related to _____.
   a. war
   b. loss and grief
   c. sonnets and ballads
   d. happiness

_____ 8. What does Brooks personify as a tempting lover?
   a. happiness
   b. war
   c. death
   d. motherhood

_____ 9. How did the speaker's lover feel about going to war?
   a. mildly displeased
   b. dutiful
   c. angry and resentful
   d. pleased and proud

_____ 10. Understanding how Brooks's words, actions, and images contribute to the poem's meaning depends upon a reader's ability to _____.
   a. envision   c. clarify details
   b. predict outcomes   d. interpret

Vocabulary and Grammar

In the blank, write the letter of the one best answer.

_____ 11. Which of the following sentences contains a gerund?
   a. We were hiking when the storm suddenly began.
   b. Crouching beneath the rocks, we watched the lightning flash.
   c. The storm slowed us down, but it didn't stop us from climbing.
   d. We are camping at the summit tonight.

_____ 12. By using appositives a writer
   a. provides details about characters without adding extra sentences.
   b. slows down the pace of a story and makes it sound choppy.
   c. modifies a noun or pronoun by telling _what kind_ or _which one_.
   d. renames the subject of a sentence.

____ 13. Which of the following sentences correctly uses the words *accept* or *except*?
  a. I excepted almost everything you said to me.
  b. Except for her love of hot chocolate, her tastes rarely included sweets.
  c. Would you mind accepting me from the invitation list for the camping trip?
  d. I except your gift with the greatest gratitude.

____ 14. What is the function of the infinitive phrase in the following sentence?
  In *Dancers, Pink and Green*, each ballerina is caught in a characteristic pose as she waits to go onstage.
  a. adverb   c. adjective
  b. direct object   d. object of a preposition

____ 15. The word *amiably* means _____.
  a. friend
  b. friendly
  c. unfriendly
  d. in a friendly way

____ 16. The word root *–cent-* means _____.
  a. coins
  b. hundred
  c. middle
  d. language

____ 17. Which of the following sentences *misuses* an adverb containing the suffix *–ly*?
  a. He nonchalantly walked into the front room.
  b. "What is a dragon?" he asked imperiously.
  c. All eyes were drawn to his nonchalantly walk.
  d. He audaciously mentioned subjects that were supposed to be secret.

____ 18. Which of the following words is *not* related to the word *disreputable*?
  a. reputation
  b. repute
  c. repertory
  d. disrepute

____ 19. In which sentence are the present participial phrase and the word it modifies both italicized?
  a. That night he buried the bicycle in the little clearing in the bush where the *dead* of the camp, *including his own youngest son*, were buried.
  b. That night he buried the bicycle in the little clearing in the bush where the dead of the *camp, including his own youngest son*, were buried.
  c. That night he buried the *bicycle* in the little *clearing in the bush* where the dead of the camp, including his own youngest son, were buried.
  d. That night he *buried* the *bicycle* in the little clearing in the bush where the dead of the camp, including his own youngest son, were buried.

____ 20. The Latin term *status quo* means _____.
  a. for a specific purpose
  b. the existing state of things
  c. in reality
  d. *terra firma*

Essay Questions

21. Sometimes a dramatic event leads a person to expand his or her horizons by thinking or behaving in new ways. Choose a selection from this unit that features such a dramatic event (such as "Civil Peace" or "The Street of the Cañon") and write an essay in which you explain how the event affects a particular character. Be sure to describe how the character thinks, feels, and behaves before and after the crucial event. Also include a clear explanation of how the event encourages (or forces) this person to change.

22. The world of nature can awaken us to new ways of using our senses and of thinking, feeling, and behaving. Choose a selection from this unit, such as "A Storm in the Mountains," "The Orphan Boy and the Elk Dog," or "In the Orchard," and explain how natural forces or events expand a character's sense or understanding of the world.

23. From their earliest moments, human beings gain new perspectives as they grow older, and this process does not stop with the end of childhood or adolescence. Choose one or more selections from this unit addressing questions of aging, such as "In the Orchard," "Old Friends," or "The Bean Eaters." In an essay, discuss how the horizons of a character or speaker in these works expand as he or she regards the passage of time and his or her own life.

24. In times of social or political upheaval, people can gain dramatic new perspectives on their lives in a relatively short period of time. Making reference to a selection from this unit, such as "The Orphan Boy and the Elk Dog" or "Civil Peace," write an essay in which you discuss how homelessness, poverty, or exile from one's homeland could expand one's horizons.

25. It is not only cataclysmic natural or historical events that can bring fresh perspectives to people. Art can have an almost magical power to change or broaden the way people experience the world. Using a selection in this unit—such as "A Tree Telling of Orpheus" or "What Makes a Degas a Degas?"—write an essay in which you discuss how art can expand an individual's horizons in profound and lasting ways.

"The Open Window" by Saki

Selection Test

Critical Reading

In the blank, write the letter of the one best answer.

____ 1. Why is Framton Nuttel visiting the Sappletons in the country?
    a. He hopes to go on a hunting expedition.
    b. He hopes to rest and relax his nerves.
    c. He is attending a family reunion.
    d. He is delivering a message from his sister.

____ 2. Why does Vera confirm the fact that Framton Nuttel does not know her aunt well at all?
    a. She wants to prepare him for her aunt's strange behavior if he does not know her.
    b. She believes she has seen him at the house before.
    c. She must confirm the fact that he does not know her aunt before she decides that she does not like him.
    d. She must confirm the fact that he does not know her before she creates her fictional tale about her aunt and the open window.

____ 3. Until Mr. Sappleton returns, Framton believes that Mrs. Sappleton is
    a. sadly deranged.
    b. rather cold-hearted.
    c. exceptionally boring.
    d. perfectly normal.

____ 4. In what does Framton seem to be mainly interested?
    a. Vera's coquettish behavior
    b. the masculine atmosphere
    c. Mrs. Sappleton's mood
    d. his own problems

____ 5. Why does Framton flee the house when Mr. Sappleton returns?
    a. He is suddenly taken ill and requires urgent care.
    b. He thinks Mr. Sappleton has come back from the dead.
    c. He is afraid he will be suspected of flirting with Mrs. Sappleton.
    d. He was once chased by dogs into a freshly dug grave.

____ 6. When Mr. Sappleton returns at the end of the story, we realize that
    a. Mr. Sappleton is a ghost.
    b. Vera played a trick on Framton.
    c. Vera is a mental patient.
    d. Framton understands the joke.

____ 7. Based on details in "The Open Window," what caused Vera to tell Framton the story of her aunt's "great tragedy"?
    a. She wanted him to understand her aunt's present state of mind.
    b. She was upset and felt that Framton was someone she could talk to.
    c. She had no self-control and blathered on about private family matters.
    d. She found Framton's company insufferable and wanted to get rid of him.

____ 8. What is the story's central conflict?
   a. Mrs. Sappleton's wish to see her husband again
   b. Vera's wish to get rid of Framton
   c. Framton's wish to get rest and relaxation
   d. Framton's fear of dogs

____ 9. What is humorous about Mrs. Sappleton's remark, "One would think he had seen a ghost?"
   a. She does not realize that Framton believes he has seen a ghost.
   b. Framton definitely has seen a ghost.
   c. Mrs. Sappleton does not understand why Framton leaves.
   d. Mrs. Sappleton seems annoyed with Framton.

____ 10. What occurs at the climax of this story?
   a. A cyclist collides with Framton.
   b. Vera tells Mrs. Sappleton that Framton is afraid of dogs.
   c. Mrs. Sappleton announces the return of the men from their hunting trip, and Framton sees them.
   d. Mrs. Sappleton introduces herself to Framton.

____ 11. Which off the following events occurs first in "The Open Window"?
   a. Vera makes up a story about Framton's fear of dogs.
   b. Framton grabs his belongings and runs frantically from the house.
   c. Framton goes into detail about his ailments and infirmities.
   d. Mrs. Stappleton announces that her husband and brothers will soon return from shooting.

____ 12. Why is Vera able to fool Framton so easily?
   a. Framton was planning to leave early anyway.
   b. Framton seems tired and lacking in good judgment.
   c. Vera is shrewd and manipulative, while Framton is self-absorbed and conventional.
   d. Vera has tricked other house guests into leaving.

____ 13. In what way is the central conflict of the story resolved?
   a. Framton is finally able to rest.
   b. The hunting party returns and Framton flees.
   c. Mrs. Sappleton finally meets Framton.
   d. Vera explains why Framton leaves.

____ 14. What does the following line about Vera mean?
      Romance at short notice was her specialty.
   a. She is adventurous and loves meeting new people.
   b. She encourages loving relationships between people.
   c. She frequently falls in love with strangers.
   d. She is able to invent fantasy tales quickly.

____ 15. "The Open Window" by Saki is mostly about
   a. how to behave around particularly boring visitors.
   b. how misinformation affects our perceptions.
   c. the unexpected effects of playing tricks.
   d. the possibility that ghosts really exist.

____ 16. Which of the following is a central idea of "The Open Window"?
   a. It is impossible to please everyone.
   b. Young people care only about themselves.
   c. Self-centered people tend to be gullible.
   d. Dealing with strangers can be risky.

Vocabulary and Grammar

____ 17. What word or phrase is modified by the word *only* in the following sentence?
> When Framton arrives at the Sappleton home, he knows only minimal details about the Sappleton family.
   a. minimal details
   b. knows
   c. Sappleton family
   d. When Framton arrives

____ 18. Which of the following is the best meaning of the word *delusion* as it is used in the following sentence?
> Framton at first thinks that Mrs. Sappleton's sighting of her husband is the result of a delusion.
   a. practical joke
   b. fact
   c. false belief
   d. promise

____ 19. What word or phrase is modified by the word *just* in the following sentence?
> Framton left when the men were just preparing to enter the open window.
   a. preparing
   b. the men
   c. Framton left
   d. the open window

____ 20. Which of the following is the best meaning of the word *imminent* as it is used in the following sentence?
> A cyclist coming along the road had to run into the hedge to avoid imminent collision.
   a. loud
   b. imaginary
   c. threatening
   d. violent

Essay Questions

21. In an essay, analyze Framton Nuttel's expectations. Explain what Framton expects before he arrives at the Sappleton home, and show how these expectations are violated. What do his actions reveal about his character?

22. In an essay, describe the plot of "The Open Window." Explain the exposition, inciting incident, central conflict, and resolution of the story. How does the author build suspense around the story's central conflict?

23. In an essay, contrast the character of Vera with the characters of Framton Nuttel and Mrs. Sappleton. What details provided by the author show why Vera is able to manipulate the events of the story so effectively? In what way is she different from the other characters?

"Leiningen Versus the Ants" by Carl Stephenson

Selection Test

Critical Reading

In the blank, write the letter of the one best answer.

____ 1. The central conflict in "Leiningen Versus the Ants" can best be characterized as one between
    a. courage and fear.
    b. men and ants.
    c. pride and reality.
    d. intelligence and nature.

____ 2. Which of the following statements best describes Leiningen's character?
    a. He is arrogant but not intelligent.
    b. He is brilliant but not organized.
    c. He is brave but not foolhardy.
    d. He is compassionate but not sentimental.

____ 3. When they learn the ants are coming, Leiningen's employees remain calm because they
    a. are fatalistic about death.
    b. have confidence in Leiningen.
    c. do not understand the danger.
    d. are aware of Leiningen's plans.

____ 4. Based on these words from Leiningen early in the story, which prediction is most reasonable?
> With me, the brain isn't a second blind gut; I know what it's there for. . . . And now I'm ready for anything and everything—including your ants.
    a. Leiningen will battle the ants with his wits.
    b. The ants will single out Leiningen in their attack.
    c. Leiningen will defeat the ants on their first approach.
    d. Leiningen will face several setbacks before defeating the ants.

____ 5. Which of the following represents an external conflict?
    a. Leiningen orders his men to defend the ditch.
    b. The peons believe the ants are thinking deadly thoughts.
    c. The flow of petrol from the cistern into the ditch becomes blocked.
    d. Leiningen forces himself to his feet after stumbling to the ground.

____ 6. What technique does the author use to increase the suspense of the story?
    a. He describes Leiningen's struggle as a series of triumphs and failures.
    b. He explains that Leiningen is well prepared for the ants.
    c. He imagines a clever way for the ants to cross the water ditch.
    d. He has Leiningen sleep through each night of the battle.

____ 7. What internal conflict is at work among Leiningen's men?
    a. their pride in the plantation versus their desire to escape
    b. their concern for their families versus their duty to their boss
    c. their respect for Leiningen's plans versus their terror of the ants
    d. their fear of the ants versus their confidence in Leiningen

____ 8. The morning after the ants' first siege, Leiningen "almost regretted that the fight had ended so soon and so simply." One can reasonably predict that
     a. the ants will retreat from the plantation.
     b. Leiningen will provoke the ants to attack.
     c. the ants will make another assault.
     d. Leiningen's men will desert him.

____ 9. Which of the following is most responsible for the failure of Leiningen's defenses?
     a. the ants' sheer numbers
     b. the plantation's great size
     c. the workers' lack of training
     d. the ants' superior intelligence

____ 10. During the story, Leiningen's attitude toward the ants changes from
     a. indifference to terror.
     b. excitement to desperation.
     c. curiosity to dislike.
     d. anger to resignation.

____ 11. What does Leiningen hope will be the effect of ferrying the women and children across the river?
     a. The safety of the women and children will be ensured.
     b. His workers will not be distracted.
     c. The women and children will seek help from other plantations.
     d. His workers will no longer fear the ants.

____ 12. Which of the following lines about Leiningen marks the climax of the story?
     a. "And now he was sure he would prove more than a match for the 'irresistible' ants."
     b. "Victory had been snatched from the very jaws of defeat."
     c. "Then all at once he saw . . . the pampas stag. In six minutes—gnawed to the bones. He couldn't die like that!"
     d. "Would he recover? 'He won't die,' said the old man who had bandaged him, 'if he doesn't want to.'"

____ 13. Based on the fact that Leiningen decides to make the daring run to the dam, which of the following predictions is most *unlikely*?
     a. Leiningen will reach the dam.
     b. The dam won't open.
     c. The ants will attack Leiningen.
     d. Leiningen will flood the plantation but die in the process.

____ 14. Which of the following lines best captures Leiningen's approach to his war with the ants?
     a. " . . . intelligence directed aright, invariably makes man the master of his fate."
     b. " '. . . I'm not going to run for it just because an elemental's on the way.' "
     c. " . . . during his three years as planter, Leiningen had met and defeated drought, flood, [and] plague. . . ."
     d. " 'Act of God, my eye!' "

Vocabulary and Grammar

_____ 15. The District Commissioner is not used to _____ people like Leiningen who *flout* his warnings.
   a. brave
   b. contemptuous
   c. cautious
   d. adventurous

_____ 16. There _____ a slight _____ that if he dams the river completely, he can flood the plantation and wash away the ants
   a. are, chance   c. is, chance
   b. are, chances   d. is, chances

_____ 17. A horde of army ants is one of nature's more frightening _____.
   a. phenomenon
   b. phenomenons
   c. phenomena
   d. phenomenas

_____ 18. When the petrol ignites, the throng of ants _____ in a wide circle and _____ for the concrete to cool, before approaching again.
   a. retreat, wait   c. retreats, wait
   b. retreats, waits   d. retreat, waits

_____ 19. The leaves that once were _____ for the ants become _____ at turns in the ditch.
   a. provender; fomentations
   b. fomentations; weir
   c. alluvium; peons
   d. provender; alluvium

_____ 20. In which of the following sentences do the subject and verb not agree?
   a. The ants' vast moving shadow covers the hill.
   b. There is at least twenty million ants approaching the plantation.
   c. Every single one of the ants is a fiend from hell.
   d. Leiningen, with the help of his men, has built defenses.

Essay Questions

21. "Leiningen Versus the Ants" is a suspense story. In an essay, explain how knowing the plots of other suspense stories affects your predictions about "Leiningen Versus the Ants." Were your predictions correct, or were you surprised by the outcome of some situations? Support your answers with examples from the story.

22. The conflicts in "Leiningen Versus the Ants" are internal as well as external. In an essay, analyze what type of conflict defines the story. Use examples from the story to defend your position.

23. In an essay, analyze the character of Leiningen. Describe his positive attributes and those that are problematic. Explain how he is a heroic figure. Support your answers with examples from the story.

"By the Waters of Babylon" by Stephen Vincent Benét

Selection Test

Critical Reading

In the blank, write the letter of the one best answer.

_____ 1. John is driven to the Place of the Gods by his desire for _____ .
    a. power
    b. knowledge
    c. metal
    d. dreams

_____ 2. Legends about the ground that "burns forever" refer to
    a. a belief that the city is Hell.
    b. intense heat from power plants.
    c. contamination of the earth.
    d. sunlight reflected by skyscrapers.

_____ 3. For John's society, which period represents "the beginning of time"?
    a. before the evolution of the human species
    b. before the onset of the Industrial Revolution
    c. after human beings learned to use fire
    d. after the destruction of modern civilization

_____ 4. In what way is John's civilization different from the one that preceded it?
    a. Priests govern the society.
    b. Books no longer exist.
    c. People eat only plants.
    d. There is no warfare.

_____ 5. Given John's references to gods and magic, the reader can conclude that
    a. John is ignorant.
    b. the People of the Hills are very spiritual.
    c. people of the future lack the capacity to understand technology.
    d. the Great Burning was a recent event.

_____ 6. *Only* a first-person narrator
    a. refers to himself with the personal pronoun "I."
    b. comments on the actions of other characters.
    c. relates story events.
    d. has thoughts and feelings.

_____ 7. John's exploration of the Place of the Gods demonstrates his _____ .
    a. timidity
    b. gullibility
    c. agility
    d. open-mindedness

_____ 8. What is the most reasonable conclusion drawn from the following details?
   There was also the shattered image of a man or a god. It had been made of white stone and he wore his hair tied back like a woman's. His name was ASHING, as I read on the cracked half of a stone.
   a. The gods had a leader named ASHING.
   b. The image is a statue of Washington.
   c. Some people considered Washington a god.
   d. The gods had greater respect for men than for women.

_____ 9. When John sees the city "as it had been when the gods were alive," he is seeing
   a. New York City as it had been.
   b. a view of another planet.
   c. the future.
   d. a myth.

_____ 10. John's empathy and respect for the man who died in the chair suggest
   a. the virtues of a modern technological society.
   b. an unwillingness to face difficult truths.
   c. the continuity of fundamental human values.
   d. a tendency to sentimentalize human history.

_____ 11. John's discovery that the "gods" were men makes him realize that
   a. he can no longer be considered a priest.
   b. New York City was once a sacred place.
   c. the Hill People are completely insignificant.
   d. his people are capable of similar feats.

_____ 12. If John were to reveal his discoveries, the People of the Hills would probably
   a. move to the Place of the Gods.
   b. denounce him.
   c. decode the old writings.
   d. embrace his ideas.

_____ 13. First-person point of view in "By the Waters of Babylon" creates
   a. a flat, unemotional tone.
   b. historical validity.
   c. intimacy.
   d. a predictable plot line.

_____ 14. What is the theme of "By the Waters of Babylon"?
   a. the hostility between different groups of people
   b. the cycles of human history
   c. the frailty of human constructions
   d. the end of human society

Vocabulary and Grammar

_____ 15. The priests might have _purified_ metal by
   a. bending it into different shapes.
   b. covering it with dirt.
   c. placing it in fire.
   d. throwing it away.

____ 16. What would make the following passage more engaging?

I was allowed to go into the dead houses. I searched for metal. I learned the ways of those houses. I saw bones, but I was no longer afraid. The bones are light and old. They will sometimes fall into dust if you touch them. But that is a great sin.

a. adding more details about the metal
b. varying the way the sentences begin
c. structuring each sentence in the same way
d. explaining why the bones turn to dust

____ 17. How does the following sentence begin?

Raising my eyes and looking south, I saw the Place of the Gods.

a. with a subject
b. with a prepositional phrase
c. with a participial phrase
d. with a subordinate clause

____ 18. Going east to the Place of the Gods was strictly forbidden; ____, John felt driven to make his journey.

a. purified
b. bowels
c. moreover
d. nevertheless

____ 19. Another word for *bowels* is _____.

a. pots
b. intestines
c. shelves
d. courage

____ 20. What happens when sentences consistently begin in a similar way?

a. They strengthen a story and make its meaning clear.
b. They create lively writing that engages readers.
c. They take on a monotonous rhythm that does not engage readers.
d. They help a writer highlight important details in a story.

Essay Questions

21. First-person point of view in "By the Waters of Babylon" creates a specific mood and tone. Write an essay describing the mood and tone and explaining how the narrator's point of view creates them.

22. Benét's choice of a first-person narrator is a deliberate one. What effect does the point of view have on the story? How would a different point of view change the effect? Write an essay in which you compare the story's first-person point of view to an optional point of view, such as third-person limited or third-person omniscient.

23. In "By the Waters of Babylon," modern civilization as we know it has been destroyed. What message does the story send about technology and humanity? Do you believe Benét is optimistic or pessimistic about the future? Support your opinion with details from the story.

"A Problem" by Anton Chekhov
"Luck" by Mark Twain

Selection Test

Critical Reading

In the blank, write the letter of the one best answer.

____ 1. Which of Sasha's actions causes a family problem?
a. He leaves the army in disgrace.
b. He quits his job at the Treasury.
c. He cashes a false promissory note.
d. He is arrested.

____ 2. Which line best illustrates Sasha's character?
a. "In short, the family was dear to him for many reasons."
b. "It made no difference to him where he was: here in the hall, in prison, or in Siberia."
c. "'And it's not in my character to bring myself to commit a crime.'"
d. "'When I have the money I help the poor.'"

____ 3. What does Sasha's uncle mean when he says that it would be "civic cowardice" to help Sasha?
a. that Sasha is a coward
b. that the family should not hide behind Sasha's problems
c. that civic duty is more important than family honor
d. that by protecting Sasha from punishment they would be breaking the law

____ 4. When you identify with a character, you
a. predict how the character will react in a particular situation.
b. put yourself in the character's place and share his or her experiences.
c. analyze the effect of the character's behavior on others.
d. draw conclusions about the character's personality.

____ 5. In "A Problem," how does Sasha Uskov feel when leaving the Colonel's home with his uncle after the council meeting ?
a. He feels grateful to his uncle for standing up for him.
b. He feels humbled by his uncles kindness and is determined to change.
c. He feels free and wants to party with his friends.
d. He regrets the trouble that he has caused his family.

____ 6. How do you think Ivan Markovitch feels when Sasha asks for another loan?
a. useful
b. horrified
c. happy to oblige
d. concerned

____ 7. Sasha can be considered a static character because
a. he does not change throughout the story.
b. he regrets his behavior.
c. he causes the main problem in the story.
d. he learns from his experience.

____ 8. Which of the following sentences best reflects the moral of Mark Twain's "Luck"?
   a. Military heroes invariably turn out to be frauds.
   b. Cheating always leads to a disastrous situation.
   c. Education is the key to effective leadership.
   d. Success may depend more on chance than on merit.

____ 9. As a young teacher, the clergyman coached Scoresby for final examinations to
   a. get Scoresby a commission in the army.
   b. lessen Scoresby's anticipated failure.
   c. earn extra money.
   d. prove his abilities as a teacher.

____ 10. What is the clergyman's motivation in telling the narrator his opinion of Scoresby?
   a. He is envious of Scoresby's success.
   b. He finds Scoresby's history amusing.
   c. He thinks Scoresby is a remarkable person.
   d. He wants the narrator to know how important he has been to Scoresby's career.

____ 11. Which of the following words best describes how the clergyman feels after Scoresby passes his final examinations?
   a. relieved
   b. elated
   c. remorseful
   d. proud

____ 12. In "Luck," how did the narrator feel about Scoresby after hearing the clergyman's story?
   a. He was disappointed to discover that his long-held suspicions about Scoresby were true.
   b. He felt that Scoresby was a genius and that the clergyman was envious of his success.
   c. He felt angry that such a fool had received so many honors.
   d. He was astonished that a man he had once considered a demigod was nothing more than a lucky fool.

____ 13. The Reverend can be considered a dynamic character because he
   a. comes to realize that Scoresby will always be blessed by good luck.
   b. never wavers in his opinion that Scoresby is a fool.
   c. spent much of his life trying to protect Scoresby from himself.
   d. realizes that Scoresby is a sweet and lovable person.

____ 14. Is it correct to say that the characterization of Scoresby is static?
   a. no, because he learns how to succeed in war
   b. yes, because he appears never to learn anything
   c. yes, because he is totally predictable
   d. no, because he becomes famous and admired

Vocabulary and Grammar

____ 15. The word *vestibule* means
   a. a high point.
   b. real or genuine.
   c. a small entrance hall.
   d. a person's visage or appearance.

____ 16. What noun or pronoun is modified by the restrictive adjective clause in the following sentence?

> To outsiders who have no personal interest in the matter such questions seem simple.

    a. outsiders
    b. who
    c. interest
    d. questions

____ 17. Sasha's other paternal uncle, a _____ man, sits silently throughout Ivan Markovitch's defense of Sasha.

    a. prodigious
    b. sublime
    c. guileless
    d. taciturn

____ 18. The word *countenance* means

    a. the expression of a person's face.
    b. a noble person.
    c. the appearance of being genuine.
    d. an incalculable amount.

____ 19. Identify the restrictive adjective clause in the following sentence.

> So I took my poor little capital that I had saved up through years of work and grinding economy and went with a sigh and bought a cornetcy in his regiment, and away we went to the field.

    a. So I took my poor little capital
    b. that I had saved up through years of work and grinding economy
    c. and went with a sigh and bought a cornetcy in his regiment
    d. and away we went to the field.

____ 20. Identify the nonrestrictive adjective clause in the following sentence.

> He went through on that purely superficial "cram," and got compliments, too, while others, who knew a thousand times more than he, got plucked.

    a. He went through on that purely superficial "cram," and got compliments, too
    b. while others
    c. who knew a thousand times more than he
    d. got plucked.

Essay Questions

21. In Chekhov's story "A Problem," Sasha Uskov's behavior causes "a problem" for his family. In an essay, describe what the serious problem that Uskov causes, how he reacts to the problem, how his family reacts to the problem, and how his family goes about trying to resolve the problem. Use details from the story to support your answer.

22. Describe in an essay what makes Arthur Scoresby and Sasha Uskov static characters. Then contrast one of these main characters with a dynamic character from the same story. Use examples from the stories to illustrate the difference between static and dynamic characters.

23. The clergyman in Twain's story "Luck" describes in detail how he feels about Scoresby's "accomplishments." But what about Scoresby himself? Write an essay describing how Scoresby might feel about his military record, based on what you know about him. How would you feel in a similar situation?

"There Will Come Soft Rains" by Ray Bradbury

"The Garden of Stubborn Cats" by Italo Calvino

Selection Test

Critical Reading

In the blank, write the letter of the one best answer.

____ 1. In "There Will Come Soft Rains," human beings
   a. have all been destroyed by the automated house.
   b. have all been destroyed in a nuclear war.
   c. have left the planet for a safer destination.
   d. are prisoners of the technology they have invented.

____ 2. What mood is created by a setting in which all domestic functions are performed by machines and none by human beings?
   a. cheerful and exhilarating
   b. repulsive and horrifying
   c. homey and reassuring
   d. impersonal and chilling

____ 3. The story is told from the point of view of
   a. an omniscient observer.
   b. the cleaning robot mice.
   c. a human survivor.
   d. the main program of the house.

____ 4. Which of the following sentences from the story contributes directly to the setting?
   a. "Today is Mr. Featherstone's birthday.'"
   b. "Bridge tables sprouted from patio walls."
   c. "It repeated the date three times for memory's sake."
   d. "A dog whined, shivering on the front porch."

____ 5. What can the reader infer about the McClellan family based on the way their house is programmed?
   a. They live a quiet, orderly life.
   b. They are active in politics.
   c. Both parents have full-time jobs.
   d. Mrs. McClellan is blind.

____ 6. Why did Bradbury choose a fully automated house instead of a factory or a school as the setting for "There Will Come Soft Rains"?
   a. A factory or school would require less automation than the house.
   b. It is unlikely that a larger building would survive the blast.
   c. The homey details emphasize the horror of nuclear destruction.
   d. A house is small enough to describe in a short story.

____ 7. By portraying the house as "alive" and the family as painted silhouettes, the author
   a. stresses the importance of strong family values.
   b. expresses the idea that human life is insignificant.
   c. reverses expectations of human and nonhuman roles.
   d. shows how technology can enhance human lives.

____ 8. The setting of "There Will Come Soft Rains" suggests that human beings
   a. are dependent on machines.
   b. have evolved into androids.
   c. view nature as distasteful.
   d. have no free choice.

____ 9. Given the events that took place shortly before the story begins, the automated house may represent the
   a. last hope for humane family values.
   b. answer to the problem of global war.
   c. dangers of technology.
   d. inherent evil of totalitarian systems.

____ 10. Which of the following details helps you clarify what is going on at the beginning of "There Will Come Soft Rains"?
   a. "Somewhere in the walls, relays clicked, memory tapes glided under electric eyes."
   b. "This was the one house left standing."
   c. "The rooms were acrawl with the small cleaning animals, all rubber and metal."
   d. "Until this day, how well the house had kept its peace."

____ 11. Bradbury's main purpose in "There Will Come Soft Rains" is to contrast the
   a. beauty of poetry with the horrors of nuclear war.
   b. frailty of human life with the power of technology.
   c. programming of the house with the needs of survivors.
   d. cleanliness of the house with inevitable death and decay.

____ 12. Which of the following details from "The Garden of Stubborn Cats" explains the statement, "The city of cats and the city of men exist one inside the other, but they are not the same city"?
   a. Buildings now fill courtyards and gardens that cats and people once shared.
   b. No cat can follow the itinerary of its ancestors.
   c. Because he brought his lunch, Marcovaldo had time to observe the cats on his lunch break.
   d. To see the Biarritz, one had to assume the posture of a cat.

____ 13. The description of changes in architecture at the beginning of "The Garden of Stubborn Cats" helps clarify
   a. Marcovaldo's interest in the well-fed cat with the blue ribbon.
   b. Marcovaldo's decision to catch the fish from above.
   c. the Marchesa's reasons for not selling her property.
   d. the vast population of cats in the overgrown garden.

____ 14. The setting of "The Garden of Stubborn Cats" is
   a. New York.
   b. an unnamed modern city.
   c. an ancient city of fable.
   d. Turin, Italy.

____ 15. In "The Garden of Stubborn Cats," after the Marchesa's death, it is implied that
   a. the cats block the redevelopment of the property.
   b. the cats had caused her death.
   c. Marcovaldo assumes responsibility for the cats and the garden.
   d. the neighbors understood the Marchesa's actions.

Vocabulary and Grammar

____ 16. The word *paranoia* refers to
   a. unexplainable events beyond the realm of reason.
   b. an example of the highest order, quality, or rank.
   c. the inability to move one's limbs.
   d. a mental disorder involving fears of persecution.

____ 17. In which sentence are the parallel elements italicized?
   a. It *fed upon Picassos and Matisses* in the upper halls, like delicacies, *baking off the oily flesh, tenderly crisping the canvases* into black shavings.
   b. It fed upon Picassos and Matisses *in the upper halls*, like delicacies, baking off the oily flesh, tenderly crisping the canvases *into black shavings*.
   c. It fed upon Picassos and Matisses in the upper halls, like delicacies, *baking off the oily flesh, tenderly crisping the canvases* into black shavings.
   d. It fed upon Picassos and Matisses in the upper halls, like delicacies, *baking off the oily flesh, tenderly crisping the canvases into black shavings.*

____ 18. The word *itinerary* means _____ .
   a. purpose
   b. destiny
   c. lifestyle
   d. route

____ 19. The word *indigence* means _____ .
   a. outrage
   b. inactivity
   c. poverty
   d. foolishness

____ 20. Which of the following sentences uses parallel structure?
   a. Marcovaldo smoked a half-cigar while he waited for work to resume.
   b. Marcovaldo, venturing into more and more cattish places, was able to catch a glimpse of the line by climbing roofs and railings.
   c. The steam shovels dug down to great depths; into the iron armatures, cement poured; a high crane passed beams to the workmen.
   d. The waiter dipped the net into the tank, pursued the appointed trout, captured it, and headed for the kitchens.

Essay Questions

21. Near the end of Bradbury's "There Will Come Soft Rains" he pays tribute to poet Sara Teasdale by including a poem she wrote. What effect does this poem have on the story? Write an essay that discusses the meaning of the poem and its effect on the story.

22. "There Will Come Soft Rains" is set in the future. Why doesn't Bradbury place less sophisticated equipment in the empty house and set the story in a war-torn past? How does the theme of the story depend on the setting? Write an essay that explains why the setting is such a critical element in the story's effect.

23. A fable is a short, simple tale, usually with a message or moral, often using animals to make its point. In what ways are these two stories fables? In an essay, discuss two elements of each story that seem fable-like. Use examples from the stories to support your ideas.

"The Princess and All the Kingdom" by Pär Lagerkvist
"The Censors" by Luisa Valenzuela

Selection Test

Critical Reading

In the blank, write the letter of the one best answer.

_____ 1. In "The Princess and All the Kingdom," what does the prince do to win the princess?
a. He wins a contest.
b. He battles his way through the country.
c. He defeats the other princes who want to marry the princess.
d. He single-handedly breaks down the walls of the city in which the princess lives.

_____ 2. In what way can a reader challenge the message in "The Princess and All the Kingdom"?
a. decide if the message holds true in real life
b. see if the message matches that of other authors
c. apply it to another story and see if it's still true
d. decide if the action in the story is believable or realistic

_____ 3. In "The Princess and All the Kingdom," what is the chancellor's message to the prince?
a. The people are opposed to him because he has laid waste the countryside.
b. The princess, though charmed at first, is having second thoughts.
c. In addition to the princess, he has won the entire kingdom.
d. The prince may have the princess, but the kingdom is ruined and worthless.

_____ 4. In "The Princess and All the Kingdom," from the prince's response to the chancellor, we can tell the prince is
a. confused and thrilled.
b. resentful and disgusted.
c. alarmed and intimidated.
d. surprised and disappointed.

_____ 5. Why does the prince in "The Princess and All the Kingdom" respond the way he does to the chancellor's words?
a. He once thought the princess's father would continue to rule.
b. He expected to go away with the princess and now sees complications.
c. He is a spoiled young man who has always had things his own way.
d. He set his sights only on the princess; it never occurred to him that he would not win her.

_____ 6. In what way is the theme of "The Princess and All the Kingdom" universal?
a. Everyone can relate to being conquered.
b. Everyone hopes to find happiness.
c. Everyone dreams of finding true love.
d. Everyone hopes to have a kingdom some day.

_____ 7. How is the writer's message revealed in "The Princess and All the Kingdom"?
a. by the reaction of the prince at the end of the story
b. by the prince's method of attaining his goal
c. through the words of the chancellor
d. through the prince's actions

_____ 8. In "The Censors," why does Juan take a job with the Censorship Division?
a. He feels he has particular skills for the work.
b. He wants to work from the inside to disrupt the entire system.
c. He hopes to intercept his letter to Mariana.
d. He wants to promote the Government's efforts to control opposition.

_____ 9. In The Censors," why does Juan report the co-worker who tries to organize a strike?
a. He believes strikes are illegal.
b. In his desire to keep his job, he thinks it will serve his own best interests to report the man.
c. He disagrees with the man's reasons for the proposed strike.
d. He thought the man was trying to undermine the mission of the Censorship Division.

_____ 10. In "The Censors," what is the author implying through Juan's absorption in his work?
a. Modern-day workers are workaholics and should lead more balanced lives.
b. It's good to be devoted to your job.
c. People can get carried away by ideas or actions and not realize what they are doing.
d. Censorship takes concentration and dedication.

_____ 11. What is Juan's "noble mission" that soon gets blurred by his becoming absorbed in censoring?
a. protecting Mariana
b. protecting the Government
c. earning promotions
d. helping to support his mother

_____ 12. Which of the following universal themes is addressed in "The Censors"?
  I. greed
 II. censorship
III. power
IV. ambition
    a. I and III   b. II and III   c. II and IV   d. III and IV

_____ 13. By what means is the theme of "The Censors" revealed?
a. directly, through the narrator's words
b. indirectly, through Juan's thoughts
c. through the structure of the Censorship Division, as described in the story
d. through the circumstances of the story's events and its outcome

_____ 14. Which of the following questions states Valenzuela's message in "The Censors"?
a. Could a person who objects to a system really become a part of that system as Juan does?
b. Is there a place in the world where letters are censored in the way described?
c. Should people get jobs when their only motive is an ulterior one?
d. What countries practice corporal punishment?

Vocabulary and Grammar

_____ 15. In "The Censors," Juan had an *ulterior* motive for getting a job as a censor because
a. he did not state why he really wanted the job.
b. it was his last chance.
c. he lied about his skills.
d. he disapproved of the censorship process.

_____ 16. The prince covers the princess's hand with ardent kisses. *Ardent* implies that
   a. the princess resisted the kisses.
   b. the prince gave her hand lots of little kisses.
   c. the prince had strong feelings.
   d. the prince was apologetic for the damage he had done to the kingdom.

_____ 17. In the following sentence, all the verbs are in the _____ tense.
   He dared his life; he battled his way step by step through the country.
   a. present   c. past
   b. present perfect   d. past perfect

_____ 18. Someone who is *venerable*
   a. is known for being associated with a famous story or event.
   b. is worthy of respect.
   c. has a certain illness.
   d. has few skills and is difficult to employ.

_____ 19. Which sentence contains mixed verb tenses?
   a. The whole city decked itself out for the festival and the wedding was celebrated with rejoicing, pomp, and splendor.
   b. When in the evening he went to enter the princess's bedchamber, he was met outside by the aged chancellor.
   c. I have not fought for sordid gain; I have fought merely to win her whom I love.
   d. I have conquered but ask for nothing, only to live happily with the only thing of value in life.

_____ 20. The censors _____ between the lines of each and every letter; they will check its tiniest comma and most accidental stain.
   a. read   c. had read
   b. have read   d. will read

Essay Questions

21. Do you feel that "The Princess and All the Kingdom" is a pessimistic or an optimistic story? In an essay, explain why you think the ending is a happy one or a sad one. What do you think is the author's general outlook on life?

22. In "The Censors," a worker gets caught up in a system he originally opposed. In an essay, explore what this system represents, how it is connected to the story's universal theme, and what aspect of society the author is commenting on.

23. Both Lagerkvist and Valenzuela have comments to make about people and society. How do they make these comments—directly or indirectly? In an essay, state each writer's message and explain how it is revealed. Finally, explain whether the messages hold up in the real world or whether they apply only to the situations in the stories.

Unit Test: Short Stories

Critical Reading

In the blank, write the letter of the one best answer.

The questions below are based on the following selection.

The following excerpt comes from the short story "Mushrooms in the City" *by Italo Calvino.*

. . . Thus, one morning, as he was waiting for the tram that would take him to Sbav and Co., where he was employed as an unskilled laborer, he noticed something unusual near the stop, in the sterile, encrusted strip of earth beneath the avenue's line of trees; at certain points, near the tree trunks, some bumps seemed to rise and, here and there, they had opened, allowing roundish subterranean bodies to peep out.

Bending to tie his shoes, he took a better look: they were mushrooms, real mushrooms, sprouting right in the heart of the city! To Marcovaldo the gray and wretched world surrounding him seemed suddenly generous with hidden riches; something could still be expected of life, beyond the hourly wage of his stipulated salary, with inflation index, family grant, and cost-of-living allowance.

On the job he was more absent-minded than usual: he kept thinking that while he was there unloading cases and boxes, in the darkness of the earth the slow, silent mushrooms, known only to him, were ripening their porous flesh, were assimilating underground humors, breaking the crust of clods. "One night's rain would be enough," he said to himself, "then they would be ready to pick." And he couldn't wait to share his discovery with his wife and his six children.

"I'm telling you!" he announced during their scant supper. "In a week's time we'll be eating mushrooms! A great fry! That's a promise!"

And to the smaller children, who did not know what mushrooms were, he explained ecstatically the beauty of the numerous species, the delicacy of their flavor, the way they should be cooked: and so he also drew into the discussion his wife, Domitilla, who until then had appeared rather incredulous and abstracted.

"Where are these mushrooms?" the children asked. "Tell us where they grow!"

At this question Marcovaldo's enthusiasm was curbed by a suspicious thought: Now if I tell them the place, they'll go and hunt for them with the usual gang of kids, word will spread through the neighborhood, and the mushrooms will end up in somebody else's pan! And so that discovery, which had promptly filled his heart with universal love, now made him wildly possessive, surrounded him with jealous and trusting fear.

"I know where the mushrooms are, and I'm the only one who knows," he said to his children, "and God help you if you breathe a word to anybody . . ."

____ 1. Which of the following best describes Marcovaldo's behavior during the day and evening after he discovers the mushrooms?
   a. volatile
   b. confident
   c. exuberant
   d. defensive

2. Why do mushrooms growing in a "sterile, encrusted strip of earth" beside the tram stop make such an impression on Marcovaldo?
   a. Wild mushrooms are one of Marcovaldo's favorite vegetables.
   b. They could be a source of income for Marcovaldo and his family.
   c. He is starved for natural beauty and wonder in the city.
   d. They symbolize his belief in the greatness of the modern city.

3. What is the effect of the details of the setting involving mushrooms, soil, and rain?
   a. The sensuous details provide the reader with evidence that the mushrooms are merely a figment of Marcovaldo's imagination.
   b. The sensuous details establish a conflict between nature and the modern world.
   c. The sensuous details place the story's events in a specific place and time.
   d. The sensuous details contrast sharply with Marcovaldo's dull, plodding work.

4. What feeling does the discovery of the mushrooms inspire in Marcovaldo?
   a. amusement
   b. hope
   c. contentment
   d. suspicion

5. In the course of this passage, a conflict is seen to develop
   a. between Marcovaldo and his family.
   b. between Marcovaldo and the mushrooms.
   c. within Marcovaldo.
   d. between Marcovaldo and the world.

6. To clarify the meaning of the term *unskilled laborer*, it would be best to
   a. review what you have already learned about Marcovaldo's job.
   b. read ahead for more information about Marcovaldo's job.
   c. look up the word *unskilled* in a dictionary.
   d. read other works by Italo Calvino.

7. Whom does Marcovaldo distrust in regard to the mushrooms?
   a. his children
   b. his coworkers
   c. everyone
   d. himself

8. A dynamic character in a work of fiction
   a. changes during the course of the story.
   b. grows up during the course of the story.
   c. is the most interesting and energetic person in the story.
   d. remains the same during the course of the story.

9. Which of the following would *not* be useful to employ at the conclusion of reading this passage?
   a. identifying persuasive messages in the text
   b. identifying cause and effect relationships in the text
   c. identifying the order in which events occur
   d. identifying which events are of greater or lesser importance

10. The information you receive when you hear or read a story is influenced by the _____ of the storyteller.
    a. gender
    b. character
    c. imagery
    d. point of view

Vocabulary and Grammar

Choose the word or words closest in meaning to the word in italics.

_____ 11. A cyclist coming along the road had to run into the hedge to avoid an *imminent* collision.
a. distant
b. apt to be dangerous
c. rapid
d. likely to happen soon

_____ 12. I was well aware that the Reverend was a man of strict *veracity*.
a. truthfulness
b. talkativeness
c. discipline
d. slander

_____ 13. *Ulterior* motives couldn't be overlooked by the Censorship Division, but they needn't be too strict with those who applied.
a. obvious
b. undisclosed
c. exterior
d. conspiratorial

In the blank, write the letter of the one best answer.

_____ 14. Which of the following does *not* apply to the use of parallel structure?
And one voice, with sublime disregard for the situation, read poetry aloud in the fiery study, until all the film spools burned, until all the wires withered and the circuits cracked.
a. It adds rhythm and balance to writing.
b. It expresses ideas of equal importance in dissimilar ways.
c. It create links between related ideas.
d. Form reflects meaning.

_____ 15. It is best to place modifiers such as *only* and *just* _____ the word or words they modify.
a. immediately after
b. near
c. immediately before
d. in the same clause as

_____ 16. Each of the following sentences contains an adjective clause. Which sentence contains a nonrestrictive adjective clause that should be set off with a pair of commas?
a. He went through on that purely superficial "cram," and got compliments too, while others who knew a thousand times more than he got plucked.
b. The strictest measures were taken that the Uskovs' family secret might not leak out and become generally known.
c. To outsiders who have no personal interest in the matter, such questions seem simple; for those who are so unfortunate as to have to decide them in earnest, they are extremely difficult.
d. Orders were given that no one was to be admitted.

_____ 17. Many of the men who _____ behind the ditch _____ to worry.
a. stand, begins
b. stands, begins
c. stands, begin
d. stand, begin

___ 18. Which of the following is not a conjunctive (or connecting) adverb?
   a. finally
   b. slowly
   c. moreover
   d. nevertheless

___ 19. The meaning of the Latin root –ultra- is ____.
   a. further; beyond
   b. not believable
   c. nearby
   d. underneath; beside

___ 20. Which of the following words is not built around the Latin root –ver-, meaning "speaking truly"?
   a. verdict
   b. veracity
   c. very
   d. verify

Essay Questions

21. Choose a selection from this unit—such as "A Problem," "Luck," or "The Princess and All the Kingdom"—that contains both static and dynamic characters. Identify at least one static and one dynamic character, and, in an essay, give a clear and thorough explanation of your classification. Use references from the text.

22. In some short stories an author's use of a particular literary element—such as setting, conflict, or point of view—is crucial to the overall meaning of the work. Choose a selection in which one literary element is particularly notable. Explain in an essay how the author's use of this literary element contributes to the total effect of the story.

23. Two writers can treat a similar subject matter in remarkably unique ways. Compare and contrast the ideas and literary characteristics of "There Will Come Soft Rains" and "By the Waters of Babylon."

24. Most short stories have clear and identifiable plot structures. Choose a selection from this unit and analyze its plot structure. In your essay, explain what information is introduced in the exposition; identify the inciting incident and the central conflict; describe the rising action and identify the climax; and finally, describe the story's resolution or end.

25. Like other writers of imaginative literature, short-story writers are interested in communicating themes to the reader. Choose a selection—such as "The Censors," "Leiningen Versus the Ants," or "By the Waters of Babylon"—and demonstrate your understanding of the work by writing an essay that analyzes the author's ideas and explains how the author uses those ideas to convey the theme of the story.

Name _____ Date _____

"**The Marginal World**" by Rachel Carson

Selection Test

Critical Reading

In the blank, write the letter of the one best answer.

____ 1. What is the central idea of "The Marginal World"?
a. The most beautiful forms of plant and animal life can be easily found in shore areas.
b. The shore is an especially apt place to examine the variability and adaptability of plant and animal life.
c. The first forms of life on this planet developed in shore areas and evolved over a period of thousands of years.
d. Shore areas provide important clues about problems that humans are likely to face in the future.

____ 2. What is Carson's pattern of organization in "The Marginal World"?
a. Carson organizes her essay in chronological order, the order in which events occur.
b. Carson organizes her essay by describing different places at different times.
c. Carson organizes her essay by classifying the different types of life found at the edge of the sea.
d. Carson organizes her essay by comparing and contrasting the ebb tide and the flood tide.

____ 3. The information presented in the selection would be most useful for an expository essay on which of the following topics?
a. Transformation and Continuity in Nature
b. Scientific Observation and Environmental Protection
c. The Future of the Species
d. Adapting to Climatic Change

____ 4. Which of the following is an effect of the low tide described in this essay?
a. Herons are a popular shore bird.
b. The author reveals how the past shapes the present.
c. Delicate flowers are visible on a cave's roof.
d. The author evaluates the relationship between land and sea life.

____ 5. What is the pattern of organization in the following passage from "The Marginal World"?
Visibly, it carpets the intertidal rocks; or half hidden, it descends into fissures and crevices, or hides under boulders, or lurks in the wet gloom of sea caves. Invisibly, where the casual observer would say there is no life, it lies deep in the sand, in burrows and tubes and passageways. It tunnels into solid rock and bores into peat and clay. It encrusts weeds or drifting spars or the hard, chitinous shell of a lobster.
a. comparison and contrast   c. classification
b. spatial order   d. chronological order

____ 6. What pattern of organization does Carson use in the following passage?
The sequence and meaning of the drift of time were quietly summarized in the existence of hundreds of small snails. . . . Once their ancestors had been sea dwellers, bound to the salt waters by every tie of their life processes. Little by little over the thousands and millions of years the ties had been broken. . . .
a. cause and effect   c. order of importance
b. chronological order   d. comparison and contrast

The Marginal World **145**

7. What does Carson mean when she says that the shore has a dual nature?
   a. The shore is an unstable environment.
   b. The shore at night is very different from the shore during the day.
   c. The shore has two primary functions.
   d. On the ebb tide, the shore belongs to the land; on the flood tide, it belongs to the sea.

8. What point is Carson making about the "blackness of the night" in the following passage?

   > The blackness of the night possessed water, air, and beach. It was the darkness of an older world, before Man.

   a. It is very dark.
   b. It is primeval.
   c. It is frightening.
   d. It makes the beach difficult to see.

9. What do you think the hydroid Tubularia, "the most delicately beautiful of the shore's inhabitants," symbolizes for Carson?
   a. the fragility of tidal pool life
   b. the unreal nature of marine life
   c. the adaptability of marine life
   d. the beauty, tenacity, and functionality of tidal pool life

10. What word or phrase best describes the sense Carson evokes in her description of twilight on the Georgia coast?
    a. loneliness
    b. awe
    c. remoteness
    d. peacefulness

11. When Carson writes, "Today a little more land may belong to the sea, tomorrow a little less. Always the edge of the sea remains an elusive and indefinable boundary," she is describing
    a. the set boundary between land and sea.
    b. the mutable nature of the shore.
    c. the formidable power of the sea.
    d. the dependability of the shore.

12. An expository essay is a piece of short nonfiction writing that
    a. narrates a series of events.
    b. describes a person, place, or object.
    c. informs by explaining, defining, or interpreting an idea, an event, or a process.
    d. relates a personal event in the writer's life.

13. In the following passage, how does Carson present her observations to the reader?

    > Invisibly, where the casual observer would say there is no life, it lies deep in the sand, in burrows and tubes and passageways. It tunnels into solid rock and bores into peat and clay. It encrusts weeds or drifting spars or the hard, chitinous shell of a lobster.

    a. by classifying the types of life she sees
    b. by explaining the relationship between animal and plant life
    c. by comparing and contrasting shore and sea life
    d. by explaining the cause-and-effect relationship between the shore and sea

_____ 14. Which of the following passages does *not* reflect Carson's overall pattern of organization in "The Marginal World"?

     a. In my thoughts of the shore, one place stands apart for its revelation of exquisite beauty. It is a pool hidden within a cave that one can visit only rarely and briefly . . .

     b. In a different way the same sense of remoteness and of a world apart came to me in a twilight hour on a great beach on the coast of Georgia.

     c. The sense of creation comes with memories of a southern coast, where the sea and the mangroves, working together, are building a wilderness of thousands of small islands . . .

     d. The flats took on a mysterious quality as dusk approached.

Vocabulary and Grammar

_____ 15. The word *marginal* means

     a. occupying the borderland.   c. capable of change.

     b. ancient or primitive.   d. relating to the universe.

_____ 16. Carson describes the edge of the sea as _____ because of the effects of the crashing surf and changing tides.

     a. primeval   b. marginal   c. mutable   d. ephemeral

_____ 17. Which sentence uses the superlative form of an adverb?

     a. The flats were astir with birds, and the voice of the willet rang insistently.

     b. The hydroid Tubularia is one of the most delicately beautiful of all the shore's inhabitants.

     c. The willets cried more urgently than the ghost-like sanderlings.

     d. You can enter the cave only when the lowest of the year's low tides fall below it.

_____ 18. Which sentence uses the comparative form of an adjective?

     a. There had been ominous showers in the night, with rain like handfuls of gravel flung on the roof.

     b. In the moment when I looked into the cave, an elfin starfish hung down, suspended by the merest thread.

     c. Only the most hardy and adaptable can survive in a region so mutable.

     d. It is tougher to survive between the tide lines than deep in the ocean because the region is so mutable.

_____ 19. The positive form of an adjective or adverb

     a. compares one thing.   c. modifies another word.

     b. compares two things.   d. compares more than two things.

_____ 20. The word *essence* means

     a. appearance or evidence.   c. passing quickly.

     b. real nature of something.   d. essential or necessary.

Essay Questions

21. At the beginning of "The Marginal World," Carson writes, "The edge of the sea is a strange and beautiful place." In an essay, analyze how Carson's pattern of organization enables her to demonstrate this idea effectively.

22. In describing a marginal world, Carson also creates a sense of a long-lost time—a time "before Man." In an essay, describe how Carson evokes this sense of time and explain what purpose it serves in her essay.

23. In "The Marginal World," Carson describes three distinct places and the marine life found in each. Write an essay in which you compare and contrast these three places. What makes each place unique? What features do they share?

from *The Way to Rainy Mountain* by N. Scott Momaday
from "Nobel Lecture" by Alexander Solzhenitsyn
"Keep Memory Alive" by Elie Wiesel

Selection Test

Critical Reading

In the blank, write the letter of the one best answer.

_____ 1. In *The Way to Rainy Mountain*, which of the following statements about the grand-mother is true?
   a. She died alone in her house near Rainy Mountain.
   b. She had seven sisters and a brother.
   c. She was one of the last remaining elders of the Kiowas.
   d. She lived out her long life in the shadow of Rainy Mountain.

_____ 2. In *The Way to Rainy Mountain*, which of the following best describes how the Kiowas felt when they entered the southern Plains?
   a. confused
   b. contented
   c. fearful
   d. liberated

_____ 3. In *The Way to Rainy Mountain*, the reader learns that the Kiowas created a legend at the base of Devil's Tower in order to
   a. help them deal with their fear of the unknown.
   b. demonstrate their reverence for the sun.
   c. recognize the important role that women play in Kiowa society.
   d. ask God to protect their children.

_____ 4. Why does Momaday tell readers in *The Way to Rainy Mountain* about what was hap-pening to the Kiowas when his grandmother was a child?
   a. He wants to compare her childhood with his own.
   b. He wants to give readers a complete sense of his grandmother and her life.
   c. He wants to emphasize the Kiowas' former power.
   d. He wants to explain how the landscape has changed since her childhood.

_____ 5. The author's purpose in *The Way to Rainy Mountain* is to
   a. demonstrate the vigor of Kiowa culture.
   b. describe the world of his ancestors.
   c. expose the mistreatment of the Kiowas.
   d. explore the meaning of religion.

_____ 6. A major theme of *The Way to Rainy Mountain* is that
   a. the Kiowas should have stayed at their original homeland in western Montana.
   b. the most effective way to come to terms with the death of an aged relative is to think about the person's youth.
   c. young people should devote greater attention to the traditions of their forebears.
   d. the culture of the Kiowas is strongly influenced by the physical world in which they live.

_____ 7. According to Solzhenitsyn, what is the world's most powerful force?
   a. literature
   b. truth
   c. friendship
   d. violence

_____ 8. Which of the following best characterizes Solzhenitsyn's relationship to other European writers mentioned in the excerpt from "Nobel Lecture"?
   a. appreciative
   b. antagonistic, but supportive
   c. hostile and contemptuous
   d. uncomprehending

_____ 9. What is the theme of the excerpt from "Nobel Lecture"?
   a. Writers all over the world form a writing fraternity.
   b. Literary critics have devalued world literature.
   c. We are moving toward an international language and literature.
   d. The writer must be a force for political and social reform.

_____ 10. According to the excerpt from "Nobel Lecture," which of the following influenced Solzhenitsyn's writing the most?
   a. winning the Nobel Prize for Literature
   b. his imprisonment
   c. his desire for fame
   d. literary critics

_____ 11. What was Solzhenitsyn's purpose in writing "Nobel Speech"?
   a. to make a gracious acceptance for a major award
   b. to articulate his understanding of the writer's role in the contemporary world
   c. to denounce the horrors of Soviet oppression
   d. to praise the European community of writers

_____ 12. In the excerpt from "Nobel Lecture," what kind of relationship does Solzhenitsyn suggest exists between violence and lying?
   a. casual
   b. unknowing
   c. incompatible
   d. interconnected

_____ 13. Which of these probably brings the greatest pain to the author of "Nobel Lecture"?
   a. exile from Europe
   b. creation of a world government
   c. an end to his life as a writer
   d. lack of recognition as an artist

_____ 14. A central idea in the excerpt from "Nobel Lecture" is Solzhenitsyn's belief that humankind will be saved by
   a. a recognition of the interdependence of all peoples.
   b. the obliteration of national boundaries.
   c. the defeat of communism.
   d. the widespread availability of world literature.

_____ 15. What does Wiesel say about neutrality in the final statements of "Keep Memory Alive"?
   a. Neutrality keeps people from getting involved with things that are best left alone.
   b. Neutrality helps keep people out of trouble.
   c. Neutrality helps the oppressor, never the victim.
   d. Neutrality is a sign of indecision, and should be avoided.

____ 16. Which of the following best describes the persuasive technique Wiesel uses in "Keep Memory Alive"?
   a. He relates his own concentration camp experience in detail to bring home the horrors of the Holocaust.
   b. He recalls the events of the Holocaust and tells readers that if they forget, they will share responsibility for it.
   c. He rages about the awful things that happened to the Jews.
   d. He relates a series of historical events from the twentieth century.

Vocabulary and Grammar

____ 17. By speaking out against injustice, people help make the world a _____ place.
   a. best
   b. more better
   c. most better
   d. better

____ 18. A person who exhibits *wariness* is _____.
   a. cautious
   b. worn out
   c. rude or speaks sharply
   d. especially sensitive

____ 19. If Jim's action *transcends* Bill's action, then Jim's action
   a. is different from Bill's.
   b. cancels out Bill's.
   c. adds to Bill's.
   d. surpasses or exceeds Bill's.

____ 20. What is the comparative form of the word *ill*?
   a. more iller
   b. most ill
   c. worst
   d. worse

Essay Questions

21. In an essay, analyze the excerpt from *The Way to Rainy Mountain*. Explain what characteristics identify it as a reflective essay, what message the author conveys, and how he conveys it. Support your answers with examples from the text.

22. Consider why the author works to "keep memory alive." In an essay, explain why he believes that people must remember the Holocaust and what effect remembering the atrocities experienced by the Jews has on us.

23. In the excerpt from "Nobel Lecture," Solzhenitsyn states that writers are the spokespersons of their countries and can be helpful in a world full of injustice and suffering. In an essay, explain Solzhenitsyn's position on violence, injustice, and suffering. Include discussion on how writers can help improve the world and keep governments honest.

"A Child's Christmas in Wales" by Dylan Thomas
"Marian Anderson: Famous Concert Singer" by Langston Hughes

Selection Test

Critical Reading

In the blank, write the letter of the one best answer.

____ 1. Dylan Thomas's "A Child's Christmas in Wales" is primarily a
   a. portrait of traditional Welsh Christmas celebrations.
   b. poetic Christmas fantasy.
   c. collection of the author's Christmas memories.
   d. description of the author's family.

____ 2. Which of the following details from the selection illustrates the difference between autobiography and biography?
   a. the story of Mrs. Prothero's fire
   b. the distinction between Useful Presents and Useless Presents
   c. the names of the narrator's childhood friends
   d. the identification of various aunts and uncles

____ 3. What word best describes the narrator's attitude toward his family?
   a. amused   b. bewildered   c. affectionate   d. embarrassed

____ 4. What is the author's purpose in describing the scene with the two boys blowing their dog whistles?
   a. to demonstrate the camaraderie of the boys
   b. to describe the narrator's triumph over a boyhood rival
   c. to provide an adult perspective on a conflict between boys
   d. to show the competitive nature of the boys' world

____ 5. Which of the following lines contains information available only to the author of an autobiography?
   a. ". . . caves that smelt like Sunday afternoons in damp front farmhouse parlors . . ."
   b. ". . . leaving huge deep footprints on the hidden pavements."
   c. "Auntie Hannah laced her tea with rum . . ."
   d. "Mistletoe hung from the gas brackets in all the front parlors."

____ 6. Which of the following phrases best describes the narrator of "A Child's Christmas in Wales"?
   a. quiet and observant   c. shy and affectionate
   b. shrewd and clever   d. fanciful and imaginative

____ 7. What conclusion can you draw about Auntie Hannah from the following sentence?
   Auntie Hannah, who had got on to the parsnip wine, sang a song about Bleeding
   Hearts and Death, and then another in which she said her heart was like a Bird's
   Nest . . .
   a. Auntie Hannah drank only at Christmas time.
   b. Alcohol made Auntie Hannah melancholy.
   c. Alcohol made Auntie Hannah maudlin and sentimental.
   d. Whenever she had a glass of wine, Auntie Hannah tended to confuse religion with love.

8. How would you describe the author's attitude in "A Child's Christmas in Wales" toward the Christmases of his childhood?
   a. sad and wistful
   c. angry and regretful
   b. nostalgic and warm
   d. cold and indifferent

9. Langston Hughes's primary purpose in "Marian Anderson: Famous Concert Singer" is to
   a. analyze the singing style of Marian Anderson.
   b. explain why music audiences loved Marian Anderson.
   c. describe how Marian Anderson triumphed over racial prejudice with talent and hard work.
   d. demonstrate the generosity of Marian Anderson.

10. Which of the following best explains why the author begins "Marian Anderson: Famous Concert Singer" with a discussion of famous black singers?
    a. to compare different forms of black musical expression
    b. to examine major influences on Marian Anderson's singing style
    c. to describe the development of black music in America
    d. to explain the significance of Marian Anderson's achievements

11. The author of "Marian Anderson: Famous Concert Singer" most likely relied on newspaper accounts for which of the following parts of the selection?
    a. comparison of Anderson with other famous black singers
    b. description of Anderson's European tours
    c. examination of the discrimination Anderson faced in southern cities
    d. discussion of Anderson's youth in Philadelphia

12. The author describes Marian Anderson's youth in Philadelphia chiefly to
    a. explain the significance of religious themes in her music.
    b. show how her family and community supported her development as a singer.
    c. explain why she became a singer rather than a violinist.
    d. identify the obstacles she had to overcome during the early stages of her career.

13. Which of the following best explains why so many Americans were angered when the Daughters of the American Revolution refused to allow Marian Anderson to sing at Constitution Hall?
    a. Anderson was a world-renowned vocal artist.
    b. Previous proprietors of the hall had made it available to everybody.
    c. The action violated basic national values.
    d. The Daughters of the American Revolution was not a popular organization.

14. In recounting Marian Anderson's life and career, the author emphasizes incidents in which the singer
    a. benefits from the help of others.
    b. overcomes adverse circumstances.
    c. shows a talent for investing her money wisely.
    d. learns how to avoid criticism.

15. In the selection, the author reveals his attitude toward Marian Anderson by emphasizing which of the following aspects of Anderson's character?
    a. aggressiveness and ambition
    c. curiosity and independence
    b. humility and self-denial
    d. dedication and perseverance

16. The central idea of "Marian Anderson: Famous Concert Singer" is that
    a. musical talent knows no racial or national boundary.
    b. publicity is the key to success in the music business.
    c. Europeans are the best judges of good music.
    d. concert performers are the best trained musical vocalists.

Vocabulary and Grammar

____ 17. In the following sentence, identify the appositive and tell whether or not it is restrictive or nonrestrictive.

Marian and her husband, an architect, settled in a country home in Connecticut.

a. architect, restrictive
b. architect, nonrestrictive
c. husband, restrictive
d. husband, nonrestrictive

____ 18. Which of the following is the best meaning of the word *sidle* as it is used in the following sentence?

Sleek and long as jaguars and horrible-whiskered, spitting and snarling, they would slink and sidle over the white back-garden walls, . . .

a. roll happily
b. move abruptly
c. move slowly and gracefully
d. move sideways in a sneaky manner

____ 19. In the following sentence, identify the appositive and tell whether or not it is restrictive or nonrestrictive.

My friend Jim and I ran into the house with snowballs.

a. friend, restrictive
b. friend, nonrestrictive
c. Jim, restrictive
d. Jim, nonrestrictive

____ 20. Which of the following is the best meaning of the word *staunch* as it is used in the following sentence?

Marian Anderson's mother was a staunch church worker who loved to croon the hymns of her faith . . .

a. loyal   b. casual   c. bitter   d. sad

Essay Questions

21. In a short essay, describe Dylan Thomas's attitude toward his childhood. Which incidents described in "A Child's Christmas in Wales" reveal this attitude? How has the passage of time affected Thomas's memories of the incidents?

22. In an essay, analyze Langston Hughes's attitude toward Marian Anderson as a singer and as a person. Which incidents presented in "Marian Anderson: Famous Concert Singer" reveal his feelings toward her? What does he consider her role in history?

23. In an essay, compare and contrast the autobiographical style of "A Child's Christmas in Wales" with the biographical style of "Marian Anderson: Famous Concert Singer" by answering the following questions: Which details presented in Thomas's piece are not likely to be known by a biographer? How would this piece be different written by a biographer? In what way does Hughes's objectivity add to his portrait of Marian Anderson? How would the piece be different if it were autobiographical?

"Flood" by Annie Dillard

Selection Test

Critical Reading

In the blank, write the letter of the one best answer.

_____ 1. The author's primary purpose in the selection is to
  a. describe her feelings and observations during a flood.
  b. analyze the causes and consequences of a flood.
  c. examine how communities react to floods.
  d. demonstrate the destructiveness of floods.

_____ 2. Which of the following sentences from "Flood" is a factual statement?
  a. "I look at the creek at my feet."
  b. "It's hard to take it all in, it's all so new."
  c. "It takes a bit of nerve even to stand on the bridge . . ."
  d. "It smashes under the bridge like a fist . . ."

_____ 3. At the beginning of the essay, why has the rainy summer day "an air of menace" for the speaker?
  a. The water is rising in Tinker Creek.
  b. She is surrounded by wildlife.
  c. She remembers a devastating flood that occurred exactly a year ago.
  d. She hears garbage trucks, school buses, and loud cars.

_____ 4. What is different about Tinker Creek on the morning of the flood?
  a. Animals are in the water.
  b. The water does not stop rising, even when it is beyond its banks.
  c. The water is especially cold.
  d. The creek does not make any noise.

_____ 5. The author's use of descriptive language in "Flood" is intended mainly to
  a. persuade readers to accept her point of view.
  b. entertain readers with interesting anecdotes.
  c. inform readers about people's behavior in an emergency.
  d. help readers share her experience.

_____ 6. The author's account of her initial reaction to the flood conveys a feeling of
  a. anger and bitterness.
  b. desperation and fear.
  c. frustration and disappointment.
  d. impotence and confusion.

_____ 7. Which of the following sentences from the selection best expresses an opinion?
  a. "When the rain stopped today I walked across the road to the downed log by the steer crossing."
  b. "The steers were across the creek, a black clot on a distant hill."
  c. "Still, the day had an air of menace."
  d. "A knot of yellow, fleshy somethings had grown up by the log."

_____ 8. The feature of "Flood" most characteristic of a descriptive essay is the author's
        a. analytical style.
        b. use of imagery.
        c. detached perspective.
        d. focus on nature.

_____ 9. What does Dillard's standing on the bridge above the flood waters reveal about her feelings toward the flood and nature?
        a. She is unaware of the true power of nature.
        b. She is paralyzed by fear.
        c. Her intense curiosity overrides any fear she might have.
        d. She is concerned mainly with her personal safety.

_____ 10. Which of the following sentences best appeals to the reader's senses of sight, feeling, and hearing?
        a. "I hear a roar, a high windy sound more like air than like water, like the run-to-gether whaps of a helicopter's propeller after the engine is off . . ."
        b. "All the familiar land looks as though it were not solid and real at all, but painted on a scroll like a backdrop, and that unrolled scroll has been shaken, so the earth sways and the air roars."
        c. "Everywhere windfall and flotsam twigs and leafy boughs, wood from woodpiles, bottles, and saturated straw spatter the ground or streak it in curving windrows."
        d. "The river leaps its bank and smashes into the woods where the motorbikes go, devastating all but the sturdiest trees."

_____ 11. Why does Dillard describe the many people and items that she expects to see carried by the flooded creek?
        a. to show her powers of observation
        b. to convey to readers the apparent power of the flooded creek
        c. to convey her fear that her own property will be destroyed by the flood
        d. to give readers an impression of her community

_____ 12. Why is Dillard concerned about which animals will survive the flood?
        a. She fears nature's entire food chain might be disrupted.
        b. She fears she will no longer be able to admire wildlife.
        c. She believes the animals might be able to help in rebuilding the area.
        d. She fears there will be too many spores and larvae.

_____ 13. The description of the children's interaction with the snapping turtle and rattlesnake evokes a feeling of
        a. fear and separation.
        b. nature's abundance and strangeness.
        c. innocence and novelty.
        d. playfulness and pain.

_____ 14. Which part of the following passage expresses an impression rather than a fact?
        They're waving a broom handle at it in hopes that it will snap the wood. . . . But the turtle is having none of it. It avoids the broom handle with an air of patiently re-pressed rage. They let it go, and it beelines down the bank, . . .
        a. They let it go
        b. with an air of patiently repressed rage
        c. it beelines down the bank
        d. They're waving a broom handle at it in hopes that it will snap the wood

_____ 15. A major theme of "Flood" is that
- a. the human capacity for adaptation is limitless.
- b. natural disasters cause greater emotional damage than physical destruction.
- c. the balance between order and chaos in nature is fragile.
- d. natural disasters make people more appreciative of what they have.

_____ 16. The author of "Flood" would most likely agree with which of the following statements?
- a. People tend to behave irrationally during moments of great danger.
- b. We must be willing to accept nature in its destructive as well as its tranquil moments.
- c. Floods are the most destructive form of natural disaster.
- d. Animals are better able to adjust to natural disasters than human beings.

Vocabulary and Grammar

_____ 17. Which word is the best meaning of _obliterates_ as it is used in the following passage?
> Our creek splashes transparently over a jumble of rocks; the high creek obliterates everything . . .
- a. moves
- b. destroys
- c. moistens
- d. soils

_____ 18. First some dolls zipped by and _____ some bottles, moving almost faster _____ she could see.
- a. then, than
- b. then, then
- c. than, than
- d. than, then

_____ 19. Which phrase is the best meaning of the word _mauled_ as it is used in the following passage?
> It's all I can do to stand. I feel dizzy, drawn, mauled.
- a. quietly at ease
- b. roughly handled
- c. treated gently
- d. confident of succeeding

_____ 20. Which of the following sentences uses _then_ or _than_ incorrectly?
- a. Dillard describes the rain falling in the morning and then again in the afternoon.
- b. Dillard thinks that the rain sounds more like air than like water.
- c. The floodwater became so high that it was higher than the bank.
- d. Dillard believes that it is necessary for the creek to flood because it is more itself then at any other time.

Essay Questions

21. In an essay, explain why "Flood" is a good example of a descriptive essay. Cite examples of descriptive passages that make you feel as if you are there witnessing the flood.

22. In an essay, analyze how the author uses a combination of facts and personal impressions to bring home the reality of the flood. Discuss what these impressions reveal about the power of nature.

23. In an essay, comment on Dillard's theme of order and chaos in nature. What images specifically address this theme? What does the writer learn from witnessing the flood?

"Star Wars—A Trip to a Far Galaxy That's Fun and Funny . . ." by Vincent Canby
"Star Wars: Breakthrough Film Still Has the Force" by Roger Ebert

Selection Test

Critical Reading

In the blank, write the letter of the one best answer.

_____ 1. Vincent Canby's review, "Star Wars—A Trip to a Far Galaxy That's Fun and Funny . . . ," was written
  a. the day after the movie originally opened.
  b. to celebrate the movie's twentieth anniversary.
  c. just before the movie came out.
  d. after the phenomenal financial success of the movie.

_____ 2. Canby's review primarily
  a. explains how the special effects were made.
  b. focuses on the conflict between good and evil.
  c. introduces the movie and praises it.
  d. explains the story in specific detail.

_____ 3. Canby includes references to Buck Rogers and King Arthur in order to
  a. demonstrate his knowledge of the medium.
  b. characterize the feeling of the story.
  c. assess the role of the movie in cinema history.
  d. explain how the tales have changed.

_____ 4. How does Canby support his belief that the two robots are "the year's best new comedy team"?
  a. He describes them as special effects.
  b. He explains the status of robots in this society.
  c. He contrasts their physical appearance.
  d. He compares them to Laurel and Hardy.

_____ 5. According to Canby, who are the true stars of Star Wars?
  a. Mark Hamill, Harrison Ford, and Carrie Fisher
  b. director George Lucas and his writers
  c. robots C-3PO and R2-D2
  d. the production designer and special effects crew

_____ 6. Why should the film not be approached with expectations of cosmic implications?
  a. The intent of the movie is fun.
  b. The many references go by too quickly to track.
  c. The plot is insufficient to carry the references.
  d. The references are well known to science-fiction followers.

_____ 7. By quoting the bartender as saying, "We don't serve their kind in here," Canby is providing evidence
  a. of social commentary in the film.
  b. that the scene is funny.
  c. of the successful special effects.
  d. that the plot is weak.

_____ 8. What weakness does Canby see in _Star Wars_?
   a. the special effects
   b. the acting
   c. the plot
   d. the theme

_____ 9. Why are performances in a film like this difficult to judge?
   a. The actors are all unknowns.
   b. Acting with effects added later complicates the task of the performer.
   c. The special effects are so distracting that we can't focus on the actors.
   d. This type of film typically places a low premium on acting.

_____ 10. The overall purpose of Canby's review is to
   a. determine how long _Star Wars_ will remain popular.
   b. note the weaknesses of the film for viewers.
   c. familiarize the audience with the film and recommend it.
   d. trace the history and references to other works in the film.

_____ 11. Roger Ebert's review, "_Star Wars_: Breakthrough Film Still Has the Force," was written
   a. before Vincent Canby's review was published.
   b. when the movie first appeared.
   c. when the movie was restored and re-released.
   d. at the height of the _Star Wars_ craze.

_____ 12. Why does Ebert think the movie has "colonized our imaginations"?
   a. It is one of the most profitable films of all time.
   b. It is so effective it seems to be real.
   c. Its characters and story are now part of our culture.
   d. It has been so successful that nothing negative can be said about it.

_____ 13. What, according to Ebert, does _Star Wars_ have in common with _Birth of A Nation_ and _Citizen Kane_?
   a. All three films are about the struggle for justice.
   b. All three films exploited new techniques for movies.
   c. All three films were immediate box office smashes.
   d. All three films made stars of their casts.

_____ 14. What recommendations does Ebert have for improving the film?
   a. more explanation of the philosophy and shorter battle scenes
   b. more character development between battle scenes
   c. modernized planet scenes, which haven't aged well
   d. more romance between Skywalker and Princess Leia

_____ 15. What is Ebert's overall purpose in writing his review?
   a. to claim a place for _Star Wars_ as a movie classic
   b. to assess changes in the re-released version
   c. to dispute Canby's assertion that the film is mere fun
   d. to discuss changes in the way we view the film now

Vocabulary and Grammar

_____ 16. Canby includes an _eclectic_ list of items that are associated with _Star Wars_. This means the list is
   a. widely accepted by most movie-goers.
   b. controversial and not agreed upon.
   c. composed of material from various sources.
   d. chosen especially by Canby from his own preferences.

_____ 17. Which of the following sentences uses *good* or *well* incorrectly?
   a. Canby prepares viewers well, by advising them to approach the film with a sense of humor.
   b. Canby makes a good analogy when he compares R2-D2 and C-3PO to Laurel and Hardy.
   c. Ebert feels the art design, set decoration and special effects in *Star Wars* do a good job of advancing the story.
   d. Ebert feels that *2001: A Space Odyssey*, made ten years before *Star Wars*, holds up good.

_____ 18. Ebert writes that *Star Wars* was a "technical watershed." A *watershed* is
   a. a moment or event after which nothing is the same.
   b. something that sets a standard that can never be matched.
   c. a box office hit of astronomical proportions.
   d. a high point, as in a process, beyond which quality decreases.

_____ 19. Ebert lists special effects, advanced sound, and new photographic techniques as methods that were "ripe for synthesis" in the movie-making industry. *Synthesis* means
   a. human-made or manufactured.
   b. a grouping of items or ideas developed for review.
   c. a separation of something from the original object or entity.
   d. a whole made up of separate elements put together.

_____ 20. The word *well*
   a. is always used as an adjective.
   b. is used only after linking verbs such as *feel, look, smell, taste,* and *seem.*
   c. is always used as an adverb describing health.
   d. often describes how skillfully something is done.

Essay Questions

21. These selections are two reviews of the same movie, though written twenty years apart. In an essay, compare and contrast the two reviews. Describe how they express similar ideas. Also explain the essential purpose of each review. Use examples from the texts to support your ideas.

22. Both Vincent Canby and Roger Ebert praise *Star Wars* in reviews written twenty years apart. What if you didn't like the movie, or had already seen it? Would you read these reviews the same way? Would they still be worth reading? Write an essay that explains the value of critical reviews.

23. Roger Ebert, in his review "*Star Wars*: Breakthrough Film Still Has the Force," cites other movies and stories to make much of his argument about why *Star Wars* still works. He mentions the movies *Birth of a Nation, Citizen Kane, 2001: A Space Odyssey,* and the stories *Don Quixote, David Copperfield,* and *Huckleberry Finn.* Write an essay that explains why Ebert cites these works, and how they enhance his argument.

Name _____ Date _____

"Mothers & Daughters" by Tillie Olsen and Estelle Jussim

Selection Test

Critical Reading

In the blank, write the letter of the one best answer.

_____ 1. Which sentence best summarizes Estelle Jussim's main point about capturing the mother-daughter relationship in photographs?
a. Everyone possesses the visual language needed to understand such images.
b. Mother-daughter portraits demonstrate a vast range of emotional experiences.
c. Any interpretation of a photograph reveals as much about the viewer as it does about the subjects in the photograph.
d. It is impossible to capture the relationship's emotional nuances on film.

_____ 2. According to Sage Sohier, "a photograph is a sort of daughter" because
a. the photographer's hopes for her photograph may never be realized.
b. both are beautiful.
c. a photographer can never understand her own work.
d. photographs convey a variety of emotions.

_____ 3. Which photograph best supports Tillie Olsen's words "Here is joy, joy, joy in each other"?
a. *Untitled*, Sage Sohier
b. *Untitled*, Bruce Horowitz
c. *Tang Chung, Lisa Lu, Lucia and Loretta*, Carla Weber
d. *Nellie G. Morgan and Tammie Pruitt Morgan, Bicentennial Celebration*, Roland Freeman

_____ 4. When Tillie Olsen describes the photographs in *Mothers & Daughters* as "a welter of images. Multi, multi-form," she means that
a. the images in a single photograph have many layers of meaning.
b. the photographs convey an astonishing variety of emotions.
c. each photograph illustrates a different emotional state.
d. only by looking at many different images of mothers and daughters can one understand the relationship.

_____ 5. How are the mother and daughter in *Bicentennial Celebration* alike?
a. Both are smiling.
b. Neither is smiling.
c. Both wear glasses.
d. Both wear dresses made of the same material.

_____ 6. Eudora Welty remembers constantly asking her mother to
a. read to her.
b. take her photograph.
c. play games with her.
d. teach her emotional lessons.

_____ 7. Which visual detail most strongly echoes the blank expressions worn by the mother and daughters in *August*, New Mexico, 1979?
a. the barren landscape
b. the clouds
c. the raincoats
d. the faces turned toward the camera

8. Which background detail in Sage Sohier's photograph adds the strongest emotional element?
   a. the mirrored door   c. the bed
   b. the poster of a teary-eyed man   d. the floor

9. In the photograph by Bruce Horowitz, the mother's state of mind is best revealed by
   a. the background.   c. the daughter's facial expression.
   b. the mother's body language.   d. the lighting.

10. Which passage conveys a point most similar to that in *August,* New Mexico, 1979?
    a. She was teaching me one more, almost her last, lesson: emotions do not grow old.
    b. One's relationship to [a photograph] consists largely of carting it around and having hopes for it.
    c. The eye seeks deeper vision.
    d. Here is the family resemblance in face, expression, stance, body.

11. The text that accompanies Sage Sohier's photograph implies that
    a. the mother in the photograph may not be the best interpreter of her daughter's life.
    b. the daughter defies her mother.
    c. the mother hopes the best for her daughter.
    d. the mother and daughter have come to terms with their differences.

12. What primary impression is conveyed by the body language in *Tang Chung, Lisa Lu, Lucia and Loretta*?
    a. resentment   b. playfulness   c. admiration   d. estrangement

13. Which two photographs most strongly contrast with each other?
    a. *August,* New Mexico, 1979, and *Untitled,* Bruce Horowitz
    b. *Tang Chung, Lisa Lu, Lucia and Loretta* and *Bicentennial Celebration*
    c. *Untitled,* Sage Sohier, and *Untitled,* Bruce Horowitz
    d. *Tang Chung, Lisa Lu, Lucia and Loretta* and *August,* New Mexico, 1979

14. Which statement most closely echoes Tillie Olsen's text about mothers and daughters?
    a. It has been widely recognized that even the greatest portrait can capture only so much of an individual's personality and character, and certainly not an ascribable mood.
    b. A photograph is a sort of daughter.
    c. To portray two persons defined as mother and daughter is to define a relationship fraught with cultural and emotional overtones.
    d. Emotions do not grow old.

Vocabulary and Grammar

15. The teenager looks _____ at the photographer as her mother _____ hugs the cat.
    a. sullen, affectionately
    b. sullen, affectionate
    c. sullenly, affectionate
    d. sullenly, affectionately

____ 16. A photograph's *implicit* meaning would most likely be discovered by
   a. reading the photograph's title.
   b. glancing at the photograph.
   c. interpreting the expressions of the people in the photograph.
   d. analyzing the photograph's technical qualities.

____ 17. In which of the following sentences are the adjectives and adverbs used correctly?
   a. The landscape looks surprisingly flat, scraggly and dryly.
   b. The mother and daughter pose proudly before the American flag.
   c. The bespectacled grandmother is wearing a garishly dress.
   d. The mother's rigid demeanor suggests that she is impatient tolerating the photographer.

____ 18. The mother's *beaming* smile conveyed her _____.
   a. hue   b. sullenness   c. fervor   d. rapture

____ 19. In Sage Sohier's photograph, the daughter's look might be described as one of ____.
   a. hue   b. sullenness   c. fervor   d. rapture

____ 20. Which modifier is used incorrectly in the following passage?
   In "Mothers and Daughters," one writer makes the observation that trying to show the relationship between a mother and daughter is to show a relationship filled with culturally and emotional elements.
   a. exceedingly
   b. impossible
   c. culturally
   d. emotional

Essay Questions

21. According to Estelle Jussim, we need a "grasp of visual language" to understand the portraits of mothers and daughters. What visual language can you "read" in the photographs? How do body language, background, distance between subjects, and other visual details help you translate the photograph's meaning? Choose one photograph and in a brief essay comment on its visual language.

22. Tillie Olsen writes that the photographs of mothers and daughters reveal "sullenness, anger or controlled anger, resentment; admiration, distaste; playfulness, pride; joy, joy, joy in each other; estrangement; wordless closeness or intense communion." Choose two photographs that convey contrasting emotions. In an essay, describe the connection between Olsen's words and the images. Identify key phrases that reveal the meaning of the images.

23. Sage Sohier accompanies her photograph with the metaphor of a photograph being a "sort of daughter." In an essay, explore how the text helps you interpret the photograph. Does it in any way limit your interpretation? Explain.

"Imitating Nature's Mineral Artistry" by Paul O'Neil
"Work That Counts" by Ernesto Ruelas Inzunza

Selection Test

Critical Reading

In the blank, write the letter of the one best answer.

____ 1. In comparison with natural gems, synthetic gems
    a. are identical in chemistry and crystalline structure.
    b. are often more brilliant or "flashy."
    c. have a wider range of available colors and shapes.
    d. are softer and more likely to crack or break.

____ 2. Why is synthesizing diamonds particularly difficult?
    a. Scientists have trouble getting synthetic diamonds to look as sparkly as natural diamonds.
    b. It takes many ingredients, some of which are difficult to obtain.
    c. Diamond crystals form irregularly and the process is hard to control in the laboratory.
    d. It takes enormous pressures and temperatures to pack diamond components—carbon atoms—together.

____ 3. Why doesn't the flame-fusion method work for synthesizing some gems?
    a. Some gems have different requirements for crystal growth.
    b. The components of some gems simply don't melt.
    c. The components of some gems are explosive when heated.
    d. The components of some gems decompose when heated.

____ 4. Given the description of the processes of synthesizing gems, what kind of knowledge would a gem synthesizer need most?
    a. knowledge of natural gems and their value
    b. knowledge of chemical reactions and processes
    c. knowledge of how to heat things to extremely high temperatures
    d. knowledge of how to polish and cut gemstones

____ 5. The chemical ingredients of ruby are
    a. aluminum oxide with a chromium coloring agent.
    b. titanium dioxide and hydrogen.
    c. beryllium and aluminum.
    d. silicone and beryllium.

____ 6. Why would it be wrong for a gem seller to represent synthetic gems as natural gems?
    a. Each type of gem has a different value and a seller should not misrepresent a product.
    b. Synthetic gems are superior in quality and cost more to manufacture.
    c. Natural gems are superior in quality and cost less to process.
    d. Synthetic gems are considered fake and should not be sold as gems at all.

____ 7. Which of the following characteristics identifies "Imitating Nature's Mineral Artistry" as a technical article?
    a. It includes technical diagrams with captions.
    b. It includes illustrations.
    c. It explains a procedure using specialized language.
    d. It has footnotes that explain technical terms.

8. The title "Work That Counts" refers to two ideas in the article. What are they?
   I. the tedium of trying to count flying birds
   II. the worthwhile nature of Inzunza's job
   III. the job of counting the migrating birds
   IV. the difference between casually watching birds and actually watching them for a living
   a. both I and III
   b. both I and IV
   c. both II and III
   d. both II and IV

9. According to "Work That Counts," what condition (or conditions) in this particular area of Mexico helps birds migrate?
   a. the topography and the ocean
   b. the bottleneck created by the land formations
   c. the abundance of available food
   d. the tail winds and warm thermal updrafts

10. According to "Work That Counts," why is the bird migration called "River of Raptors"?
    a. because so many birds of prey fly over the area during migration
    b. because the birds land on rivers and lakes to rest at night
    c. because some birds actually float on the rivers sometimes
    d. because the birds fly such a long way to catch their prey

11. Choose the list of items that contains examples of specialized vocabulary found in "Work That Counts."
    a. binoculars, species, canyon
    b. hawks, circles, broad-winged
    c. thermal column, raptor, avian
    d. Gulf of Mexico, energy, migrating

12. According to "Work That Counts," why does Veracruz have the highest count of migrating birds in the world?
    a. The area is unspoiled and naturally attracts birds.
    b. Birds traveling from all portions of North America converge there.
    c. It has a high bird population year-round, which contributes to the migratory count.
    d. In other places in the world, birds aren't counted as carefully as they are in Veracruz.

13. How does the author add interest to the facts he relates in the technical article "Work That Counts"?
    a. He presents facts in a chart so the reader can see them easily.
    b. He includes them all in one paragraph.
    c. He writes as if he is taking the reader along on a bird-watching tour.
    d. He writes in a very informal manner and uses only simple words that all readers can understand.

14. In a technical article, a diagram contributes by
    a. breaking up the text on the page.
    b. adding information or enhancing the information in the text.
    c. replacing the text with visual information.
    d. adding visual interest, though it doesn't really tell the reader anything new.

Vocabulary and Grammar

____ 15. Which word is modified by the italicized phrase in the following sentence?
> This article states that Chatham and Gilson had a process for making emeralds *that depended on a technique called flux growth.*

a. process　　　　　　　c. technique
b. both　　　　　　　　d. details

____ 16. Which sentence contains a misplaced modifier?

a. Being easy to obtain, relatively common chemical compounds are used for man-made gems.
b. Using the flame-fusion method, the rubies were produced by the scientists.
c. Using the Hydraulic Pressure method, Hall succeeded in making the first man-made diamond.
d. Distinguishing between synthetic and natural gemstones, experts must pay close attention to the details.

____ 17. An event that is *fortuitous*

a. is both accidental and beneficial.
b. brings wealth to the people involved.
c. has unhappy consequences.
d. is an act of nature.

____ 18. One factor that contributes to Veracruz's attraction for migrating birds is its *topography*, or

a. height.
b. location with respect to the equator.
c. climate.
d. surface features.

____ 19. To *divulge* something is to _____ it.

a. eat　　　　b. sell　　　　c. reveal　　　　d. invest

____ 20. Which is the best revision of the following sentence?
> Popular, opaque, semi-precious stones, scientists easily reproduce opals in laboratories.

a. Popular and opaque, scientists easily reproduce semi-precious opals in laboratories.
b. Popular, opaque opals, semi-precious stones, scientists easily reproduce in laboratories.
c. Scientists easily reproduce opals—popular, opaque, semi-precious stones— in laboratories
d. No change needed.

Essay Questions

21. In his technical article "Work That Counts," Inzunza writes in the first person, using the words *I* and *we*. In an essay, analyze what effect this perspective has on the reader, noting what makes the article technical rather than a first-person account. Support your answer with examples from the text.

22. In an essay, explain why Inzunza's bird-counting work is important, based on his explanation in "Work That Counts." What could variations in the bird counts or the migratory patterns indicate? What do we learn by studying the migrations of birds? Support your answers with examples from the text.

23. Would you like to own a synthetic emerald or ruby? Or, would you rather have a natural one? Why? In an essay, analyze the appeal and the importance of the process of synthesizing gems. Support your opinions with facts and details from the text.

Unit Test: Nonfiction

Critical Reading

In the blank, write the letter of the one best answer.

The questions below are based on the following selection.

The following selection is the beginning of the essay "The Creative Process in Music" by Aaron Copland.

Most people want to know how things are made. They frankly admit, however, that they feel completely at sea when it comes to understanding how a piece of music is made. Where a composer begins, how he manages to keep going—in fact, how and where he learns his trade—all are shrouded in impenetrable darkness. The composer, in short, is a man of mystery to most people, and the composer's workshop an unapproachable ivory tower.

One of the first things most people want to hear discussed in relation to composing is the question of inspiration. They find it difficult to believe that composers are not as preoccupied with that question as they had supposed. The layman always finds it hard to realize how natural it is for the composer to compose. He has a tendency to put himself into the position of the composer and to visualize the problems involved, including that of inspiration, from the perspective of the layman. He forgets that composing to a composer is like fulfilling a natural function. It is like eating or sleeping. It is something that the composer happens to have been born to do; and, because of that, it loses the character of a special virtue in the composer's eyes.

The composer, therefore, confronted with the question of inspiration, does not say to himself: "Do I feel inspired?" He says to himself: " Do I feel like composing today?" And if he feels like composing, he does. It is more or less like saying to yourself: "Do I feel sleepy?" If you feel sleepy, you go to sleep. If you don't feel sleepy, you stay up. If the composer doesn't feel like composing, he doesn't compose. It's as simple as that.

_____ 1. According to the author, why don't composers worry much about inspiration?
   a. It is not commonplace.
   b. Worrying about it would compromise their self-confidence.
   c. It is not especially important to them.
   d. Composing is completely natural to them.

_____ 2. Which of the following is not a common method of developing an expository essay?
   a. describing a subject using sensory details
   b. analyzing and interpreting information
   c. presenting causes and effects
   d. comparing and contrasting ideas

_____ 3. Based on the first four paragraphs of Aaron Copland's essay, which of the following best describes his purpose in writing "The Creative Process in Music"?
   a. to entertain the reader with his impressions of composition
   b. to inform the reader about how music comes into being
   c. to persuade the reader to compose music
   d. to inform the reader about how different types of music affect listeners

_____ 4. Aaron Copland believes that
   a. composers should compose each and every day.
   b. composers must feel inspiration in order to create.
   c. composers can create without feeling inspired.
   d. inspiration and composition are inseparable.

_____ 5. Why is it difficult for a nonmusician to understand how composers regard the concept of inspiration?

    a. A composer's and a non-musician's perspectives are essentially different.

    b. Nonmusicians are rarely inspired themselves.

    c. Composers are more intelligent than most nonmusicians.

    d. Only artists can understand how inspiration can be coaxed forth and harnessed.

_____ 6. In these paragraphs Copland

    a. compares composers to tradespeople.

    b. analyzes the role of inspiration to a composer.

    c. interprets the meaning of music for an audience of laymen.

    d. classifies musical works as inspired or uninspired.

_____ 7. Which of the following ideas is a fact rather than an impression?

    a. Composers are mysterious.

    b. Composing to composers is like fulfilling a natural function.

    c. Copland hopes that his musical compositions are inspired.

    d. Copland was born to compose.

_____ 8. Which of the following is _not_ one of the author's main points?

    a. Non-musicians and composers think differently about music.

    b. Composers rarely ask themselves if they feel inspired.

    c. Composers must work in absolute silence.

    d. Most people have limited understanding of how music is composed.

_____ 9. In the third and fourth paragraphs, Copland draws a distinction between

    a. sleeping and composing.

    b. inspiring music and feeling inspired to compose music.

    c. recognizing genius and having genius

    d. needing inspiration to compose and composing in an inspired way

_____ 10. Which of the following terms best describes Aaron Copland's subject in this expository essay?

    a. a process

    b. an idea

    c. an event

    d. an issue

Vocabulary and Grammar

In the blank, write the letter of the one best answer.

_____ 11. In words like _comfortable_ or _perishable_, the suffix _–able_ means _____.

    a. giving

    b. capable of being

    c. relieving; lessening

    d. a process

_____ 12. The connotations of a word are its _____.

    a. roots, prefixes, and suffixes

    b. dictionary definitions

    c. inferences

    d. shades of meaning

____ 13. Which of the following words does *not* contain the prefix *mal-*, meaning "bad, evil"?
   a. malady
   b. malignant
   c. malty
   d. malevolent

____ 14. In which sentence is the word *then* used incorrectly?
   a. There is no greater sadness then witnessing the loss of one's home.
   b. Dillard observed first the damage to wildlife and then to people's homes.
   c. When the waters recede, then all that is left is the struggle to rebuild.
   d. Dillard writes that she watched the water rise; then recede.

____ 15. The cry of the willet was _____ than that of the other birds.
   a. urgent
   b. urgenter
   c. more urgent
   d. more urgenter

____ 16. Which of the following is the *least* appropriate synonym for the word *synthetic*?
   a. artificial
   b. man-made
   c. unnatural
   d. shiny

____ 17. A stock of songs that a singer knows and is ready to perform is called his or her
   _____.
   a. anthems
   b. repertoire
   c. arias
   d. repertory

____ 18. _____ down, in the land of the Crows and Blackfeet, the plain is yellow.
   a. Farther
   b. Further
   c. More far
   d. Furthest

____ 19. Which of the following sentence does *not* contain a nonrestrictive appositive?
   a. When she was graduated from high school, the Philadelphia Choral Society, a Negro group, sponsored her further study and secured for her one of the best local teachers.
   b. However, the Scandinavian people, who had fallen in love with her, kept asking her to come back there.
   c. In 1924 the famous conductor, Arturo Toscanini, listened to her sing at Salzburg.
   d. In his book, *Marian Anderson,* her longtime accompanist, Vehanen, tells of hotel accommodations being denied her, and service in dining rooms often refused.

_____ 20. This collection makes no pretense of offering more than an _____ sifting of contemporary imagery, which, upon examination, can reveal much about contemporary life and our _____ ideologies concerning motherhood.
   a. intelligent, implicitly
   b. intelligently, implicit
   c. intelligent, implicit
   d. intelligently, implicitly

Essay Questions

21. In "Mothers & Daughters," words and images combine to convey information to a reader. In a short essay, explain how the written text helps you appreciate the photographs more deeply and the photos help you appreciate the text more deeply.

22. Despite the dictionary definition of the word *nonfiction*, this type of writing contains not only facts but also impressions. Choose one of the biographical or autobiographical selections in this unit and, explain how the author uses facts, impressions, or both in his portrait of a person's life and times.

23. Nonfiction writing comes in an impressively wide array of forms. Choose one of the technical articles in this unit, and compare and contrast it with an example of a different type of nonfiction writing from this unit. In your essay, you might analyze the purposes, audiences, central ideas, and characteristics of each selection.

24. Two examples of nonfiction—even the same form of nonfiction—can be as distinct from each other as are two poems, two short stories, or two plays. Compare and contrast the persuasive essays by Alexander Solzhenitsyn and Elie Wiesel. What is each writer's central message, audience, and tone? In your opinion, how successful is each writer in achieving his purpose?

25. Depending on the purpose and disposition of the writer, a critical review can occupy a position anywhere between an expository and a persuasive essay. Choose one of the two critical reviews in this unit, and analyze the writer's use of devices associated with these two types of nonfiction writing.

Antigone, **Prologue through Scene 2,** by Sophocles

Selection Test

Critical Reading

In the blank, write the letter of the one best answer.

____ 1. Which of these events in *Antigone* took place first?
  a. the assault on Thebes
  b. the death of the brothers
  c. the decree of Creon
  d. the crime of Oedipus

____ 2. Which of the following best explains Antigone's motive for saying to Ismene, "And now you can prove what you are:/A true sister, or a traitor to your family"?
  a. She is afraid to act alone.
  b. She wants to make a strong emotional appeal.
  c. She hates her sister.
  d. She suspects Ismene is plotting with Creon.

____ 3. Ismene pleads with Antigone not to defy Creon because she
  a. fears challenging authority herself.
  b. feels that Antigone loved their brother more than she.
  c. believes that Creon will punish her for Antigone's actions.
  d. must assert her will over others.

____ 4. Antigone's motive for burying Polyneices is her _____ .
  a. stubbornness
  b. pride
  c. loyalty
  d. hatred

____ 5. Antigone defies Creon's decree because she
  a. wants to overthrow him.
  b. wishes to join her dead brothers.
  c. wants to die rather than marry Haimon.
  d. believes in obedience to a higher law.

____ 6. Which one of the following is a conflict in the play?
  a. conflict between Choragos and the chorus
  b. conflict between Creon and Choragos
  c. conflict between the laws of man and the laws of the gods
  d. conflict between Antigone and Polyneices

____ 7. The play's antagonist is _____ .
  a. Antigone
  b. Ismene
  c. Creon
  d. Choragos

____ 8. Which of the following best explains Creon's motivation for decreeing that Polyneices should go unburied?
   a. He believes the gods have commanded it.
   b. He has a strong affection for Eteocles.
   c. He does not want to honor a traitor.
   d. He wants to harm the family of Oedipus.

____ 9. Creon insists on executing Antigone because
   a. he wants to make an example of her.
   b. he despised her father, Oedipus.
   c. he refuses to take orders from a woman.
   d. she will not admit her guilt.

____ 10. Which of the following best summarizes Creon's argument against burying Polyneices?
   a. This is Polyneices' destiny as a son of Oedipus.
   b. His punishment is a deterrent.
   c. The city cannot afford funerals for its enemies.
   d. Religion forbids the burial of enemies of the state.

____ 11. Which of the following best illustrates the protagonist's struggle with the antagonist?
   a. ANTIGONE: Ismene, I am going to bury him. Will you come?
   b. SENTRY: How dreadful it is when the right judge judges wrong!
   c. CHORAGOS: Like father, like daughter; both headstrong, deaf to reason! She has never learned to yield.
   d. ANTIGONE: There is no guilt in reverence for the dead.

____ 12. The major conflict exposed in this selection is between
   a. Creon and himself.
   b. Creon and Antigone.
   c. Antigone and Ismene.
   d. Antigone and herself.

____ 13. What primary characteristic does Creon reveal in the following words?
   This girl is guilty of a double insolence, / Breaking the given laws and boasting of it. / Who is the man here, / She or I, if this crime goes unpunished?
   a. wisdom
   b. anger
   c. pride
   d. fairness

____ 14. The struggle of protagonist against antagonist in *Antigone* is best described as pitting
   a. Antigone's obedience to a higher law against Creon's desire for order.
   b. Creon's stubbornness against Antigone's selfishness.
   c. Antigone's humility against Creon's arrogance.
   d. Creon's strength against Antigone's weakness.

Vocabulary and Grammar

____ 15. Antigone wants to protect her brother's body from _____ birds.
   a. carrion
   b. sated
   c. anarchist
   d. sultry

_____ 16. Which character would best be grouped with anarchists?
   a. Creon
   b. Antigone
   c. Ismene
   d. sentry

_____ 17. What *transcends* Antigone's fear of death?
   a. Creon's decree
   b. her fear of discovery
   c. Ismene's reluctance to join her
   d. her devotion to a higher law

_____ 18. What is the objective pronoun in the following sentence?
   Antigone felt that burying their brother was the least that she and her sister could do for him.
   a. him
   b. her
   c. she
   d. their

_____ 19. Creon tells Antigone that her death gives _____ everything he wants from _____.
   a. he, her
   b. him, her
   c. him, she
   d. he, she

_____ 20. In the following sentence, what is the function of the pronoun *her*?
   Ismene wants to die as well, but Antigone does not want to give her the satisfaction.
   a. a direct object
   b. the object of a preposition
   c. an indirect object
   d. the object of an infinitive

Essay Questions

21. Like all good dramas, *Antigone* centers on a conflict between a protagonist and an antagonist. In a brief essay, identify the protagonist and antagonist of this play, and describe the characteristics of each character that add to the conflict.

22. Antigone declares to Ismene and to Creon that she acts out of honor and obedience to the laws of the gods. Are these really her motives? Do her actions and words reveal different motives? In a brief essay, analyze Antigone's motives and draw conclusions about why she acts as she does. Support your opinion with evidence from the selection.

23. As the new head of state, Creon makes his declaration forbidding Polyneices' burial. Write an analysis of Creon's speech in Scene I. Determine what it reveals about Creon's abilities as a politician and the strengths and flaws of his character.

Antigone, **Scenes 3 through 5,** by Sophocles

Selection Test

Critical Reading

In the blank, write the letter of the one best answer.

_____ 1. Which of the following quotations best expresses the theme of *Antigone?*
a. "The only crime is pride."
b. "The truth is always best."
c. "The generation of kings has/always loved brass."
d. " . . . it is a sorry thing when a wise man/Sells his wisdom . . ."

_____ 2. Which of the following words best describes Creon's character?
a. ambitious
b. stubborn
c. dignified
d. forgiving

_____ 3. Readers can sympathize with Antigone because of her
a. struggle to do what she feels is right.
b. prideful refusal to give in to Creon.
c. arranged marriage to Haimon.
d. royal lineage.

_____ 4. Haimon believes that authority rests with the _____ .
a. gods
b. king
c. people
d. traditions

_____ 5. Antigone might be considered a tragic character because
a. she suffers the loss of her father and brothers.
b. she hangs herself.
c. her refusal to give in to Creon results in her downfall.
d. her situation elicits sympathy from the reader.

_____ 6. By identifying with Haimon, readers can best understand
a. Creon's tragic flaw.
b. Antigone's obstinacy.
c. Eurydice's grief.
d. the atmosphere in Thebes following Creon's decree.

_____ 7. What is the meaning of Haimon's statement, "[Antigone's] death will cause another"?
a. If Antigone must die, then so must Ismene.
b. Eurydice's grief will lead her to suicide.
c. Haimon will kill Creon.
d. Haimon will kill himself in grief over Antigone's death.

_____ 8. It is difficult to identify with the Choragos because he is
a. an unpleasant character.
b. not personally involved in the play's conflict.
c. prejudiced against Antigone.
d. in alliance with Creon.

Unit 8: Drama

____ 9. Creon might be considered a tragic character because he
   a. suffers greatly because of a flaw in his character.
   b. loses everything that is dear to him.
   c. gives up his great power in sorrow.
   d. ruled Thebes for only a short time.

____ 10. What is the meaning of Teiresias' statement, "The generation of kings has/always loved brass"?
   a. Kings are always insolent and defiant.
   b. Kings come from high military rank.
   c. Kings enjoy martial music.
   d. Kings always seek apparent rather than real value.

____ 11. Which of the following is not a factor in making Creon a tragic character?
   a. his refusal to listen to Haimon's argument
   b. his kinship to Oedipus
   c. his grief over the deaths of Haimon and Eurydice
   d. his belated decision to release Antigone

____ 12. Which of the following makes Creon relent?
   a. He sees that his judgment is unwise.
   b. He fears punishment from the gods.
   c. He believes in forgiving his enemies.
   d. He does not want to break Haimon's heart.

____ 13. Does the Choragos agree with Creon's final statement, "Fate has brought all my pride to a thought of dust"?
   a. Yes, because he believes that Fate caused the tragedy.
   b. Yes, because he believes that Creon is reduced to dust.
   c. No, because he believes Creon's pride caused his ruin.
   d. No, because he believes Creon is not fully destroyed.

____ 14. What is the effect of Creon's change of heart in Scene 5?
   a. He is no longer a tragic character, because he can be flexible.
   b. He is no longer a sympathetic character, because he is weak.
   c. His downfall is more pitiable, because he repented in vain.
   d. He is transformed from the antagonist to the protagonist.

Vocabulary and Grammar

____ 15. Creon expects _____ from others, even though he is not willing to give it himself.
   a. deference
   b. piety
   c. blasphemy
   d. lamentation

____ 16. Which pronoun best completes the following sentence?
   Let's lose to a man, at least! Is a woman stronger than _____?
   a. I
   b. me
   c. us
   d. we

____ 17. It is unlikely that a person filled with _____ would commit a _____ action.
   a. lamentation; deference
   b. piety; vile
   c. blasphemy; vile
   d. deference; piety

____ 18. Each of the following sentences contains a pronoun in an elliptical clause. In which ones are the correct pronoun case used?
        I. Ismene believed that Creon was stronger than her.
       II. Ismene believed that Creon was stronger than she.
     III. Like Antigone, Ismene felt grief, but the grief seemed greater to Antigone than her.
    IV. Like Antigone, Ismene felt grief, but the grief seemed greater to Antigone than she.
    a. I and II
    b. I and III
    c. II and III
    d. III and IV

____ 19. Creon is furious that Haimon loves Antigone more than _____.
    a. he
    b. him
    c. her
    d. them

____ 20. What is Creon's act of *blasphemy*?
    a. forbidding the burial of Polyneices
    b. arresting Antigone
    c. ignoring Teiresias' warning
    d. saying prayers for Polyneices

Essay Questions

21. Identifying with a character gives readers a deeper understanding of a literary work. With which character in *Antigone* did you identify most strongly? In an essay, explain how you identified with this character and, consequently, what you discovered about the character and the play.

22. Centuries of critics and readers have debated who the tragic character is in *Antigone*—the title character or Creon. Which one do you believe is the tragic character? In an essay, state your opinion and support it with reasonable evidence from the play.

23. What, in your opinion, accounts for the strong appeal *Antigone* has had for centuries of readers? Write an essay in which you explain why Sophocles' classic tragedy remains relevant to modern life. Support your opinion with evidence from the play.

Unit 8: Drama

Name _____ Date _____

The Tragedy of Julius Caesar, Act I, by William Shakespeare

Selection Test

Critical Reading

In the blank, write the letter of the one best answer.

_____ 1. In Act I, Scene i, why do Flavius and Marullus try to disrupt the festivities?
   a. They think the holiday profanes the feast of Lupercal.
   b. They resent the defeat and murder of Pompey.
   c. They worry that Caesar will be offended by the smell and manners of the crowd.
   d. They feel that Caesar will be embarrassed by the festival.

_____ 2. Shakespeare distinguished commoners from noblemen in his play by having commoners
   a. speak in prose.   c. carry their tools.
   b. speak in verse.   d. make many puns.

_____ 3. Which of the following facts or events is revealed in Act I, Scene i, and serves as part of the exposition?
   a. The Lupercal footrace takes place.
   b. Cassius and Brutus first meet and express disapproval of Caesar.
   c. Flavius and Marullus scold the people for celebrating Caesar's triumph.
   d. Caesar refuses to allow Antony to crown him as king.

_____ 4. In the following passage, refer to lines 67 and 68 and text aid 22. Why is it helpful to know when Lupercal takes place?

   FLAVIUS. . . Go you down that way toward the Capitol;
   [65] This way will I. Disrobe the images,
         If you do find them decked with ceremonies.[21]
   MARULLUS May we do so?
         You know it is the feast of Lupercal.[22]
   FLAVIUS It is no matter; let no images
   [70] Be hung with Caesar's trophies . . .

   21. Disrobe the images . . . decked with ceremonies: Strip the statues . . . covered with decorations.
   22. feast of Lupercal: An ancient Roman festival celebrated on February 15.

   a. It explains which season of the year it is.
   b. It helps readers envision the type of weather that is occurring.
   c. Becoming familiar with ancient Roman festivals is vital to understanding the play.
   d. It establishes the time setting, which will take on significance in the next scene.

_____ 5. In the preceding passage, what information is revealed in lines 69 and 70 that helps establish the readers' knowledge of the situation?
   a. Not everyone is celebrating Caesar's triumph.
   b. The commoners are easily intimidated by Roman officials.
   c. It is the custom, during festivals, to decorate statues.
   d. Grown men, such as the speakers in this passage, act like pranksters during festivals.

_____ 6. Combined with the actions of Cassius, the soothsayer's warning suggests that
   a. Brutus will be exiled.   c. Caesar will be overthrown.
   b. Flavius will be arrested.   d. Calpurnia will have a child.

_____ 7. In Act I, Scene ii, Cassius characterizes Caesar as
   a. sincere and proud.   c. weak and gentle.
   b. kind and gentle.   d. fierce and warlike.

8. Casca's description of Caesar's behavior when he is offered the crown in Act I, Scene ii, suggests that Caesar owes his success most of all to

a. his family connections and wealth.

b. his personal heroism and charisma.

c. the support of a few noblemen.

d. his manipulation of the masses.

9. How do the noblemen react to the people's acclamation of Caesar?

a. approvingly

b. disapprovingly

c. joyfully

d. timidly

10. According to the following passage and text aids, what is the significance of saying that Caesar is "like a Colossus"?

[135] **CASSIUS** Why, man, he doth bestride the narrow world
Like a Colossus,⁴⁶ and we petty men
Walk under his huge legs and peep about
To find ourselves dishonorable⁴⁷ graves.

46. Colossus: A gigantic statue of Apollo, a god of Greek and Roman mythology, which was set at the entrance to the harbor of Rhodes about 280 B.C. and included among the seven wonders of the ancient world.
47. dishonorable: Shameful (because they will not be of free men).

a. Cassius is suggesting that a statue of Caesar be made.

b. Cassius is recognizing Caesar's power to become a mythical figure, like Apollo.

c. Cassius is comparing Caesar and his importance to that of the god Apollo.

d. Cassius is suggesting that Caesar is about as sensible as a statue.

11. Which is the best restatement of the following passage?

Men at some time are masters of their fates:

[140] The fault, dear Brutus, is not in our stars,⁴⁸
But in ourselves, that we are underlings.⁴⁹

48. stars: Destinies. The stars were thought to control people's lives.
49. underlings: Inferior people.

a. Sometimes men are in control of their fates: it's not our destinies that are at fault, Brutus, it's the fact that we are by nature inferior people.

b. At some point, men master their fates: Brutus, we fault not the stars but our inferior selves.

c. Men sometimes are masters: their flaw, Brutus, lies not in Destiny but in the fact that they are inferior beings.

d. Men sometimes master their destinies, whether the fault is in the stars or in their inferiority.

12. Which of the following images is meant to convey a sense of suspicion and distrust?

a. Cassius as a mirror for Brutus

b. Caesar offering his bared throat

c. Caesar as a colossus

d. Cassius with a lean and hungry look

13. At the beginning of Scene ii, Casca and Cicero discuss troubling events. What is the nature of these events?

a. the attempt to crown Caesar as king

b. the conspiracy being formed by Cassius and Brutus

c. the removal of the decorations from the statues

d. the unusually violent thunderstorm

14. What is the Roman attitude toward suicide expressed by Cassius and Casca in Act I, Scene iii?

a. It is against the law and flouts public opinion.

b. It is a mortal sin and an offense to God.

c. It is an honorable alternative to disgrace.

d. It is a cowardly solution to problems.

15. What is the effect of the image of alchemy in this speech by Casca?

. . . that which would appear offense in us, / [Brutus's] countenance, like richest alchemy, / Will change to virtue and to worthiness."

a. It makes the conspirators appear ignoble.

b. It suggests that Brutus has uncanny powers.

c. It indicates that Brutus will overlook the offense.

d. It shows that Casca considers himself unworthy.

Vocabulary and Grammar

____ 16. Choose the item that restates the following sentence in the subjunctive mood.

   The crowd cheered for Caesar as if he was a king.

   a. The crowd cheered for Caesar as though he was a king.
   b. The crowd cheered for Caesar asking him to be king.
   c. The crowd cheered for Caesar as if he had been a king.
   d. The crowd cheered for Caesar as if he were a king.

____ 17. Caesar wanted to blame anything he had done wrong on his infirmity, or

   a. weakness.
   b. imbalance.
   c. lack of good judgment.
   d. political ambition.

____ 18. Casca believes that the strange happenings are *portentous*, meaning that they are

   a. important.
   b. signs of events to come.
   c. signals of great natural disturbances.
   d. significant for anyone who sees them.

____ 19. Which of the following sentences is in the subjunctive mood?

   a. I wish you could go to the play tonight.
   b. Mrs. Taggert asks that we meet at 6:30 near the front entrance.
   c. She wonders whether anyone wants to meet earlier.
   d. We were all thrilled to be able to go.

____ 20. The subjunctive mood is used to express

   a. a direct command or an order.
   b. a strong opinion.
   c. a suggestion or a contrary-to-fact statement.
   d. the thoughts of one character about another.

Essay Questions

21. In this play, Shakespeare uses the superstitions of ancient Romans to foreshadow what is going to happen. In Act I, a soothsayer makes a prediction, and a number of unusual, apparently natural, phenomena occur. The characters respond to them as Romans would have. In an essay, describe some of these events or omens. Discuss how they affect the play, how they are related to the situation in Rome in Act I, and how Shakespeare uses them to create drama.

22. A play's exposition serves to introduce characters, setting, the situation, and any other details vital to the play's action. What does Act I, Scene i—the exposition of *The Tragedy of Julius Caesar*—tell you about the play? What do you learn about important characters, the setting, and the situation? How does Shakespeare reveal information—through characters' actions or words? How is this information significant to what happens in the other scenes in Act I? Answer these questions in an essay.

23. Some of Caesar's supporters wanted to make him king. What if the supporters of a popular American president began a movement to make that president a king? In what ways does this go against the American governmental system? Why would most people not support the movement? What connotations does "kingship" have that "presidency" does not? In an essay, relate your answers to these questions to the situation in Shakespeare's Rome. For what reasons would people object to Caesar being king? If possible, cite evidence from the play to support your explanation.

The Tragedy of Julius Caesar, Act II, by William Shakespeare

Selection Test

Critical Reading

In the blank, write the letter of the one best answer.

_____ 1. When Brutus delivers a soliloquy in his orchard at the beginning of Act II, he is
a. changing his mind about the conspiracy.
b. preparing his argument to persuade Cassius to kill Antony.
c. justifying his decision to attack Caesar.
d. interpreting Portia's frightening dreams.

_____ 2. What is Brutus' motivation for joining the conspiracy?
a. He wants to protect Rome against tyranny.
b. He hopes to become king himself.
c. He seeks revenge for Pompey's death.
d. He wants to see Cassius on the throne.

_____ 3. When Brutus says, "And therefore think him as a serpent's egg/Which hatched, would as his kind grow mischievous,/And kill him in the shell," he is
a. trying to understand Cassius' motivation.
b. recommending a course of action to the Senate.
c. expressing disgust with Caesar.
d. explaining why the conspirators must act now.

_____ 4. What is suggested by Brutus' image of Caesar as a snake?
a. the threat of deception
b. the likelihood of war
c. the danger of tyranny
d. the prospect of a conspiracy

_____ 5. The meter of blank verse is typically
a. ionic hexameter.
b. five iambic feet per line, with some variation.
c. perfectly regular, broken only by minor characters or couplets.
d. entirely irregular, as the term implies.

_____ 6. As the conspirators enter Brutus' house, he says, "Where wilt thou find a cavern dark enough/to mask thy monstrous visage? Seek none, conspiracy/Hide it in smiles and affability." In this speech, Brutus expresses
a. his mixed emotions about the plot.
b. a plan for escape after the assassination.
c. the need for secrecy.
d. his contempt for Caesar.

_____ 7. The conspirators finally agree not to attack Antony. Why do they make this decision?
a. They cannot be sure that Antony will be present.
b. They fear Antony's military skills.
c. They fear turning public opinion against them.
d. They hope Antony will succeed Caesar.

_____ 8. The conspirators want Caesar to go to the Senate House so they can
    a. kill him.
    b. present him to the people.
    c. offer him the crown.
    d. deliver Artemidorus' letter.

_____ 9. When Caesar appears in Act II, Scene ii, he seems to be
    a. bold and reckless.
    b. timid and superstitious.
    c. sneaky and conspiratorial.
    d. trusting and dignified.

_____ 10. In Acts I and II, the reports of strange occurrences in Rome create which of the following atmospheres?
    a. exciting, vivid, inspiring
    b. terrifying, bloody, grotesque
    c. mysterious, magical, fantastic
    d. foreboding, ominous, threatening

_____ 11. Shakespeare uses blank verse for
    a. most of the speeches of major characters.
    b. rhyming dramatic lines.
    c. all speeches by minor characters.
    d. the soliloquies at the beginning of each act.

_____ 12. Why does Calpurnia ask Caesar not to go to the Senate?
    a. She has heard rumors of the conspiracy.
    b. Her strange dreams have made her ill.
    c. She believes her frightening dreams are omens.
    d. She is uncertain what the Senate might do.

_____ 13. Caesar says, "Cowards die many times before their deaths;/The valiant never taste of death but once." This line means that
    a. death is inevitable but fear is a choice.
    b. anyone who fears death is a coward.
    c. no one can kill a valiant person.
    d. cowards should be put to death.

_____ 14. Which of the following creates suspense in Act II?
    a. Brutus' confession to Portia
    b. the meeting of the conspirators
    c. the wild, foreboding weather
    d. the many warnings to Caesar

_____ 15. The fact that the reader, but not Caesar, knows that his "friends" plan to kill him makes Caesar appear _____ .
    a. vulnerable
    b. foolish
    c. dangerous
    d. ambitious

Vocabulary and Grammar

_____ 16. The word _augmented_ means _____ .
    a. predicted
    b. intended
    c. delayed
    d. increased

_____ 17. Which of the following sentences uses a form of *who* incorrectly?
     a. Brutus, who is not ambitious, thinks only of the good of the country.
     b. Who's interpretation of the dream does Caesar believe?
     c. To whom does the power shift within the group of conspirators?
     d. If you had been a Roman citizen, whose side would you have chosen?

_____ 18. Someone who has *entreated* has _____ .
     a. repaired
     b. pleaded
     c. abandoned
     d. provided for

_____ 19. Something that is *imminent* is _____ .
     a. short-lived
     b. famous
     c. about to happen
     d. unfavorable

_____ 20. _____ does Brutus send to see _____ at the gate?
     a. Who, whose
     b. Whom, who's
     c. Whom, whose
     d. Who, who's

Essay Questions

21. Brutus is a patriot and a nobleman, well off and well thought of in Roman society. He has the respect and admiration of all, and Caesar is his personal friend. Yet he embarks on a course of treachery. How do you explain his behavior? Write an essay that explains Brutus' reasons for his actions. Use examples from the play to support your ideas.

22. As the conspirators part, Cassius worries whether Caesar will leave home, noting the "unaccustomed terror of this night." What omens and portents occur in Act II, and what role do they play in the growing suspense of the play? Write an essay that discusses some of the omens in the play and how Shakespeare uses them to further his plot. Use examples from the play to support your ideas.

23. The conspirators elect not to attack Antony. Cassius is not so sure they've chosen wisely in the matter, but Brutus brushes his argument aside. Why does Brutus decide to leave Antony unharmed and how is this decision consistent with other aspects of Brutus' character? Write an essay that explains how Brutus' nature leads him to this fateful decision. Use examples from the play to support your ideas.

Name _____ Date _____

The Tragedy of Julius Caesar, **Act III**, by William Shakespeare

Selection Test

Critical Reading

In the blank, write the letter of the one best answer.

____ 1. Why do the conspirators ask Caesar to pardon Publius Cimber in Act III of *The Tragedy of Julius Caesar?*
   a. They need Publius Cimber's political support.
   b. They want to divert Caesar's attention from the assassination.
   c. They want to prove Caesar is just and kind.
   d. Publius Cimber is a rival for Caesar's crown.

____ 2. In Caesar's last few speeches, when he refuses to pardon Publius Cimber, his tone is
   a. proud and arrogant.   c. reasonable and accommodating.
   b. excited and irrational.   d. kind and sympathetic.

____ 3. When Antony first shakes hands with the conspirators, it suggests that he
   a. knows nothing about the assassination.
   b. plans to join them to kill Caesar.
   c. accepts the murder and supports the conspirators.
   d. wishes they would kill him as well.

____ 4. Which choice is the best paraphrase of this passage from Scene i?
   ANTONY O pardon me, thou bleeding piece of earth,
   [255] That I am meek and gentle with these butchers!
   Thou art the ruins of the noblest man
   That ever livèd in the tide of times.
   Woe to the hand that shed this costly blood!
   a. Forgive me, Caesar, for being friendly with your murderers. You are the noblest man that ever lived, and you are ruined. I wish misfortune on the hand that made your wounds.
   b. Antony addresses Caesar's corpse and pledges to get revenge on his killers.
   c. Pardon me, bloody earth, that I did not kill these butchers! You have ruined the noblest man, regardless of the times. That hand that shed this blood will pay.
   d. Forgive me for being meek. These butchers have ruined a noble man. This blood has been shed by a woeful hand.

____ 5. When Antony delivers a dramatic speech over Caesar's body, he is alone onstage. A speech delivered under these circumstances is called a(n) _____ .
   a. aside   b. soliloquy   c. monologue   d. eulogy

____ 6. What are the connotations of Antony's image of Caesar as a hart, or deer?
   a. untamed, shy, hidden   c. timid, weak, quick to flee
   b. gentle, attractive, tender   d. free, noble, proud

____ 7. How are Antony's true feelings about the conspirators first revealed?
   a. in dialogue with the conspirators   c. in his funeral oration for Caesar
   b. in his soliloquy over Caesar's body   d. in a series of asides in conversation

____ 8. In his oration, how does Antony show that the conspirators were not honorable ?
   a. He contrasts Caesar's deeds with the reasons for the assassination.
   b. He attacks their character directly.
   c. He gives examples of their past acts of dishonor.
   d. He explains the meaning of honor.

_____ 9. Choose the item that most accurately paraphrases the following lines.

> When that the poor have cried, Caesar hath wept;
> Ambition should be made of sterner stuff.

    a. Poor people and Caesar cried; they are not stern enough to be ambitious.

    b. Caesar wept right along with his poor citizens; if he's ambitious he ought to be tougher than that.

    c. Caesar cried with the poor people who cry because Caesar's ambition is stern.

    d. When is it that the poor have cried, when Caesar has cried? Ambition should be more stern.

_____ 10. Antony's speech at Caesar's funeral is interrupted by the plebeians' reactions in several places. Because Antony delivers the speech to other characters on stage, it is considered a(n) _____.

    a. conversation   b. aside   c. dialogue   d. monologue

_____ 11. Why does Antony point to the wounds on Caesar's body and the tears in his cloak and identify whose dagger made each one?

    a. It shows that Antony saw the murder and knows who is responsible.

    b. It increases Antony's credibility with the crowd.

    c. It emphasizes the treachery involved and makes each conspirator personally responsible for Caesar's death.

    d. He is so horrified by the crime that he can't help exclaiming over it.

_____ 12. What do Antony's speeches in Act III reveal about his character?

    a. He uses the deeds of others to his advantage.

    b. He is a loyal and clever supporter of Caesar.

    c. He did not truly care for Caesar.

    d. He is unaware of his effect on others.

_____ 13. What news is reported to Antony at the end of Scene ii?

    a. The conspirators are celebrating in the city streets.

    b. Caesar's funeral is over.

    c. Octavius has arrived in Rome.

    d. The mob is on the way to declare him king.

_____ 14. Which statement sums up the purpose of Scene iii, in which a group of plebeians attacks Cinna the poet?

    a. The poet was a murderer.   c. Romans are barbarians.

    b. Workers hate the arts.   d. Mob rule now governs.

_____ 15. What impression does Shakespeare give of the plebeians in Act III?

    a. They are easily manipulated.   c. They respect the noblemen.

    b. They are men of principle.   d. They do not care for politics.

_____ 16. The purpose of a paraphrase is to

    a. restate a passage as briefly as possible.   c. find hidden meaning in a passage.

    b. interpret a passage.   d. restate a passage in one's own words.

Vocabulary and Grammar

_____ 17. Which of the following sentences contain reflexive pronouns?

    I. If I live a thousand years, I shall not find myself so apt to die.

    II. Only we ourselves will take responsibility for the deed.

    III. Do you consider yourself so vile that you will not love your country?

    IV. I tell you that which you yourselves do know.

    a. I and II   c. II and III

    b. I and III   d. III and IV

____ 18. When Antony and Brutus first speak after the assassination, Brutus speaks of *mal-ice*, which means _____ .

a. ill will   b. regret   c. suspicion   d. violence

____ 19. Which of the following statements is false?

a. A reflexive pronoun ends in *-self* or *-selves*.
b. A reflexive pronoun points back to a noun or pronoun in the same sentence.
c. A reflexive pronoun adds information to a sentence.
d. A reflexive pronoun always follows a linking verb.

____ 20. Both Brutus and Antony make an oration at Caesar's funeral. An oration is

a. a funeral speech.   c. a formal speech.
b. a personal way of showing grief.   d. an ancient Roman custom at funerals.

Essay Questions

21. Lines 148–163 of Act III, Scene i, contain Antony's first public words following the assassination of Caesar. He has just gained permission to speak to the conspirators in safety. Examine the monologue carefully, and in an essay, relate Antony's message in the speech. Describe Antony's tone and discuss what he hopes to accomplish with this speech. What are Antony's motives? Why doesn't Shakespeare have Antony deliver this speech as a soliloquy, with no other characters on stage?

22. The surprise and the power of Act III lie in Antony's words and actions. In an essay consider Antony's dual roles in Act III. What are those dual roles? How does he switch from one role to the other? Finally, how does Scene iii add to the drama of the act?

23. In lines 175–190 of Act III, Scene ii, Antony has just asked the plebeians to allow him to step down and to gather around Caesar's body so that he can read the will. Upon viewing Caesar's body again, Antony apparently gets distracted and delivers the words in the speech. Paraphrase the speech. Then, in an essay, consider the words of Antony. Why does he speak the way he does to the crowd? Why does he mention Brutus' and Caesar's relationship specifically? What effect do these words have on the plebeians? Keep in mind that this is the third of four major sections of Antony's funeral oration.

***The Tragedy of Julius Caesar*, Act IV**, by William Shakespeare

Selection Test

Critical Reading

In the blank, write the letter of the one best answer.

____ 1. At the beginning of Act IV, what are Antony, Octavius, and Lepidus discussing?
   a. how best to honor Caesar's will
   b. which Romans must die so that they can secure their power
   c. how they might work peacefully with Brutus and Cassius
   d. to which Romans they might offer leadership roles in government

____ 2. In Antony's conversation with Octavius in Act IV, Scene i, of *The Tragedy of Julius Caesar,* we learn that Antony is _____ .
   a. loyal
   b. trustworthy
   c. sentimental
   d. unscrupulous

____ 3. Which of the following best describes relations among the triumvirate?
   a. open conflict and envy
   b. mutual trust and respect
   c. manipulation and suspicion
   d. petty quarrels and disagreements

____ 4. Which of the following is a source of conflict between Cassius and Brutus?
   a. Brutus believes that Cassius has taken bribes.
   b. Brutus regrets the murder of Caesar.
   c. Cassius believes that Portia has died in a strange way.
   d. Antony blames both Brutus and Cassius for Caesar's death.

____ 5. Which of the following best illustrates the change in Brutus and Cassius's friendship in Act IV?
   a. Brutus admits he was ill-tempered with Cassius.
   b. Brutus and Cassius argue and disagree with each other.
   c. Brutus asks Cassius not to speak of Portia's death.
   d. Brutus and Cassius both command armies.

____ 6. How are Brutus and Cassius characterized in Act IV, Scene iii?
   a. wise, generous, sensible
   b. timid, hesitant, fearful
   c. gentle, accommodating, understanding
   d. ambitious, petty-minded, quarrelsome

____ 7. When Brutus receives confirmation of Portia's death, he is
   a. openly relieved.
   b. apparently unmoved.
   c. seemingly devastated.
   d. quietly sorrowful.

© Prentice-Hall, Inc.

Unit 8: Drama

8. How do the temperaments of Brutus and Cassius differ?
   a. Brutus is mean-spirited and greedy, while Cassius is gentle and generous.
   b. Brutus is emotional, while Cassius is stoical.
   c. Brutus is stoical, while Cassius is emotional.
   d. Brutus is hot-tempered, while Cassius is calm.

9. What does the conflict between Brutus and Cassius probably indicate about their ability to face the challenges that lie ahead of them?
   a. If they cannot form a united front and focus on important matters, they probably will not be able to defeat Antony.
   b. Their anger toward each other will probably drive them to victory.
   c. Their fighting shows that they do not really want to succeed as leaders, and so they will not.
   d. Although they fight among themselves, they are able to agree on a solid strategy.

10. Which of the following best summarizes Brutus' argument in Act IV, Scene iii, in which he urges Cassius to be honest?
    a. We killed Caesar to end corruption; now we do not have the right to corrupt ourselves.
    b. We killed Caesar because he was a tyrant; our tyranny invites a similar fate.
    c. By killing Caesar we have gained great wealth; we do not need to extort money.
    d. We pretended to kill Caesar to ensure justice, but he was honest.

11. On what plan of action do Cassius and Brutus finally agree?
    a. They agree to wait for their enemies to come to them.
    b. They agree to surrender to Antony at Philippi.
    c. They agree to march to Philippi to meet their enemies.
    d. They agree to hide.

12. In the following lines that Brutus addresses to Lucius, what is Shakespeare trying to show about Brutus' character?
    > What, thou speak'st drowsily? / Poor knave, I blame thee not; thou art o'er-watched. / Call Claudius and some other of my men; / I'll have them sleep on cushions in my tent.
    a. He is close-minded.
    b. He is condescending to his men.
    c. He is kind and thoughtful.
    d. He is foolish.

13. What is the significance of the ghost's promise to see Brutus at Philippi?
    a. Philippi is where he is to meet Antony's troops, and the ghost's promise to be there is probably a bad omen.
    b. Philippi is where he is to meet Antony's troops, and the ghost should bring him good luck.
    c. Philippi is where Caesar was killed.
    d. The ghost is urging Brutus to leave for Philippi immediately.

14. Brutus asks his servants why they cried out in their sleep because
    a. he was asleep and dreamed of Caesar.
    b. he thinks they dreamed of the ghost.
    c. he wants to know if they saw the ghost.
    d. they disturbed his much-needed rest.

15. What does Caesar's ghost symbolize?
    a. justification for Brutus' actions
    b. Brutus' guilty conscience
    c. the disorder of Brutus' army
    d. Caesar's forgiveness

Vocabulary and Grammar

_____ 16. Which of the following is the best meaning of the word *covert* as it is used in this sentence?

> Antony, Octavius, and Lepidus make covert plans to secure their power.

a. Simple
b. Complicated
c. Secret
d. Entertaining

_____ 17. What is the antecedent of *them* in the following sentence?

> Octavius, though we lay these honors on this man, to ease ourselves of divers slanderous loads, he shall bear them as the ass bears gold.

a. Octavius
b. loads
c. man
d. honors

_____ 18. Cassius denies _____ accusations related to his honesty.

a. philosophical
b. ridiculous
c. slanderous
d. covert

_____ 19. Which of the following sentences about the selection contains an error in pronoun and antecedent agreement?

a. After Caesar was murdered, his death was discussed by Octavius, Antony, and Lepidus.
b. Brutus accused Cassius of taking bribes, which they denied.
c. Sleep wouldn't come to Brutus because he was visited by Caesar's ghost.
d. Brutus decided to meet the enemy who was not far off.

_____ 20. Which of the following is the best meaning of the word *chastisement* as it is used in the following line?

> The name of Cassius honors this corruption, / And chastisement doth therefore hide his head.

a. Sympathy
b. Humor
c. Honor
d. Criticism

Essay Questions

21. In a short essay, describe the conflict between Antony and Brutus and Cassius. What drives Antony to battle with Brutus and Cassius? What in Antony's character makes him a difficult enemy to have? At what point in Act IV does he reveal his character?

22. In what ways does Brutus suffer in Act IV? What changes occur in his personal life? What happens to his friendship with Cassius? What threats does he face? How does he handle his difficult circumstances? Given the events of Act IV, what do you guess the future holds for Brutus? Answer these questions in an essay.

23. In an essay, compare and contrast the characters of Antony, Brutus, and Cassius. In what ways do they differ from one another? What traits do they share? Give concrete examples to back up your statements about each character.

The Tragedy of Julius Caesar, **Act V,** by William Shakespeare

Selection Test

Critical Reading

In the blank, write the letter of the one best answer.

_____ 1. How might you best describe the meeting between Brutus, Cassius, Antony, and Octavius at the beginning of Act V?
a. friendly
b. hostile
c. long
d. quietly restrained

_____ 2. According to the following statement, what mistake is the cause of Cassius' problems?

> Flatterers! Now, Brutus, thank yourself; / This tongue had not offended so today, / If Cassius might have ruled.

a. not following his instincts and killing Antony along with Caesar
b. not paying enough attention to the words of Antony
c. not flattering Antony to get on his good side
d. not inviting Antony to join the conspiracy against Caesar

_____ 3. What is the effect of Cassius' belief that he is doomed to die?
a. He tries to enjoy each moment of his life.
b. He takes unnecessary risks.
c. He loses all hope of surviving the battle.
d. He fears being captured.

_____ 4. What do Brutus and Cassius say to each other before they depart for battle?
a. They speak angry words to each other.
b. They discuss quitting the battle and leaving Rome forever.
c. They bid each other farewell in case they do not see each other again.
d. They say a quick good-bye and plan to meet again in a few hours.

_____ 5. How might you describe the feelings of Brutus and Cassius as they head into battle?
a. unconfident
b. angry
c. excited
d. eager

_____ 6. What is Cassius' fatal mistake?
a. He believes that they will never win and kills himself out of frustration.
b. He forgets where he is supposed to be stationed.
c. He mistakenly believes Titinius has been captured and kills himself out of guilt.
d. He mistakenly walks into a trap set by Antony's army.

_____ 7. Which of the following statements by Brutus on the death of Cassius is most reflective of his stoicism?
a. "O Julius Caesar, thou art mighty/yet!"
b. "Friends, I owe/more tears/To this dead man than you will see me pay./I shall find time, Cassius; I shall find time."
c. "Are yet two Romans living such/as these?"
d. "Where, where, Messala, doth his/body lie?"

8. In Act V, Scene iv, to what does Brutus attribute the suicides of Cassius and Titinius?
   a. the power of Caesar's ghost
   b. the enemy's superior numbers
   c. his own men's cowardliness
   d. his errors in judgment

9. Which of the following is a good argument against Cassius' being described as the noble hero who is brought low through his own fault?
   a. He is greedy and dishonest rather than noble and heroic.
   b. He is not heroic because he was afraid to kill himself.
   c. He does not fail because he dies a free man.
   d. His death is not his fault because it was fated.

10. Which of the following words best characterizes the attitude of Antony and Octavius toward Brutus' followers when they have been captured?
    a. pity
    b. mercy
    c. contempt
    d. vengeance

11. Which of the following events convinces Brutus that he was wrong to kill Caesar?
    a. his ethical disagreement with Cassius
    b. Antony's reproaches of the killers
    c. the mysterious death of Portia
    d. the apparition of Caesar's ghost

12. What is the main reason why Brutus does not want to be captured and taken back to Rome?
    a. He is afraid of seeing Antony face to face.
    b. Being captured would be a disgrace and rob him of honor.
    c. He no longer wishes to rule Rome.
    d. He feels his army will be unable to function without him.

13. What is an important effect of Brutus' death?
    a. Antony surrenders.
    b. Cassius is deemed the hero of the battle.
    c. Brutus' army is chased away.
    d. Antony recognizes Brutus as noble and virtuous.

14. Why is The Tragedy of Julius Caesar considered a tragedy?
    a. A main character is involved in a struggle that ends in disaster.
    b. The plot features a battle.
    c. The plot features a power struggle between two leaders, one of whom dies.
    d. More than one person dies by the final act.

15. Which of the following may be used to argue that Brutus is the tragic hero of The Tragedy of Julius Caesar?
    a. He is defeated by a supernatural being.
    b. He was devoted to the cause of liberty.
    c. His own actions caused his downfall.
    d. He was unfairly manipulated by Cassius.

16. Which of the following best expresses the theme of The Tragedy of Julius Caesar?
    a. Mercy to the losing faction is more noble than vengeance.
    b. Individuals can affect events even from beyond the grave.
    c. Good consequences cannot result from an evil deed.
    d. Philosophy is no help in times of great crisis.

Vocabulary and Grammar

____ 17. Which of the following passages from Act V contains a word of direct address?
   a. "They stand, and would have parley."
   b. "Upon the right hand I; keep thou the left."
   c. "What says my general?"
   d. "Stand fast, Titinius, we must out and talk."

____ 18. Which of the following is the best meaning of the word *presage* as it is used in this sentence?

   Cassius' feelings of doom are influenced by symbols that seem to presage disaster.
   a. foretell
   b. protect against
   c. recall
   d. fight

____ 19. What is a word of direct address in the following passage from Act V?

   O Cassius, Brutus gave the word too early, / Who, having some advantage on Octavius, / Took it too eagerly; his soldiers fell to spoil, / Whilst we by Antony are all enclosed.
   a. Antony
   b. Who
   c. Brutus
   d. Cassius

____ 20. Which of the following is the best meaning of the word *envy* as it is used in the following line from Act V?

   All the conspirators save only he / Did that they did in envy of great Caesar . . .
   a. admiration
   b. anger
   c. jealousy
   d. forgetfulness

Essay Questions

21. How does Antony's attitude toward Brutus change by the end of Act V? What is the reason for this change? According to Antony, why were Brutus' actions against Caesar different from those of the other conspirators? Answer these questions in an essay.

22. In an essay, discuss cause and effect in *The Tragedy of Julius Caesar*. What are the effects of Caesar's death? What are some of the events that lead to the play's tragic ending in Act V?

23. Write an essay in which you discuss Brutus as a tragic hero. In your essay, answer the following questions: What are his heroic qualities? When in the play does he exhibit these qualities? What is his tragic flaw? When in the play is this flaw most obvious? Why is his death so tragic?

Unit Test: Drama

Critical Reading

In the blank, write the letter of the one best answer.

The questions below are based on the following selection.

The following excerpt is from Act II Scene vii of William Shakespeare's comedy As You Like It. *In this play, Duke Frederick has usurped and then banished his brother from one of the great dukedoms of France. The brother, the lawful duke, takes refuge in a forest with a group of loyal supporters. In this famous monologue, Jaques, a lord attending the lawful duke in the forest, expresses his ideas about life.*

Jaques. All the world's a stage, / And all the men and women merely players: / They have their exits and their entrances; / And one man in his time plays many parts, / His acts being seven ages. At first the infant, / Mewling and puking in the nurse's arms. / Then the whining school-boy, with his satchel / And shining morning face, creeping like snail / Unwillingly to school. And then the lover, / Sighing like furnace, with a woeful ballad / Made to his mistress's eyebrow. Then a soldier, / Full of strange oaths, and bearded like the pard, / Jealous in honour[1], sudden and quick in quarrel, / Seeking the bubble reputation / Even in the cannon's mouth. And then the justice, / In fair, round belly with good capon-lined, / With eyes severe and beard of formal cut, / Full of wise saws[2] and modern instances; / And so he plays his part. The sixth age shifts / Into the lean and slipper'd pantaloon, / With spectacles on nose and pouch on side, / His youthful hose[3], well saved, a world too wide / For his shrunk shank[4]; And his big, manly voice, / Turning again toward childish treble, pipes / And whistles in his sound. Last scene of all, / That ends this strange eventful history, / Is second childness and mere oblivion, / Sans[5] teeth, sans eyes, sans taste, sans every thing.

_____ 1. To what does Jaques compare the world?
   a. a nurse's arms
   b. exits and entrances in a theater
   c. the stage of a theater
   d. men and women

_____ 2. What does this monologue describe as the "acts" of a man's life?
   a. the theatrical performances a man enjoys in his lifetime
   b. the stages of his life from birth to death
   c. the teachers and nurses in a man's life
   d. the different jobs a man holds during his life

_____ 3. How many complete sentences are in the following passage of blank verse from the selection?

   All the world's a stage, / And all the men and women merely players: / They have their exits and their entrances; / And one man in his time plays many parts, / His acts being seven ages.

   a. one
   b. two
   c. three
   d. four

[1] eager for fame and protective of one's reputation
[2] wise sayings
[3] type of outer garment worn on the legs by men
[4] the leg
[5] without

Unit 8: Drama

4. According to Jaques, what is a man's attitude toward school in the second stage of his life?
   a. He loves it.
   b. He is intimidated by it.
   c. He dislikes going to school.
   d. He appreciates its importance.

5. Which choice is the best paraphrase of the following passage?
   > Then a soldier, / Full of strange oaths, and bearded like the pard, / Jealous in honour, sudden and quick in quarrel, / Seeking the bubble reputation / Even in the cannon's mouth
   a. As a soldier, a man vows to build a strong and lasting reputation.
   b. As a soldier, a man learns to operate a cannon in the heat of battle.
   c. As a soldier, a man fights and risks his life to gain fleeting fame.
   d. As a soldier, a man becomes quarrelsome and bitter.

6. Which of the following is the best description of the justice in the fifth stage of life?
   a. He gives advice and has an inflated opinion of his own wisdom.
   b. He is generous and kind, giving good advice to all who need it.
   c. He is modest and unsure of himself.
   d. He is well dressed and admirable.

7. Which conflict creates drama in the life of a man at his sixth stage of life?
   a. He begins to miss his childhood.
   b. His body begins to break down and his voice becomes shrill as a child's.
   c. He is unable to find friends.
   d. He has trouble finding clothing that is comfortable and attractive.

8. What does Jaques see in every stage of a man's life?
   a. interesting performances
   b. learning experiences
   c. kindness and affection
   d. struggle and unhappiness

9. How might you best paraphrase the following passage from the selection.
   > Last scene of all, / That ends this strange eventful history, / Is second childishness and mere oblivion, / Sans teeth, sans eyes, sans taste, sans every thing.
   a. In the last stage of life, a man becomes helpless as a child, his mind and body deteriorate, and he dies.
   b. In the last stage of life, a man enjoys a second childhood that is carefree and happy.
   c. In the last stage of life, a man no longer needs his sight and his sense of taste.
   d. In the last stage of life, a man thinks back on his childhood, closes his eyes, and smiles.

10. What purpose does this monologue serve?
    a. It provides valuable information about events of the play.
    b. It shows how other characters feel about Jaques.
    c. It demonstrates Jaques's negative attitude toward life.
    d. It introduces readers to words related to the theater.

Vocabulary and Grammar

Choose the word(s) that best completes each sentence.

____ 11. Cassius wishes that he _____ powerful, and he asks that Brutus _____ the conspiracy against Caesar.
   a. were . . . join
   b. were . . . joins
   c. was . . . join
   d. was . . . joins

____ 12. Brutus, _____ is Caesar's friend, worries about Caesar's ambition, so he joins the conspirators _____ are plotting to kill Caesar.
   a. whom, who   c. who, who
   b. whom, whom   d. who, whom

____ 13. Some people felt that Caesar's pride and power presented a _____ threat to Rome.
   a. spare
   b. prodigious
   c. productive
   d. confounded

____ 14. Caesar did not protect himself because he did not believe that danger was _____.
   a. surly
   b. confounded
   c. vile
   d. imminent

In the blank, write the letter of the one best answer.

____ 15. 'Tis better that the enemy seek us; so shall he waste his means, weary his soldiers, doing himself offense, whilst _____, lying still, are full of rest, defense, and nimbleness.
   a. she
   b. it
   c. we
   d. he

____ 16. Which of the following sentences contains a word of direct address?
   a. Brutus was the noblest Roman of all.
   b. Soon, we will draw our swords against the conspirators.
   c. Antony calls the conspirators villains.
   d. When, Antony, shall we give the sign of battle?

____ 17. Which of the following choices is the best meaning of the word *malice* as used in the following sentence:
      Their swords were lifted in anger and malice.
   a. a desire to frighten
   b. a desire to harm
   c. hopelessness
   d. recklessness

____ 18. Which of the following sentences from the selection contain reflexive pronouns?
      I. If this be known, Cassius or Caesar never shall turn back, for I will slay myself.
      II. If I myself must die, there is no hour so fit as Caesar's death hour.
      III. I have the same dagger for myself, when it shall please my country to need my death.
      IV. What touches us ourself shall be last served.
    a. I and II
    b. I and III
    c. II and III
    d. III and IV

The questions below consist of a related pair of words in CAPITAL LETTERS followed by four lettered pairs of words. Choose the pair that best expresses a relationship similar to that of the pair in capital letters.

____ 19. COVERT : HIDDEN ::
    a. argue : disagreement
    b. honest : truthful
    c. secret : known
    d. mystery : riddle

____ 20. CHASTISEMENT : PRAISE ::
    a. encouragment : honor
    b. angry : pleased
    c. punishment : compliment
    d. disappointment : failure

Essay Questions

21. Like real people, each of the main characters in *The Tragedy of Julius Caesar* possesses a variety of personality traits, some positive and some negative. As you read, you might have found your opinions of Caesar, Brutus, Cassius, and Antony changing. Write an essay in which you describe the character that you find most interesting and sympathetic. Explain your response by describing some of the thoughts, words, and actions of the character.

22. Characters in *The Tragedy of Julius Caesar* display different leadership styles. In an essay, compare the leadership of Antony and Octavius with the leadership of Brutus and Cassius. In what ways do their styles differ? When are these differences revealed? Whose style proves to be more effective? Explain your answer.

23. The drama of *The Tragedy of Julius Caesar* grows from a variety of different conflicts, or struggles between forces. Some of these conflicts are external—meaning they take place between two characters or groups—and some of these conflicts are internal—meaning they take place within a character. In an essay, describe one external conflict and one internal conflict in the play.

24. The dramatic situations presented in *The Tragedy of Julius Caesar* have both causes and effects. In an essay, describe some of the causes and effects that lead to the tragic death of Brutus at the end of the play. What is the immediate cause of his suicide? What are some other causes that lead to his final, desperate moment? What is the immediate effect of his death? What might be a long-term effect?

25. Write an essay in which you discuss Julius Caesar and Brutus as tragic heroes. What are their heroic qualities? What are their tragic flaws? In your essay, explain why, though they are both tragic figures, they are different from each other. Support your answer with details from the play.

"The Stolen Child" by William Butler Yeats

Selection Test

Critical Reading

In the blank, write the letter of the one best answer.

_____ 1. In "The Stolen Child," the fairies
   a. exist only by night.
   b. lead a child back to his parents.
   c. take a child from the human world.
   d. show a child their secret treasures.

_____ 2. The description of the island, herons, stolen cherries, and moonlight at the beginning of the poem help to create an atmosphere that is _____ .
   a. amusing
   b. mystical
   c. light-hearted
   d. serious

_____ 3. In "The Stolen Child," what feelings are evoked by the image of the fairies whispering to sleeping trout?
   a. feelings of playfulness   c. soothing feelings
   b. feelings of caring and kindness   d. feelings of suspicion

_____ 4. The line "We foot it all the night" means
   a. one must walk all night to find the island.
   b. humans measure the world differently from fairies.
   c. they walk all night with the abducted child.
   d. the fairies dance all night.

_____ 5. The lines "For the world's more full of weeping/than you can understand" imply
   a. that grief is a human phenomenon.
   b. that the child will cry if he doesn't go.
   c. that the fairies cannot understand human tears.
   d. that the fairies will weep if the child doesn't come.

_____ 6. The *atmosphere* of a literary work is its _____ .
   a. meaning
   b. mood
   c. setting
   d. moral

_____ 7. When responding to "The Stolen Child," you should consider
   a. how the rhyme structure compares to that of other poems.
   b. Yeats's literary background.
   c. how the images in the poem affect you.
   d. how punctuation influences the rhythm of the poem.

_____ 8. What do the fairies do to the sleeping trout?
   a. They whisper to them to disturb them.
   b. They lean out and grasp them.
   c. They cover them with ferns.
   d. They steal them from the water.

Unit 9: Poetry

_____ 9. Why do the fairies do what they do to the sleeping trout?
   a. to give them to the child
   b. to amuse themselves
   c. to hide them from humans
   d. to please the trout

_____ 10. As the fairies speak of weeping and of their activities while they lure the child, the atmosphere shifts from
   a. enchanting to disturbing.
   b. magical to ironic.
   c. mysterious to hopeful.
   d. sorrowful to happy.

_____ 11. Why do the fairies keep telling the child the world is full of weeping?
   a. The fairies and humans are united by emotions.
   b. They care about his feelings.
   c. The fairies believe he will be happier with them.
   d. They hope to persuade him to abandon the human world.

_____ 12. When the child leaves with the fairies he
   a. goes to the leafy island to share in the stolen cherries and dancing.
   b. will be solemn but will at least have no need to continue weeping.
   c. must leave human pleasures like cattle sounds, kettles singing, and scurrying mice.
   d. will become one of the supernatural woodland creatures.

_____ 13. Images of calves "lowing" on the hillside and the "kettle on the hob" suggest
   a. the tedious tasks involved in farm life.
   b. things the child doesn't want to give up in order to join the fairies.
   c. the warmth and security of the fairy world.
   d. the comforts of the human world.

_____ 14. When the price of the fairies' bargain becomes clear, the atmosphere of the poem becomes _____ .
   a. triumphant
   b. sarcastic
   c. poignant
   d. innocent

_____ 15. Although fairies don't really exist, Yeats uses the folklore to explain
   a. the persistence of belief in the supernatural.
   b. the grief caused by the death of a child.
   c. strange events happening on Irish nights.
   d. the reason why human beings weep.

Vocabulary and Grammar

_____ 16. Which pair of words correctly completes the following sentence?
   _____ determined to lure the child into _____ world.
   a. They're, their   c. There, they're
   b. Their, there   d. They're, there

_____ 17. Which sentence uses _their, there,_ or _they're_ incorrectly?
   a. The fairies tell the child that he will be happy in their world.
   b. They're not being completely honest with him.
   c. Once the fairies have him, their not likely to let him go.
   d. I wish the child had not followed them there.

____ 18. Someone who is *slumbering* is _____ .
   a. staggering
   b. struggling
   c. sleeping
   d. stammering

____ 19. The birds most like *herons* are _____ .
   a. vultures
   b. hawks
   c. storks
   d. sparrows

____ 20. If one thing *glosses* another, it _____ it.
   a. shines
   b. erodes
   c. loses
   d. expands

Essay Questions

21. The fairies in "The Stolen Child" offer a deal to the child they hope to lure: He will be free of a world full of troubles and tears, but he can never return to its pleasures. In an essay, explain how life offers tradeoffs for its pleasures and pains. Use examples from the poem or from your own experience to support your ideas.

22. In "The Stolen Child," supernatural beings lure a child to a world beyond human reach. In an essay, identify natural elements that Yeats draws on to create a supernatural world, and describe how those elements contribute to the effect of the poem's ending.

23. Yeats does not tell the story from the point of view of the child or those who know him, but in the voice of a being other than human. How does the identity of the speaker contribute to the effect of the poem? In an essay, explain how Yeats uses the speaker to provide another point of view on what it means to be alive. Use examples from the poem to illustrate your ideas.

"In Flanders Fields" by John McCrae
"The Kraken" by Alfred, Lord Tennyson
"Reapers" by Jean Toomer
"Meeting at Night" by Robert Browning
"Prayer of First Dancers" Traditional Navajo Chant

Selection Test

Critical Reading

In the blank, write the letter of the one best answer.

_____ 1. Who are the speakers of "In Flanders Fields"?
   a. poppies in a cemetery
   b. soldiers in battle
   c. soldiers killed in battle
   d. relatives of soldiers

_____ 2. What important message do the speakers of "In Flanders Fields" give to readers?
   a. Continue the important fight for which we died, or we will not be able to rest peacefully.
   b. End the quarrel with our enemy, or you will be buried in Flanders fields too.
   c. Be sure the poppies continue to grow in Flanders fields.
   d. Remove the poppies from Flanders fields.

_____ 3. In "In Flanders Fields," what does the poem's repetitive beat suggest?
   a. soldiers carrying the torch of the fallen soldiers into battle
   b. the bravely singing larks and other birds that fly over Flanders fields
   c. the sound of gunfire in Flanders fields
   d. the rows and rows of grave markers throughout Flanders fields

_____ 4. In "The Kraken," where can the Kraken be found?
   a. wandering through villages
   b. sleeping on a beach
   c. deep in the sea
   d. swimming along the surface of the ocean

_____ 5. What musical device is demonstrated by the italicized words in the following passage from "The Kraken"?
   > Below the thunders of the upper *deep*; / Far, far *beneath* in the abysmal sea, / His ancient, *dreamless*, uninvaded *sleep* / The Kraken *sleepeth*: faintest sunlights *flee*
   a. consonance
   b. assonance
   c. onomatopoeia
   d. alliteration

_____ 6. According to Tennyson's poem, what has the Kraken spent his time doing for ages?
   a. sleeping and eating huge seaworms
   b. attacking sailors
   c. rising to the surface of the ocean and roaring
   d. traveling throughout the ocean

7. What action is reflected by the repetition of sound in the following lines from "Reapers"?

> Black reapers with the sound of steel on stones / Are sharpening scythes. I see them place the hones / In their hip-pockets as a thing that's done. / And start their silent swinging . . .

   a. the squeal of the field rat
   b. the swish of the scythe blades
   c. horses driving a mower through the weeds
   d. the setting of the sun on the farm

8. What happens to the field rat in "Reapers"?
   a. It is chased away by the reapers.
   b. It is taken in as a pet.
   c. It is frightened away by the horses.
   d. It is cut with the blade of a scythe.

9. What is revealed by actions described in "Reapers"?
   a. the numbing effect on slaves of repetitive work
   b. the beauty of nature on a farm
   c. how to operate a scythe effectively
   d. the important role horses play at harvest time

10. On what type of journey has the speaker in "Meeting at Night" been?
    a. a journey walking down a long stretch of beach
    b. a journey on horseback
    c. a journey at sea
    d. a mountain journey

11. Which of the following lines from "Meeting at Night" features an example of ono-matopoeia?
    a. "And quench its speed i' the slushy sand"
    b. "Three fields to cross till a farm appears"
    c. "And a voice less loud, through its joys and fears"
    d. "The gray sea and the long black land"

12. What is the meaning of the following lines from "Meeting at Night"?

> And a voice less loud, through its joys and fears, / Than the two hearts beating each to each!

    a. The people are speechless, and the two hearts are beating with fear and anxiety.
    b. The person at the door does not speak loudly enough to be heard over the ocean waves.
    c. Voices cannot be heard over the couple's hearts, which are beating together with love and happiness.
    d. The two people meeting do not speak to each other.

13. What musical device is most noticeable in "Prayer of First Dancers"?
    a. repetition
    b. onomatopoeia
    c. assonance
    d. consonance

14. How would you describe the attitude toward the "you" being addressed in "Prayer of First Dancers"?
    a. hostile and angry
    b. welcoming and admiring
    c. nervous and fearful
    d. formal and unwelcoming

____ 15. What can you say about the Navajo attitude toward nature after reading "Prayer of First Dancers"?
   a. They view nature only as something to be used.
   b. They feel indifferent toward nature.
   c. They feel respect and reverence toward nature.
   d. They feel nature interferes with their lifestyle.

____ 16. What aspect of "Prayer of First Dancers" is most reflective of its ceremonial use?
   a. its length
   b. its references to beauty
   c. its references to children
   d. its repeated words and phrases

Vocabulary and Grammar

____ 17. Which pair of words correctly completes the following sentence?
   Nesting in its bed _____ the weeds, the startled field rat was caught _____ the blade and the ground.
   a. between, between   c. among, between
   b. between, among   d. among, among

____ 18. Which of the following is the best meaning of the word *abysmal* as it is used in the following line from "The Kraken"?
   Below the thunders of the upper deep; / Far, far beneath in the abysmal sea . . .
   a. deep   b. gloomy   c. rough   d. icy

____ 19. Which of the following sentences use *between* or *among* incorrectly?
   I. The students voted among themselves to chose the most popular poem.
   II. It came down to a choice between "Reapers" and "Meeting at Night."
   III. Of the many poems they had to choose between, those were their favorites.
   IV. If I had to choose among those two poems, I would choose "Meeting at Night."
   a. I and II   c. II and III
   b. I and IV   d. III and IV

____ 20. Which of the following is the best meaning of the word *millennial* as it is used in the following line from "The Kraken"?
   Huge sponges of millennial growth and height . . .
   a. of minimal change   c. rapid
   b. relating to a thousand-year period   d. questionable

Essay Questions

21. In an essay, describe the experience of the speaker in "Meeting at Night." Where has the speaker been? What are his feelings on arriving at the farmhouse? What specific images convey the speaker's feelings throughout the poem?

22. In an essay, explain how the poems "In Flanders Fields," "The Kraken," and "Prayer of First Dancers" focus on the handing down of something important, such as a duty, a story, or a tradition from the past. What has been handed down in each poem?

23. In an essay, explain how sound relates to meaning in the four poems you have read. What ideas are being expressed in each poem? How do rhythms, rhymes, and other repeated sounds emphasize these ideas?

"The Wind—tapped like a tired Man" by Emily Dickinson
"A Pace Like That" by Yehuda Amichai
"Metaphor" by Eve Merriam
"Right Hand" by Philip Fried

Selection Test

Critical Reading

In the blank, write the letter of the one best answer.

_____ 1. In "The Wind—tapped like a tired Man," who is the guest who enters the speaker's home?
a. a tired man   b. the wind   c. a musician   d. a humming bird

_____ 2. Which of the following lines from "The Wind—tapped like a tired Man" is the best example of personification?
a. "And like a Host—'Come in'/I boldly answered— . . ."
b. "And I became alone—"
c. " . . . like the Push/Of numerous Humming Birds at once/From a superior Bush—"
d. "His Countenance—a Billow—/His Fingers, as He passed/Let go a music— . . ."

_____ 3. How would you describe the movement of the wind in the speaker's home?
a. vicious and intense   c. rapid and agitated
b. delicate and silent   d. slow and calm

_____ 4. How might you paraphrase the following stanza from "The Wind—tapped like a tired Man"?
He visited—still flitting— / Then like a timid Man / Again, He tapped—'twas flurriedly—And I became alone—
a. Wind darted around my home and then abruptly left.
b. The wind gusted in my home. Then it broke through the window.
c. The wind became stronger and stronger until I had to seek cover.
d. The wind stayed in my home until another visitor—a timid man—knocked on my door.

_____ 5. In "A Pace Like That," what is the main reason why the speaker wants to live life at a slower pace?
a. to devote more time to his work and to studying the Torah
b. to spend more time observing the world around him
c. to devote more time to gardening and growing new trees
d. to improve his reading skills

_____ 6. Which image is used by the speaker in "A Pace Like That" to show how he wants to live his life?
a. working in a manhole   c. a child learning to read
b. sleepless nights   d. the image of reading a newspaper

_____ 7. In "A Pace Like That," what is the main reason why the speaker's life is in contrast with a Torah scroll?
a. His life is more complicated than the Torah.
b. He lives his life without paying much attention to his religion.
c. He lives in haste rather than slowly and carefully, focusing on each day.
d. His life is more simplistic.

Unit 9: Poetry

_____ 8. How might you paraphrase the following lines from "A Pace Like That"?

> The longer you live, the more people there are / who comment on your actions.
> Like a worker / in a manhole: at the opening above him / people stand around giving free advice / and yelling instructions, / but he's all alone down there in his depths.

a. Throughout your life, people will offer advice and criticism. Only you, however, know exactly what is best for your own situation.

b. You will find that spending your life working can be difficult and frustrating.

c. The older you get, the more you will appreciate the advice of others. There will be times when good advice might save you from the depths of failure.

d. The older you get, the more time you will devote to work. You will be completely alone, in contact with people only while you work.

_____ 9. What metaphor is central to the poem "Metaphor"?

a. the comparison of bright words to dark words

b. the comparison of morning to a blank sheet of paper

c. the comparison of night to dawn

d. the comparison of rest to wakefulness

_____ 10. To the speaker of "Metaphor," what does each morning present?

a. a chance for a fresh start

b. more work

c. time to deal with yesterday's problems

d. more bright words than dark words

_____ 11. How would you paraphrase the following lines from "Metaphor"?

> Whatever you want to say, / all day, / until night / folds it up / and files it away.
> The bright words and the dark words / are gone / until dawn / and a new day / to write on.

a. Night provides you with a temporary escape from the pressures of the day. When morning arrives, you must again face the problems of the previous day.

b. You should always say and do whatever you want. If you do not, you will feel as though you failed at the end of the day and at the beginning of the new day.

c. At the end of the day, all of the day's experiences are filed away. You can put the good and bad experiences of the day behind you and start fresh the next day.

d. Some days will be filled with good experiences and some days will be filled with bad experiences.

_____ 12. In "Right Hand," what does Grandfather's hand do as it irons?

a. It becomes tired and limp, thinking only of when the work will be finished.

b. It becomes expressive and self-assured, telling stories in Grandfather's native Yiddish.

c. It becomes angry and resentful, slamming the iron down on the shirts and trousers.

d. It stiffens from the pain and exhaustion caused by too many years of hard work.

_____ 13. What two things are being compared in the following simile?

> The poems this hand had proclaimed to shirts / as it moved back and forth like a
> Greek chorus / across the stage of the ironing board—

a. the ironing board and a poem

b. Grandfather's hand and a poem

c. a Greek chorus and an ironing board

d. Grandfather's moving hand and a Greek chorus

_____ 14. In what way is Grandfather himself different from his hand?

a. Grandfather is interested in poetry while his hand is concerned mainly with the work of ironing.

b. Grandfather is energetic but his hand is stiff and sore.

c. Grandfather is reserved and quiet while his hand is expressive and self-assured.

d. Grandfather speaks only in Yiddish while the hand speaks in English.

_____ 15. Why must Grandfather put his hand in his pocket in order to use English words?

    a. His hand is tired from too much ironing.

    b. His hand represents his native Yiddish and his heritage.

    c. His hand represents his knowledge of English.

    d. Having his hand in his pocket helps him to think.

Vocabulary and Grammar

_____ 16. Which of the following is the best meaning of the word _tremulous_ as it is used in the following line from "The Wind—tapped like a tired Man"?

    His fingers, as He passed / Let go a music—as of tunes / Blown tremulous in Glass—

    a. quiet   b. trembling   c. colorful   d. agitated

_____ 17. Which of the following sentences contains an elliptical clause?

    a. I planted a lemon tree.

    b. The wind timidly entered the home.

    c. I admired his hands that moved so meaningfully.

    d. Remember the way Grandfather ironed.

_____ 18. Which of the following is the best meaning of the word _decipher_ as it is used in the following sentence?

    We stand and try to decipher the inscription on an ancient tombstone.

    a. destroy   b. create   c. translate   d. change

_____ 19. Which of the following sentences contains an elliptical clause?

    a. Do you see the tree I am describing?

    b. Grandfather carried his voice in his right hand.

    c. Think about a worker who stands alone in a manhole.

    d. Music and other sounds came from the wind.

_____ 20. Which of the following is the best meaning of the word _eloquent_ as it is used in the following sentence from "Right Hand"?

    What an eloquent hand, it broke into grins/and self-assured narration whenever it opened.

    a. enormous   b. delicate   c. expressive   d. entertaining

Essay Questions

21. How is metaphor used in the poem "Metaphor" and in the poem "Right Hand"? What comparisons are being made in the poems? How do these comparisons convey the themes of the poems? Answer these questions in an essay.

22. In an essay, describe the lifestyle advocated by the speaker in "A Pace Like That." What does the speaker want to change in his life? What images does the speaker use to illustrate the way in which he wants to approach life? In what way does the experience described in "The Wind—tapped like a tired Man" reflect a similar approach to life?

23. In an essay, discuss the theme of making choices and understanding the importance of each moment in life, as it is addressed in each of the four poems. How does each poem focus on this theme? What experience does each speaker share, and what does this experience reveal about day-to-day values and choices?

"La Belle Dame sans Merci" by John Keats
"Danny Deever" by Rudyard Kipling

Selection Test

Critical Reading

In the blank, write the letter of the one best answer.

____ 1. Which of the following statements best summarizes what Keats says in "La Belle Dame sans Merci"?
   a. Being enchanted by a beautiful lady is worth all the pain.
   b. Beauty endures even in harsh seasons and lonely times.
   c. Beauty never lasts long, and when it fades it brings sadness.
   d. Beware of magic or you will be condemned to despair.

____ 2. What aspect of "La Belle Dame sans Merci" is characteristic of narrative poetry?
   a. It deals with fantasy.
   b. It tells a story.
   c. It includes a hero.
   d. It is about nature.

____ 3. Which of the following best describes the lady in "La Belle Dame sans Merci"?
   a. caring and sympathetic
   b. generous and kind
   c. enchanting and mysterious
   d. proud and conceited

____ 4. The setting of "La Belle Dame sans Merci" reflects a world that is _____ .
   a. springlike
   b. damp
   c. dangerous
   d. lifeless

____ 5. Choose the sentence that most clearly reflects the meaning of the following stanza from "La Belle Dame sans Merci."
>   I made a garland for her head,
>   And bracelets too, and fragrant zone;
>   She looked at me as she did love,
>   And made sweet moan.
   a. I brought her flowers, and she seemed embarrassed.
   b. I gathered bouquets for her, and she rejected them.
   c. I covered her with blossoms, and she looked at me tenderly.
   d. As I offered my gifts, she looked away.

____ 6. The minor characters (the kings and princes) are significant in "La Belle Dame sans Merci" because they
   a. plan to attack the knight.
   b. are victims of the lady.
   c. will eventually rescue the knight.
   d. fail to warn the knight.

_____ 7. In "La Belle Dame sans Merci," why is the lady "without pity"?
   a. She never feeds the knight.
   b. Her songs are offensive.
   c. She never says she loves the knight.
   d. She enslaves the knight with her beauty.

_____ 8. In the end, "La Belle Dame sans Merci" is a poem about
   a. optimism and cheer.
   b. love and loneliness.
   c. despair and death.
   d. courage and valor.

_____ 9. Which of the following makes the two speakers in "Danny Deever" seem more vivid and real?
   a. They speak in dialect.
   b. They are called by their titles rather than by their names.
   c. Each man speaks the same number of lines in each stanza.
   d. They speak in rhymed lines.

_____ 10. The theme of Kipling's "Danny Deever" is that
   a. harsh justice is necessary in the military.
   b. executing a soldier leads to rebellion among his comrades.
   c. people should not be punished for crimes committed in times of stress.
   d. even military men are upset by the execution of a comrade.

_____ 11. Which character in "Danny Deever" views events as the reader does?
   a. Danny Deever
   b. the Color-Sergeant
   c. the commander of the regiment
   d. Files-on-Parade

_____ 12. "Danny Deever" creates a mood full of _____ .
   a. remorse
   b. grief
   c. rage
   d. dread

_____ 13. The fact that Files-on-Parade asks the Color-Sergeant questions throughout most of "Danny Deever" suggests that Files-on-Parade is
   a. less experienced.
   b. less sympathetic.
   c. more angry.
   d. more anxious.

_____ 14. In "Danny Deever," why is Files-on-Parade especially disturbed by Danny's execution?
   a. He too has committed crimes while in the military.
   b. He was forced to cut off Danny's buttons and stripes.
   c. He was a friend of Danny's.
   d. He was a friend of Danny's victim.

_____ 15. To what is Kipling referring in the following line from "Danny Deever"?
      'E's drinkin' bitter beer alone . . .
   a. Danny's final meal
   b. Danny's solitary agony
   c. Danny's drunken death
   d. Danny's wicked crime

_____ 16. In "Danny Deever," which of the following best reflects the soldiers' feelings toward Deever?
a. "The regiment's in column, an' they're marchin' us away . . ."
b. "For 'e shot a comrade sleepin'—you must look 'im in the face . . ."
c. "The regiment's in 'ollow square—they're hangin' him today . . ."
d. "O they're hangin' Danny Deever in the mornin'!"

Vocabulary and Grammar

_____ 17. The word *thrall* means _____ .
a. excitement
b. thrash
c. slavery
d. hilltop

_____ 18. A *sojourn* is a _____ .
a. militia
b. stay
c. trip
d. record

_____ 19. Which of the following phrases uses hyphens *correctly*?
a. a so-called friend
b. two-thousand three-hundred twenty-one
c. a highly-valued prize
d. the best-laid-plans

_____ 20. Which of the following phrases uses hyphens *incorrectly*?
a. a nearly-lost cause
b. a fifty-dollar ticket
c. a one-quarter share
d. a little-known fact

Essay Questions

21. The execution of Danny Deever takes place as the speakers and the readers "watch" the action. How do the soldiers feel about Deever's death? What clues are there in the poem that provide evidence about their emotions? Write an essay in which you discuss these clues to the other soldiers' feelings, and explain how you got them.

22. On one level, "La Belle Dame sans Merci" is a story of a knight who loves and loses a beautiful woman. On a deeper level, though, the poet is commenting on the nature of love. In an essay, analyze the poet's meaning based on the knight's experiences.

23. There are three speakers in "Danny Deever"—Files-on-Parade, the Color-Sergeant, and the unnamed narrator who says "O they're hangin' Danny Deever in the mornin'!" The relationship between Files-on-Parade and the Color-Sergeant reveals itself in dialogue, but who is that third speaker? In an essay, discuss the role of the unnamed speaker of "Danny Deever." What function does that speaker perform that the other two don't, and how does that help create the poem?

"The Guitar" by Federico García Lorca
"Making a Fist" by Naomi Shihab Nye
"Jade Flower Palace" by Tu Fu
"The Moon at the Fortified Pass" by Li Po
"What Are Friends For" by Rosellen Brown
"Some Like Poetry" by Wisława Szymborska

Selection Test

Critical Reading

In the blank, write the letter of the one best answer.

____ 1. The speaker of "The Guitar" makes a direct comparison between the guitar
and _____ .
a. a singer
b. camellias
c. a wounded heart
d. snow

____ 2. Which word best describes the speaker's feelings in the following lines from "The
Guitar"?
It mourns the arrow without a target,
The evening without morning.
And the first bird dead
Upon a branch.
a. angry
b. regretful
c. disillusioned
d. sorrowful

____ 3. The preceding lines from "The Guitar" should be read as how many sentences?
a. one
b. two
c. three
d. four

____ 4. Naomi Shihab Nye's "Making a Fist" is about
a. trying to communicate with parents.
b. learning to establish independence.
c. trying to overcome a fear of death.
d. experiencing the difficulty of going to a strange place.

____ 5. What does the following, final line from "Making a Fist" suggest?
. . . clenching and opening one small hand.
a. Survival is a series of struggles.
b. The speaker is angry with her mother.
c. The speaker is now on the verge of death.
d. People stop growing and changing when they become adults.

© Prentice-Hall, Inc.

_____ 6. A central idea of "Jade Flower Palace" is that
   a. people everywhere are cruel to each other for no good reason.
   b. the ravages of time cannot fully erase the beauty of great palaces.
   c. the gold and glory of ancient princes are worthy of serious poetry.
   d. no matter how hard people hope or plan, they cannot control the future.

_____ 7. What makes the speaker of "Jade Flower Palace" so sad is the contrast between
   a. the beauty of the surrounding woods and the ugliness of the palace ruins.
   b. the prince's hopes for his palace and its current decayed state.
   c. the prince's wealth and power and the speaker's poverty.
   d. what he used to think of the prince and what he knows about him now.

_____ 8. After which word does the first stop occur in the following lines from "Jade Flower Palace"?

> The shattered pavements are all
> Washed away. Ten thousand organ
> Pipes whistle and roar. . . .

   a. all
   b. away
   c. organ
   d. roar

_____ 9. In "The Moon at the Fortified Pass," soldiers gazing at the moon think about
   _____ .
   a. battle
   b. enemies
   c. home
   d. sleep

_____ 10. The tone the poet uses in "The Moon at the Fortified Pass" is best described as
   a. grim and foreboding.
   b. bold and daring.
   c. gentle and loving.
   d. calm and expectant.

_____ 11. Unlike the speaker of "What Are Friends For," the mother in the poem
   a. cherishes her friendships.
   b. considers friendship an unwanted obligation.
   c. thinks of little ways to please her friends.
   d. has few friends.

_____ 12. Which words best summarize the speaker's feelings about friends in "What Are Friends For"?
   a. patient and kind
   b. excited and open
   c. grateful and accepting
   d. disappointed and bitter

_____ 13. The following lines from "What Are Friends For" contain how many stops or pauses?

> What are friends for, my mother asks.
> A duty undone, visit missed,
> casserole unbaked for sick Jane.

   a. two
   b. three
   c. four
   d. five

____ 14. In "Some Like Poetry," what effect is created by the repetition of the phrase "one likes"?
a. It helps the reader understand poetry.
b. It creates an intimate tone.
c. It makes poetry seem intangible.
d. It demonstrates that the word *like* cannot adequately express the speaker's feelings.

____ 15. What are the speaker's feelings about poetry?
a. She knows it is vital to her, even though few people think it is important.
b. She counts it among the many things she likes, such as chicken-noodle soup.
c. She thinks it is suitable only for students and poets.
d. She wishes more people liked it.

Vocabulary and Grammar

____ 16. If you read the poem *monotonously*, the audience will become _____.
a. enthusiastic   b. bored   c. confused   d. emotional

____ 17. The sight of a _____ might generate *pathos*.
a. parade   b. battle   c. funeral procession   d. palace

____ 18. The soldiers' *wistful* eyes in "The Moon at the Fortified Pass" might
a. blink back tears.
b. shine happily.
c. narrow in anger.
d. bulge in fear.

____ 19. Which sentence clearly conveys that Tom does not like any other kind of soup in the evening?
a. Only Tom likes chicken-noodle soup in the evening.
b. Tom likes only chicken-noodle soup in the evening.
c. Tom only likes chicken-noodle soup in the evening.
d. Tom likes chicken noodle-soup only in the evening.

____ 20. Where should the word *only* be placed in the following sentence in order to convey that no one besides Mother baked a casserole?
    Mother baked a casserole for sick Jane.
a. after *Jane*   c. between *baked* and *casserole*
b. between *mother* and *baked*   d. before *Mother*

Essay Questions

21. In an essay, explain how reading in sentences helps you understand two of the poems in this selection. Provide three examples from each poem to support your points.

22. The speakers in these lyric poems explore timeless themes, such as loss, death, war, and friendship. In an essay, explain which speaker moves you most strongly, the chief emotion the speaker expresses, and what poetic devices create this effect. Support your opinion with evidence from the poem.

23. Originally meant to be sung or read while a lyre was played, lyric poetry is known for its musical quality. Write an essay in which you explore the musical nature of lyric poetry. Use at least three examples from the poems in this selection to support your opinion.

Unit 9: Poetry

Name _____ Date _____

Sonnet 18 by William Shakespeare
"The Waking" by Theodore Roethke
Tanka by Ki no Tsurayuki and Priest Jakuren
Haiku by Matsuo Bashō and Kobayashi Issa

Selection Test

Critical Reading

In the blank, write the letter of the one best answer.

_____ 1. Sonnet 18 by William Shakespeare is mostly about
    a. the many beauties of summer.
    b. a loved woman's death.
    c. a poet's celebration of his beloved.
    d. the fact that love can be disappointing.

_____ 2. In Sonnet 18, what do we learn about the poet's beloved?
    a. We learn that she has a fair complexion and gold hair.
    b. We learn that she looks much younger than she really is.
    c. We learn little about her appearance but find out that she has a mild temper.
    d. We learn very little except that she is very attractive.

_____ 3. In describing the characteristics of a Shakespearean sonnet, which of the following is *incorrect*?
    a. fourteen-line poem
    b. written in iambic pentameter
    c. contains three quatrains
    d. consists of five unrhymed lines

_____ 4. According to Shakespeare, Death can be defeated by _____ .
    a. religion
    b. art
    c. science
    d. nature

_____ 5. What is the tone of the couplet at the end of Sonnet 18?
    a. questioning
    b. confident
    c. fearful
    d. melancholy

_____ 6. In "The Waking," what "climbs up a winding stair"?
    a. a worm
    b. a rat
    c. a plover
    d. the poet

_____ 7. The images of nature in "The Waking" connect to the poet's meaning by
    a. symbolizing the connection between life and death.
    b. creating a warm, inviting mood.
    c. appealing to the senses.
    d. explaining the metaphor for waking.

____ 8. What characteristic of a villanelle is demonstrated in the following stanza from "The Waking"?

> I wake to sleep, and take my waking slow.
> I feel my fate in what I cannot fear.
> I learn by going where I have to go.

a. an unrhymed poem of three lines of 5-7-5 syllables
b. a quatrain with an *abab* rhyme scheme
c. a simple image from nature
d. two refrain lines that appear in the first and third line of the first stanza

____ 9. In Tsurayuki's tanka, what season is it when the speaker goes to visit the girl he loves?

a. winter
b. spring
c. summer
d. autumn

____ 10. What does the image of the cold, blowing river imply about the connection between the girl and the speaker in the tanka by Tsurayuki?

a. The girl does not expect the speaker's visit.
b. The speaker cannot cross the cold river to visit the girl.
c. The speaker's love for the girl is not returned.
d. The speaker will brave even the harshest weather to be with the girl he loves.

____ 11. Envisioning the image of the cypress-mountain in Priest Jakuren's tanka helps the reader

a. feel lonely.
b. understand the speaker's feelings about loneliness.
c. find the mountain on a map.
d. identify the poem as a tanka.

____ 12. What feeling does the speaker of Issa's haiku express about the rat lapping at the river?

a. appreciation
b. disgust
c. surprise
d. fear

____ 13. The dominant mood created by Bashō's haiku is best described as _____ .

a. sad
b. meditative
c. joyful
d. regretful

____ 14. Basho's poem is a more exact example of haiku than Issa's because

a. it contains three unrhymed lines.
b. it includes an image of nature.
c. its lines have five, seven, and five syllables.
d. Bashō wrote more haiku than Issa.

____ 15. The images in the haiku appeal most strongly to the senses of

a. touch and smell.
b. smell and hearing.
c. sound and touch.
d. sight and sound.

Vocabulary and Grammar

For questions 16 and 17, choose the word or phrase that is most nearly *opposite* in meaning.

____ 16. temperate
   a. controlled
   b. extreme
   c. unpleasant
   d. stubborn

____ 17. lunar
   a. earthen
   b. polar
   c. solar
   d. aquatic

____ 18. Which of the three-word groupings below correctly completes the following sentence?

   I noticed when reading the _____ Haikus that both have _____ do with water falling _____ earth.

   a. two, to, too
   b. too, too, to
   c. to, too, too
   d. two, to, to

____ 19. Which word pair below correctly completes the following sentence?

   Summer days are sometimes _____ hot, but that doesn't bother me _____ much.

   a. too, too
   b. too, to
   c. to, too
   d. to, to

____ 20. Which of the following sentences contains an example of *two, to,* or *too* meaning *excessively?*
   a. Shall I compare thee to a summer's day?
   b. So long lives this, and this gives life to thee.
   c. Summer's lease hath all too short a date . . .
   d. When in eternal lines to time thou grow'st . . .

Essay Questions

21. The haiku and tanka in this selection are rich with imagery. How does envisioning the imagery help you understand these poems? In a brief essay, describe the imagery you envision for one haiku and one tanka. Then explain what this strategy helps you discover about each poem.

22. Writing a poem requires more than just adhering to a particular poetic form. Given the poems in this selection, which poem do you believe is most compelling, both in its formal requirements and in its content? Explain your choice in a brief essay. Support your opinion with specific examples from the poem.

23. In addition to poetic devices such as imagery and diction, a poem's form can help a poet express meaning. Write a brief essay in which you analyze how form relates to content in either Sonnet 18 or "The Waking." Pay particular attention to the poetic form's requirements for rhyme scheme and stanza structure, length, and content.

Unit Test: Poetry

Critical Reading

In the blank, write the letter of the one best answer.

The following poem, "The Splendor Falls," by Alfred, Lord Tennyson, is one of several poems written as a musical interlude within Tennyson's long, narrative poem The Princess. The Princess *tells the story of a prince who tries to marry Princess Ida, the daughter of a neighboring king, despite the fact that the princess has renounced marriage.*

The Splendor Falls

The splendor falls on castle walls / And snowy summits old in story; / The long light shakes across the lakes, / And the wild cataract[1] leaps in glory. / Blow, bugle, blow, set the wild echoes flying, / Blow, bugle; answer, echoes, dying, dying, dying. /

O, hark, O, hear! how thin and clear, / And thinner, clearer, farther going! / O, sweet and far from cliff and scar[2] / The horns of Elfland[3] faintly blowing! / Blow, let us hear the purple glens replying, / Blow, bugle; answer, echoes, dying, dying, dying. /

Oh love, they die in yon rich sky, / They faint on hill or field or river; / Our echoes roll from soul to soul, / And grow forever and forever. / Blow, bugle, blow, set the wild echoes flying, / And answer, echoes, answer, dying, dying, dying.

____ 1. According to the speaker, what has splendor?
   a. castle walls and snowy summits
   b. horns and bugles
   c. wild echoes
   d. purple glens

____ 2. Why might snowy summits be "old in story"?
   a. People walk to the top of the summits and tell stories.
   b. They are featured in many old stories.
   c. They have existed for many years.
   d. They are old and boring.

____ 3. Which of the following lines uses alliteration?
   a. The horns of Elfland faintly blowing!
   b. The long light shakes across the lakes . . .
   c. And the wild cataract leaps in glory.
   d. And thinner, clearer, farther going!

____ 4. What does the sound of the repeated phrase "dying, dying, dying" suggest?
   a. light
   b. snowy summits
   c. the death of trees
   d. the fading echo of a bugle

[1] waterfall
[2] steep, rocky place
[3] Fairyland

_____ 5. Which of the following lines features an example of personification?
   a. The splendor falls on castle walls . . .
   b. Blow, let us hear the purple glens replying . . .
   c. O, hark, O, hear! how thin and clear . . .
   d. And thinner, clearer, farther going!

_____ 6. Who or what is the speaker addressing in the following lines from the poem:
   O love, they die in yon rich sky, / They faint on hill or field or river; / Our echoes roll from soul to soul, / And grow forever and forever.

   a. the horns of Elfland
   b. nature
   c. a person the speaker loves
   d. the wild echoes

_____ 7. Which of the following images helps readers to understand the feelings of the speaker toward the object of his love?
   a. Blow, bugle, blow, set the wild echoes flying,/Blow bugle; answer, echoes, dying, dying, dying.
   b. Our echoes roll from soul to soul,/And grow forever and forever.
   c. Blow, let us hear the purple glens replying . . .
   d. They faint on hill or field or river!

_____ 8. How might you best describe the attitude of the speaker throughout the poem?
   a. emotional
   b. sad
   c. distant
   d. fearful

_____ 9. Which of the following helps readers to envision the beauty of the landscape by appealing to their sense of sight?
   a. O, hark, O, hear! how thin and clear,/And thinner, clearer, farther going!
   b. Blow, bugle, blow, set the wild echoes flying . . .
   c. The long light shakes across the lakes,/And the wild cataract leaps in glory.
   d. The horns of Elfland faintly blowing!

_____ 10. "The Splendor Falls" is most accurately classified as a _____.
   a. narrative poem
   b. lyric poem
   c. dramatic poem
   d. haiku

Vocabulary and Grammar

The questions below consist of a related pair of words in CAPITAL LETTERS followed by four lettered pairs of words. Choose the pair that best expresses a relationship _similar_ to that of the pair in capital letters.

_____ 11. MILLENNIAL : TIME ::
   a. inch : ruler
   b. annual : yearly
   c. enormous : size
   d. time : clock

_____ 12. ELOQUENT : EXPRESSIVE ::
   a. beauty : charm
   b. magnificent : impressive
   c. express : declare
   d. movement : motion

In the blank, write the letter of the one best answer.

____ 13. Which word pair below correctly completes the following sentence?

The villagers whispered excitedly _____ themselves as they traveled _____ their homes and the sacred dance circle.

a. between, between
b. between, among

c. among, between
d. among, among

____ 14. Which word pair below correctly completes the following sentence?

_____ is a leafy island near Sleuth Wood where the fairies have hidden _____ vats full of berries.

a. Their, they're
b. There, their

c. There, there
d. They're, their

____ 15. What is the best definition of the word *decipher* as it is used in the following sentence?

At what pace do you decipher the inscription on an ancient tombstone?

a. write
b. cover
c. translate
d. recite

____ 16. What is the meaning of the following sentence?

Jade likes only the poetry of Naomi Shihab Nye.

a. Jade doesn't like poetry by any other author.
b. Jade doesn't like anything else by that author.
c. Only Jade likes poetry by that author.
d. The meaning is unclear.

Choose the word that best completes each sentence.

____ 17. Many people do not know Grandfather well because of his _____ nature.

a. tremulous
b. guttural
c. eloquent
d. taciturn

____ 18. The soldiers' _____ glances revealed their homesickness.

a. wistful
b. tremulous
c. abysmal
d. temperate

____ 19. Which words below correctly complete the following sentence?

Imagining the speaker's journey _____ Cypress-Mountain, in Priest Jakuren's tanka, helps you _____ understand his feelings about loneliness.

a. to, two
b. too, to

c. to, too
d. to, to

____ 20. Which words below correctly complete the following sentence?

Through his words _____ his beloved in Shakespeare's Sonnet 18, the speaker is able _____ capture her beauty so that others may appreciate it _____.

a. to, to, too
b. to, to, to

c. to, to, two
d. to, too, to

Essay Questions

21. The poems in this unit present a variety of vivid images. In reading these poems, you were able to picture a quiet graveyard for lost soldiers, a frightening sea monster, and many different portraits of people and nature. What two images from poems in this unit did you find most striking? Write an essay in which you describe these images, and explain why you found them so effective.

22. Poets often draw their inspiration from the beautiful and unique aspects of nature. Poets who focus on nature often help readers to view the ordinary sights and sounds of nature in different ways. For example, think about Shakespeare's Sonnet 18, Roethke's "The Waking," Dickinson's "The Wind—tapped like a tired Man," or each tanka and haiku in the unit. Write an essay about two poems from the unit that focus on images of nature. What are these poems about? How does each help you view an aspect of nature in a different way?

23. Many poets featured in this unit use musical devices such as alliteration, onomatopoeia, assonance, consonance, repetition, meter, and rhyme to create certain effects in their poems. The sounds these devices create often help to enhance a poem's meaning. In an essay, describe how musical devices are used in one poem from this unit. For example, you might choose "In Flanders Fields," "Reapers," "Prayer of First Dancers," or Sonnet 18. What effect does a single musical device or many different devices create in this poem? How does the sound of the poem help to enhance meaning? Explain.

24. Many of the poems in this unit deal with the choices people make in dealing with the world. For example, think about the poems "The Stolen Child," "Metaphor," "A Pace Like That," "Right Hand," or "The Waking." Choose two poems from the unit that describe choices or express attitudes with which you can relate. Write an essay about these poems, identifying their main ideas and describing why you found them effective. What images help you to understand the poet's meaning in each poem?

25. As you read the poems in this unit, you probably noticed that some poems tell complete stories, while others focus on single incidents and experiences and the feelings of the poem's speaker. In an essay, define and then compare and contrast lyric poetry, narrative poetry, and dramatic poetry. In writing your essay, refer to specific poems in this unit.

from *Don Quixote* by Miguel de Cervantes

Selection Test

Critical Reading

On the line, write the letter of the one best answer.

_____ 1. Much of the humor in Don Quixote comes from the fact that Don Quixote sees him-self as a _____ .
a. writer
b. historian
c. squire
d. knight

_____ 2. According to the narrator, Don Quixote lost his mind as a result of
a. reading too many books of chivalry.
b. facing too many daring adventures.
c. falling victim to a sage's evil spell.
d. giving his heart to unrequited love.

_____ 3. How does Don Quixote afford his huge reading habit?
a. by working as a knight
b. by leasing out his horse
c. by selling some land
d. by writing stories of knighthood

_____ 4. Don Quixote can best be described as a _____ .
a. wanderer
b. dreamer
c. lover
d. scholar

_____ 5. Don Quixote, the priest, and the barber argue about
a. which of several knights was the greatest.
b. how a man could become a knight.
c. how a knight could serve his God and his country.
d. what attire a knight should wear.

_____ 6. La Mancha is the name of Don Quixote's _____ .
a. grandfather
b. king
c. nation
d. town

_____ 7. To Don Quixote's thinking, the name Rocinante was
a. silly and pompous.
b. foreign and awkward.
c. lofty and sonorous.
d. ancient and mysterious.

_____ 8. To Don Quixote, a knight without love is like a
a. horse without a knight.
b. squire without a knight.
c. body without a soul.
d. house without a fireplace.

_____ 9. What does Don Quixote's speech comically imitate?
   a. the language of nobles and government officials near La Mancha
   b. ornate language in books of chivalry
   c. the language of the country people of Cervantes' time
   d. the speech of scholars and priests

_____ 10. Why is Don Quixote so concerned about the wounds of Don Belianis and who the greatest knight was?
   a. because he believes the old tales to be true
   b. because the barber disagrees with him
   c. because Sancho does not understand the rules of combat
   d. because he is concerned for their well-being

_____ 11. Don Quixote expresses admiration for the "lucidity of style" of the old romances. As an example, he quotes "the reason of the unreason with which my reason is afflicted so weakens my reason that with reason I complain of your beauty." What is comic about this passage?
   a. The passage is so unclear it is almost impossible to grasp.
   b. Don Quixote has already lost his sense of reason.
   c. His desired lady, Aldonza Lorenzo, possesses no real beauty.
   d. It is about Rocinante.

_____ 12. Before combat, Sancho points out the true nature of the windmills. Quixote responds, "It is easy to see that you are not used to this business of adventures." Why does Quixote say this?
   a. Quixote is trying to quell Sancho's fear of giants.
   b. Quixote hopes to educate Sancho about the ways of chivalry.
   c. Quixote knows they are really windmills.
   d. Quixote sees only what he wants to see.

_____ 13. What does Sancho Panza do after Don Quixote jousts with windmills?
   a. He fusses over Don Quixote's wounds.
   b. He worries about the evil sage.
   c. He eats his dinner.
   d. He calls the priest for help.

_____ 14. When Don Quixote discovers that he has been fighting a windmill, he blames this on
   a. his squire's poor eyesight.
   b. his enthusiasm distorting his vision.
   c. the bad advice of the barber of La Mancha.
   d. the ill will of Sage Freston.

_____ 15. After the battle with the windmills, at what contrast between himself and Sancho does Quixote laugh?
   a. Quixote belatedly realizes what Sancho knew all along.
   b. Knights-errant may not complain of wounds but squires may.
   c. The two travelers' different manner of dress amuses Quixote.
   d. Sancho's speech is so inelegant compared to Quixote's.

Vocabulary and Grammar

_____ 16. A meeting that is _interminable_ seems _____ .
   a. hostile
   b. endless
   c. ridiculous
   d. over

_____ 17. A person who is *affable* is _____ .
   a. prosperous
   b. optimistic
   c. friendly
   d. idle

_____ 18. Something *requisite* is _____ .
   a. beautiful
   b. necessary
   c. annoying
   d. returned

_____ 19. Which words in the following sentence should begin with a capital letter?
   Don quixote tells a story to his squire about a spanish knight named diego de vargas.
   a. quixote, squire, spanish, knight, vargas   c. quixote, squire, spanish, diego, vargas
   b. quixote, squire, knight, diego, vargas   d. quixote, spanish, diego, vargas

_____ 20. Which sentence contains an error in capitalization?
   1. Cervantes writes that Don Quixote ate bacon and eggs on Saturdays, lentils on Fridays, and pigeon on Sundays.
   2. Cervantes writes that Don Quixote believes that the Knight of the Burning Sword is a better warrior than the Cid Ruy Diaz.
   3. The footnote explains that the Cid Ruy Diaz was a famous Spanish soldier; Cid being a derivation of the arabic word for *lord*.
   4. Cervantes writes that Don Quixote loved his lady Dulcinea with all his heart.

Essay Questions

21. Don Quixote is a fool in many respects. His speech is ridiculous, his ideas are hopelessly out of fashion, and he has lost touch with reality. Yet readers admire him and know immediately he is the hero of the story. In an essay, analyze how Cervantes makes us admire Don Quixote. Give examples from the selection to illustrate your ideas.

22. One of the techniques Cervantes uses throughout *Don Quixote* is to set up comparisons between Sancho and Quixote as they travel through the land. Write an essay that compares and contrasts the attitudes and points of view of these two characters and show what the contrast indicates about Cervantes' themes.

23. In an essay, analyze the narrator of *Don Quixote*. Explain who this person seems to be, and how his style of telling the tale contributes to the effect of *Don Quixote*.

Name _____ Date _____

"Morte d'Arthur" by Alfred, Lord Tennyson
"Arthur Becomes King of Britain" from *The Once and Future King*
by T. H. White

Selection Test

Critical Reading

On the line, write the letter of the one best answer.

_____ 1. The central conflict in "Morte d'Arthur" is the one between
    a. King Arthur and his conscience.   c. Francis and Everard.
    b. Sir Bedivere and the three queens. d. Sir Bedivere and King Arthur.

_____ 2. In "Morte d'Arthur," Arthur sends Bedivere to cast Excalibur into the lake. Then
    Arthur asks Bedivere what he has seen. Why does Arthur ask this question?
    a. He wants to know where the sword landed.
    b. He suspects there are enemies nearby.
    c. Arthur knows that a hand will rise up to receive the sword.
    d. In his weakness, he has forgotten what he asked Bedivere to do.

_____ 3. What do the following lines from "Morte d'Arthur" reveal about Arthur?
        Thou wouldst betray me for the precious hilt:
        Either from lust of gold, or like a girl
        Valuing the giddy pleasure of the eyes.
    a. He is aware of the sword's value and wants no one else to possess it.
    b. He knows Bedivere is greedy and likely to steal the sword.
    c. He knows Bedivere is a liar and isn't really a loyal knight.
    d. He suspects Bedivere's reason for not throwing the sword into the lake.

_____ 4. In "Morte d'Arthur," what keeps Sir Bedivere from throwing Excalibur into the lake?
    a. misunderstanding Arthur's wishes c. honor for King Arthur's memory
    b. greed for the jeweled gold hilt   d. disloyalty to Arthur

_____ 5. Which of the following passages from "Morte d'Arthur" reveals Tennyson's values
    about truth, as demonstrated through a character's words or actions?
    a. "Though Merlin sware that I should come again
        To rule once more—but let what will be be, . . ."
    b. "This is a shameful thing for men to lie."
    c. "What record, or what relic of my lord
        Should be to aftertime, but empty breath
        And rumors of a doubt? . . ."
    d. "The old order changeth, yielding place to new, . . ."

_____ 6. In "Morte d'Arthur," how does Arthur comfort Sir Bedivere in Arthur's final moments?
    a. He assures Bedivere that they will meet again.
    b. He tells Bedivere to continue leading a noble life.
    c. He asks Bedivere to believe in the power of prayer.
    d. He expresses curiosity about the afterlife.

_____ 7. In "Morte d'Arthur," what attitude about worldly riches does Tennyson reveal
    through Bedivere's actions and Arthur's responses?
    a. Anyone can be tempted by riches, but there are more important things.
    b. One should hold on to worldly goods as long as possible.
    c. It is best to throw away items of value.
    d. All riches are bad and should be avoided at all cost.

_____ 8. What do these lines from "Morte d'Arthur" reveal about Tennyson's attitude?

> And so to bed, where yet in sleep I seemed
> To sail with Arthur under looming shores,
> Point after point; till on to dawn, when dreams
> Begin to feel the truth and stir of day,
> To me, methought, who waited with the crowd,
> There came a bark that, blowing forward, bore
> King Arthur; like a modern gentleman
> Of stateliest port; and all the people cried,
> "Arthur is come again: he cannot die."

    a. Tennyson believes in dreams coming true.
    b. Tennyson views the Arthur legend as a lasting one.
    c. Tennyson thinks the narrator is easily influenced by a little storytelling.
    d. Tennyson believes Arthur never actually died.

_____ 9. How does the preceding passage from "Morte d'Arthur" express the notion that the legend will continue?
    a. It depicts a person telling the story to his friends.
    b. It repeats the part about Arthur being on a boat.
    c. It shows the narrator reliving Arthur's death scene.
    d. It depicts the narrator dreaming about Arthur's return.

_____ 10. In "Arthur Becomes King of Britain," why is the death of the old king especially significant?
    a. He died without an heir.
    b. He left a country torn apart by war.
    c. Foreign invaders are likely to take over the countryside.
    d. He didn't pull the sword out of the anvil before he died.

_____ 11. How does Wart, in "Arthur Becomes King of Britain," come upon the sword in the churchyard?
    a. He gets lost on the way to the arena.
    b. He is determined to find a sword for Kay and happens to pass by.
    c. He sets out purposely to find the sword in the stone.
    d. All of the animals from Merlyn's teachings help him.

_____ 12. In "Arthur Becomes King of Britain," why is the disappearance of Merlyn significant in the legend?
    a. It clears the way for Wart to become king.
    b. It removes a minor character from the story.
    c. It introduces the idea of magic to the story.
    d. It provides a comic tone for the story.

_____ 13. In "Arthur Becomes King of Britain," what does Merlyn represent in the legend?
    a. the inabilty of Arthur to make decisions
    b. the weakness of Arthur as a leader
    c. the magic that plays an important role in Arthur's life
    d. the religion that is more important than magic

_____ 14. In "Arthur Becomes King of Britain," what might be inferred when Wart says, "I feel strange when I have hold of this sword, and I notice everything much more clearly"?
    a. The sword provides Wart with magical powers.
    b. Wart has become delirious from touching the sword.
    c. Wart realizes that the sword has made him king.
    d. Wart will be able to joust in the tournament.

15. What does the following dialogue reveal about White's attitude toward his subject in "Arthur Becomes King of Britain"?

> "I don't know what the Church is coming to," said Sir Grummore.
> "It's in an anvil," explained the King.
> "The Church?"
> "No, the sword."

   a. He is unhappy over the Church's decline.   c. He is impatient with people's ignorance.
   b. He is critical of the disrespect shown him.   d. He is playful and humorous.

16. "Arthur Becomes King of Britain" is chiefly about
   a. mourning the death of Uther the Conqueror.   c. discovering an unknown identity.
   b. the disappearance of Merlyn.   d. being competitive at a tournament.

Vocabulary and Grammar

17. How would you correct the punctuation in the following passage?

> "Yes, and you will carry my shield and spears for the jousts, and I shall win the palm
> of everybody and be a great knight!"
> "Well, I am glad we are going," said the Wart, "for Merlyn is leaving us too".

   a. Move the commas outside the final quotation marks.
   b. Move the period inside the final quotation mark.
   c. Move the exclamation mark outside the final quotation marks.
   d. No correction is needed.

18. Which of the following punctuation rules are *not* correct?

   I. Always place a comma or a period inside the final quotation mark.

   II. Always place a semicolon or colon outside the final quotation mark.

   III. Place a question mark or exclamation mark inside the final quotation mark if the end mark is not part of the quotation.

   IV. Place a question mark or exclamation mark outside the final quotation mark if the end mark is part of the quotation.
   a. I and II   b. II and III   c. III and IV   d. I and IV

19. The three queens on the barge send up a cry that is "an agony of lamentation."
    Lamentation means _____ .
   a. mourning   b. anger   c. fear   d. revenge

20. Kay's *sumptuous* bath could also be described as
   a. cleansing and soothing.   c. warm and bubbly.
   b. necessary and required.   d. elaborate and luxurious.

Essay Questions

21. In an essay, compare and contrast the qualities of Kay and the Wart in "Arthur Becomes King of Britain." Cite specific examples of their behavior in the story. Which would you prefer to have as a friend? Explain your answer.

22. In Tennyson's epic poem, "Morte d'Arthur," Bedivere is reluctant to follow the dying Arthur's instructions. In an essay, explain what Bedivere does instead, and list the reasons he gives for not obeying Arthur. Was he justified in not obeying Arthur? Why or why not? What would you have done in Bedivere's place? Explain why.

23. In "Arthur Becomes King of Britain," Arthur fights many battles against men who don't believe in his claim to the throne. Tired of fighting, Arthur wonders whether there is a way to "harness Might so that it works for Right." In an essay, explain what you think this statement means. Then apply the statement to the Arthur described by Tennyson in "Morte d'Arthur."

Name _____ Date _____

"Rama's Initiation" from the *Ramayana* by R. K. Narayan

Selection Test

Critical Reading

On the line, write the letter of the one best answer.

_____ 1. The story is mostly about Rama's initiation into a life of
    a. searching for mystery and wonder.
    b. casting enchantment and spells.
    c. destroying evil and disorder.
    d. ruling a huge empire.

_____ 2. Sage Viswamithra was once a(n) _____ .
    a. asura
    b. hermit
    c. guard
    d. king

_____ 3. What can be inferred from Dasaratha's comment that Rama is "still learning the arts and practicing the use of arms"?
    a. Training in the arts and arms was valued in a future ruler.
    b. Rama is a skilled fighter.
    c. Only royalty received training in the arts and the use of arms.
    d. Dasaratha doubts that Viswamithra can continue Rama's education.

_____ 4. Why was the king reluctant to let Rama go with Sage Viswamithra?
    a. Rama was his only child.
    b. The king did not trust Viswamithra.
    c. The king had been childless for many years.
    d. Rama had no interest in weapons or in fighting.

_____ 5. What valuable quality does Vasishtha demonstrate when he runs after Viswamithra?
    a. humility
    b. respect for the divine
    c. courage
    d. forgiveness of others

_____ 6. Viswamithra's insistence that Rama accompany him demonstrates that an epic hero must
    a. learn from a sage.
    b. be forced to leave home.
    c. be a young boy.
    d. be approved by the gods.

_____ 7. Viswamithra helped his two disciples through the arid desert by
    a. telling them a story.
    b. singing a song that cooled and refreshed them.
    c. transmitting two mantras.
    d. chanting a prayer.

_____ 8. Given the details about Viswamithra, one can infer that in Indian culture sages
    a. were misunderstood.
    b. had little patience with kings.
    c. battled the gods.
    d. were highly respected.

_____ 9. What can be inferred about Hindu divinities from details such as Indra is the god of rain and Yama is the god of death?
    a. All Hindu divinities are male.
    b. Hindu divinities are closely linked to natural forces.
    c. Hindu divinities often come in contact with humans.
    d. Rama received the blessing of the gods.

_____ 10. Thataka may be seen as a symbol of
    a. evil and disorder.
    b. starvation and thirst.
    c. justice and kindness.
    d. goodness and harmony.

_____ 11. Which quality of an epic hero does Rama demonstrate by killing Thataka?
    a. bravery
    b. strength
    c. control
    d. kindness

_____ 12. Which word best describes the selection's tone?
    a. scholarly
    b. objective
    c. intimate
    d. adventurous

_____ 13. What initial step toward becoming an epic hero does Rama make in this selection?
    a. He makes a solo journey.
    b. He separates himself from his family.
    c. He rescues a person in distress.
    d. He sets out on a quest for self-knowledge.

_____ 14. The theme of this selection is best summarized as
    a. the triumph of good over evil.
    b. the superiority of youth over old age.
    c. the tension between political and spiritual forces.
    d. the contrast between wisdom and inexperience.

Vocabulary and Grammar

_____ 15. Grieving the loss of his son, Dasaratha shows little _____ for Rama's _____ mission.
    a. decrepitude; diminutive
    b. austerities; esoteric
    c. exuberance; sublime
    d. obeisance; secular

_____ 16. Rama demonstrates heroic qualities by mastering the _____ techniques of weaponry.
    a. sublime
    b. august
    c. diminutive
    d. esoteric

____ 17. Giving away material possessions and forgoing personal pleasures are examples of _____.
    a. austerities
    b. decrepitude
    c. obeisance
    d. exuberance

____ 18. Which of the following sentences contains an introductory subordinate clause?
    a. The new assembly hall, Dasaratha's latest pride, was crowded all day with visiting dignitaries, royal emissaries, and citizens.
    b. Since they were destroyers of life, Agasthya degraded them to demonhood.
    c. The mother was left alone and lives on here, breathing fire and wishing everything ill.
    d. This Thataka is more dreadful than Yama, the god of death, who takes a life only when the time is ripe.

____ 19. Where should a comma be placed in the following sentence?
    In the story "Rama's Initiation" the demon Thataka turns all fertile land into desert.
    a. between *story* and *Rama's*   c. between *Thataka* and *turns*
    b. between *land* and *into*   d. between *Initiation* and *the*

____ 20. Which sentence contains correct punctuation?
    a. If Dasaratha would not send Rama, Viswamithra would not take anyone else.
    b. When it became dark Rama and Lakshmana rested, at a wooded grove.
    c. When Thataka heard about her husband's death, she and her sons, swore to get revenge.
    d. While fighting, with Rama Thataka threw a flaming spear.

Essay Questions

21. The epic *Ramayana* tells fantastic stories about its hero, Rama. What qualities of an epic hero does Rama exhibit in this selection? In a brief essay, explain why Rama is an epic hero. Use details from the selection to support your explanation.

22. The details of an epic, such as the *Ramayana,* often reveal much about the culture in which the story originated. Specifically, one can infer the culture's beliefs and values from an epic. Write an essay in which you make inferences about ancient Indian values, based on details from the selection.

23. How much personal choice does Rama have in becoming a hero? Is it a role in which he makes conscious decisions about his life, or is his fate decided for him by others? Explore this question in an essay, supporting your opinion with evidence from the selection.

from *Sundiata: An Epic of Old Mali* by D. T. Niane

Selection Test

Critical Reading

On the line, write the letter of the one best answer.

_____ 1. Which adjective best describes the community's attitude toward Sogolon Djata's inability to walk?
a. sympathetic
b. mocking
c. indifferent
d. fearful

_____ 2. According to the narrator, the story of Sogolon Djata's childhood illustrates that
a. kings are not born, they are made.
b. you cannot tell people's worth from the way they look.
c. the least likely people often become kings.
d. a person's destiny is determined at birth.

_____ 3. Which words best describe Sassouma Bérété, the king's first wife?
a. kind and honest
b. resentful and vengeful
c. foolish and silly
d. happy and successful

_____ 4. What is the storyteller's main purpose in detailing Sassouma's treatment of Sogolon Djata?
a. to show her belief in fate
b. to show how much she loves her own son
c. to show the error in being jealous and mocking destiny
d. to show her unhappiness with the king

_____ 5. Before his death, what present did Naré Maghan give to his son, Sogolon Djata?
a. a huge iron rod
b. a crown
c. a griot
d. a plot of land

_____ 6. Who became all-powerful right after Naré Maghan's death?
a. Sassouma Bérété, the king's first wife
b. Dankaran Touman, Sassouma's son
c. Sogolon Djata
d. Sogolon Kedjou, Sogolon Djata's mother

_____ 7. When the king asks the soothsayer about Sogolon Djata, what does the soothsayer mean when he says "great trees grow slowly but they plunge their roots deep into the ground"?
a. Sogolon Djata will best serve the people of Mali if he is put in charge of growing and protecting trees.
b. Although Sogolon Djata is developing slowly, he will someday be a great and strong king.
c. Sogolon Djata will never be effective as a king.
d. The trees of Mali are becoming bigger and stronger every day.

8. Which of the following passages from the selection best illustrates a conflict between Sogolon Djata and society?
   a. "Through your fault I have just suffered the greatest affront of my life! What have I done, God, for you to punish me in this way?"
   b. "Sogolon Kedjou and her children lived on the queen mother's leftovers."
   c. "'Take them then, since your son is unequal to mine.' Then she laughed derisively with that fierce laughter which cuts through your flesh . . ."
   d. "As men have short memories, Sogolon's son was spoken of with nothing but irony and scorn. People had seen one-eyed kings, one-armed kings, and lame kings, but a stiff-legged king had never been heard tell of."

9. Why is Sogolon Djata's response to being tormented a calm one?
   a. He knows that when the time is right, he will be king.
   b. He knows that there is nothing he can do to change public opinion.
   c. He feels depressed and powerless.
   d. He does not like anyone in the village, so nothing they say bothers him.

10. Why was the iron bar that would help Sogolon stand already made?
    a. It was a popular item in the village.
    b. It was destiny that Sogolon Djata would someday use the bar to stand and claim power.
    c. It was originally going to be given to Dankaran Touman.
    d. It was used to help Farakourou stand.

11. What effect does the conflict between Sogolon and Sassouma over baobob leaves have on the story's central conflict?
    a. Sogolon Djata decides to visit Sassouma and her son and threaten them.
    b. Sogolon decides to leave the village because it is too humiliating for her to stay.
    c. Sogolon Djata is moved to ask for the iron rod that will help him stand and get his mother a baobob tree.
    d. Sogolon Djata crawls to a baobob tree to get his mother some leaves.

12. What is the storyteller's main purpose in describing Sogolon's heroic act of standing before the people and tearing up a baobob tree?
    a. to explain Sogolon Djata's legendary rise to power
    b. to show Sogolon Djata's weakness
    c. to show the reactions of villagers
    d. to show the work of forges

13. Which was *not* a sign of Sogolon Djata's strength?
    a. He brained other three-year-olds.
    b. He fought Dankaran Touman, son of Sassouma.
    c. He picked up an iron bar.
    d. He uprooted a baobab.

14. The story is mostly about how Sogolon Djata
    a. is a source of humiliation to his mother.
    b. finally proves his right to rule.
    c. became his father's pride and joy.
    d. got back at his evil aunt.

Vocabulary and Grammar

_____ 15. Where should a semicolon be placed in the following sentence?

Sogolon's son, from *Sundiata*, was described as having a very big head he also had large eyes which opened wide each time someone visited.

a. between *son* and *from*   c. between *head* and *he*
b. between *Sundiata* and *was*   d. between *having* and *a*

_____ 16. Which of the following is the best meaning of the word *malicious* as it is used in the following line from the selection?

Malicious tongues began to blab.

a. hopeful   c. innocently curious
b. friendly   d. intentionally harmful

_____ 17. What purpose does the semicolon serve in the following sentence?

All Niani spoke of Mari Djata's infirmity; nevertheless, the king had faith in his son's destiny.

a. joins independent clauses separated by a conjunctive adverb
b. joins independent clauses not already joined by a conjunction
c. joins independent clauses separated by a transitional expression
d. avoids confusion when an independent clause already contains commas

_____ 18. Which of the following is the best meaning of the word *fathom* as it is used in the following line from the selection?

God has mysteries which none can fathom.

a. forget   b. enjoy   c. understand   d. erase

_____ 19. Which sentence shows the correct use of semicolons?

a. No matter how great the destiny promised for Mari Djata might be; the throne could not be given to someone who had no power in his legs; if the jinn loved him; let them begin by giving him the use of his legs.
b. The king's will reserved the throne for Mari Djata, however; the council of elders took no account of Naré Maghan's wishes.
c. Naré Maghan meets with Nounfaïri, the blacksmith seer of Niani; and Nounfaïri' words, along with Doua's confidence; gave the king some assurance.
d. The king believed that Mari Djata would be king, as was foretold; that Balla Fasséké, the son of Doua, would be Mari Djata's griot, just as Doua had been his own griot; and that Boukari, son of Namadjé, would be Mari Djata's right hand.

_____ 20. Which of the following is the best meaning of the word *estranged* as it is used in the following line from the selection?

Naré Maghan became imperceptibly estranged but Gnankouman Doua never ceased reminding him of the hunter's words.

a. strange; odd   b. removed from   c. angry   d. forgetful

Essay Questions

21. In an essay, explain how this selection illustrates virtues such as honor and nobility. In your analysis, describe which characters show that they honor the values and traditions of their culture and which characters do not. Support your answer with examples of their behavior.

22. In an essay, describe specific examples of conflict in the story. How are these conflicts resolved? How do the conflicts faced by Sogolon Djata make him a more effective leader? Support your answer with examples from the selection.

23. Storytellers often have many different purposes for telling a story. In an essay, explain the storyteller's main purpose for telling the story of Sundiata, any other purposes the storyteller may have, and what specific parts of the story illustrate these purposes.

Unit Test: Epics and Legends

Critical Reading

In the blank, write the letter of the one best answer.

The questions below are based on the following selection.

The following excerpt, from Edith Hamilton's book Mythology, describes a legendary incident from the early life of Hercules, one of the greatest and most powerful heroes of Greek and Roman mythology. The incident takes place after his mother Alcema puts him and his brother Iphicles to bed for the night.

One evening Alcmena gave both the children their bath and their fill of milk and laid them in their crib, caressing them and saying, "Sleep, my little ones, soul of my soul. Happy be your slumber and happy your awakening." She rocked the cradle and in a moment the babies were asleep. But at darkest midnight when all was silent in the house two great snakes came crawling into the nursery. There was a light in the room and as the two reared up above the crib, with weaving heads and flickering tongues, the children woke. Iphicles screamed and tried to get out of bed, but Hercules sat up and grasped the deadly creatures by the throat. They turned and twisted and wound their coils around his body, but he held fast. The mother heard Iphicles' screams and, calling to her husband, rushed to the nursery. There sat Hercules laughing, in each hand a long limp body . . . They were dead. All knew then that the child was destined to great things. Teiresias, the blind prophet of Thebes, told Alcmena: "I swear that many a Greek woman as she cards the wool at eventide shall sing of this your son and you who bore him. He shall be a hero of all mankind."

_____ 1. What does Hercules do when snakes crawl into his nursery?
   a. He kills the snakes with his bare hands.
   b. He screams in terror.
   c. He hides while Iphicles kills the snakes.
   d. He wishes the snakes away.

_____ 2. What is Hercules' unusual reaction to the incident in the nursery?
   a. He hands the snakes to Iphicles.
   b. He cries out in fear.
   c. He laughs and calmly holds the snakes.
   d. He places the snakes in his crib.

_____ 3. Which of the following passages best illustrates the heroic powers of Hercules?
   a. There was a light in the room and as the two reared up above the crib, with weaving heads and flickering tongues, the children woke
   b. There sat Hercules laughing, in each hand a long limp body . . .
   c. One evening Alcmena gave both the children their bath and their fill of milk and laid them in their crib . . .
   d. . . . but Hercules sat up and grasped the deadly creatures by the throat. They turned and twisted and wound their coils around his body, but he held fast.

_____ 4. What do the actions of Hercules reveal about his character?
   a. He is extremely intelligent.
   b. He is brave and strong.
   c. He cares about his family.
   d. He is filled with anger.

_____ 5. How might you describe the attitude of the family and the community toward the actions of Hercules?
   a. They are not surprised by his actions.
   b. They are angry.
   c. They are shocked and amazed.
   d. They are frightened.

_____ 6. What can you infer about the values of people in ancient Greece, based on the selection?
   a. They valued physical strength and power.
   b. They valued children.
   c. They did not value animals.
   d. They valued humorous stories.

_____ 7. In what way is this mythical story also a legend?
   a. It is a story filled with excitement.
   b. It is a story that has been passed down for generations, and it is believed to be based in fact.
   c. It is the story of a child who proves his strength to friends and family.
   d. The events of the story are unexpected.

_____ 8. Which of the following statements is the best summary of the prophet's words to Alcema?
   a. You and your son will be the subject of much gossip among people in Greece.
   b. Your son's strength will inspire people in Greece as they go about their daily chores.
   c. Many people in Greece will tell stories and sing the praises of you and your son, who is destined to be a hero.
   d. People will talk about your son, but only you will know that he is to be the hero of mankind.

_____ 9. How do the words of the prophet emphasize the idea that Hercules has the qualities of an epic hero?
   a. They reinforce the idea that Hercules' power is truly extraordinary.
   b. They reveal that people in the community will stand behind Hercules.
   c. They reveal the fact that Hercules was lucky to have survived the fight against the snakes.
   d. They emphasize the idea that Alcmena is his mother.

_____ 10. What was probably the Greeks' main purpose for repeating this story about Hercules?
   a. to inform people about snakes
   b. to inform people about the early life of an important hero
   c. to entertain people with adventure and suspense
   d. to persuade people to protect their children from snakes

Vocabulary and Grammar

In the blank, write the letter of the one best answer.

_____ 11. Place a _____ inside the final quotation mark only if it is part of the quotation.
   a. comma
   b. period
   c. question mark
   d. semicolon

____ 12. Which sentence does *not* require a semicolon?
a. Mari Djata had a head so big that he seemed unable to support it; he also had large eyes which would open wide whenever anyone entered his mother's house.
b. Sogolon had resorted to all her talent as a sorceress to give strength to her son's legs; but the rarest herbs had been useless.
c. Naré Maghan met with Nounfaïri, the blacksmith seer of Niani; and Nounfaïri's words, along with Doua's confidence, gave the king some assurance.
d. Naré Maghan had chosen Mari Djata to succeed him; nevertheless, his wishes were ignored.

____ 13. Which words in the following sentence should begin with a capital letter?
Cervantes writes about don Quixote and his role as a spanish storyteller.
a. don, spanish
b. don, role, spanish
c. don, spanish, storyteller
d. don, role, storyteller

____ 14. Which choice is the best meaning of the word *sumptuous* as it is used in the following sentence?
We approached the king's large and sumptuous palace.
a. simple
b. dark
c. magnificent
d. empty

The questions below consist of a related pair of words in CAPITAL LETTERS followed by four lettered pairs of words. Choose the pair that best expresses a relationship similar to that of the pair in capital letters.

____ 15. INTERMINABLE : TEMPORARY ::
a. endless : eternity
b. flexible : stretch
c. memorable : outstanding
d. excitable : calm

____ 16. EXUBERANCE : ENTHUSIASTIC ::
a. disturbance : disorderly
b. difference : contrast
c. conference : discussion
d. laziness : energetic

Choose the word that best completes each sentence.

____ 17. We heard their chilling cries of agony and _____.
a. affront
b. obeisance
c. lamentation
d. adulation

____ 18. Sogolon and his mother felt hurt by the _____ words of their neighbors.
a. taciturn
b. malicious
c. affable
d. veracious

_____ 19. Where should a comma be placed in the following sentence?
    In the place where Viswamithra and Rama were standing the god Shiva used to
    pray.
    a. between *god* and *Shiva*
    b. between *standing* and *the*
    c. between *Shiva* and *used*
    d. between *place* and *where*

_____ 20. Which of the following sentences contains an introductory clause?
    a. Rama will be in my care, and he will be quite well.
    b. At some time, every human being has to depart and seek his fulfillment in his own
       way.
    c. When the daughter of Suketha grew up, she married a chieftain.
    d. Under a relentless sun, all vegetation had dried and turned to dust.

Essay Questions

21. Write an essay about the character in this unit that you found most heroic. What tradi-
    tional heroic qualities does this character possess? What did you find most interesting
    about this character's experiences?

22. Many of the epics and legends in this unit focus on cultures and time periods with which
    you might be unfamiliar. As a reader, you can think of the pieces as sources from which
    you can make inferences about these different cultures. Choose a selection from the unit
    that helped you to understand a particular culture or time period. Explain what the selec-
    tion helped you to infer.

23. Sometimes storytellers told and retold certain stories to inform people of important histori-
    cal events. Other times stories were told to pass on beliefs or influence behavior in suc-
    ceeding generations. Some stories were told and retold simply because people found them
    entertaining. Choose a selection from this unit that you feel serves one of these purposes
    particularly well. Write an essay in which you identify which aspects of the piece serve a
    particular purpose.

24. The events of most epics focus on some type of epic conflict—a situation in which a hero
    struggles against obstacles and outside forces. In an essay, describe an epic conflict in one
    of the selections from the unit. Describe the conflict and how the main character of the
    piece you choose deals with this conflict.

25. In an essay, compare and contrast the actions and values of at least three main charac-
    ters from the unit. For example, you might focus on Don Quixote, King Arthur, and
    Sundiata. What do these characters have in common? In what ways do they differ?

ANSWERS

Unit 1: On the Edge

"Contents of the Dead Man's Pocket" by Jack Finney

Selection Test (p. 1)

Critical Reading/Vocabulary and Grammar

1. d 2. c 3. b 4. d 5. b 6. b 7. c 8. a 9. a
10. d 11. b 12. a 13. c 14. b 15. a 16. d
17. a 18. b 19. a 20. c

Questions are classified in these categories:
  Comprehension 1(A), 2(E), 3(E)
  Interpretation 4(A), 6(C), 7(A), 8(C), 10(E)
  Literary Analysis 11(C), 12(A), 14(E), 15(A)
  Reading Strategy 5(A), 9(E), 13(C)
  Vocabulary 16(A), 17(A), 18(A)
  Grammar Skill 19(C), 20(A)
  E = Easy, A = Average, C = Challenging

Essay Questions

Guidelines for student response:

21. (Easy) Students should conclude that Tom's values at the beginning of the story were wrapped up in ambition and "getting ahead" of the other young men who worked at his company. His wife took second place. At the end of the story, Tom leaves his desk behind and goes to join his wife. While out on the ledge he discovers that he hasn't done much of which he is proud.

22. (Average) Two questions should arise for students upon reading the first paragraph. One has to do with the nature of the memo he loads into his typewriter. The other has to do with why he has a guilty conscience. To maintain suspense, Finney keeps readers guessing as to whether Tom will fall or not. Even the title suggests to readers that Tom won't survive. Tom's thoughts cause readers to focus on his falling and inevitable death. Tom's actions go back and forth between clinging safely and teetering frantically on the ledge. Until Tom steps into the living room, readers are kept in doubt as to his fate.

23. (Challenging) Students may suggest that people examine and/or change their values under new life circumstances (job, residence, family), in new relationships,

through experiences, and so on. Students may also indicate that observing other people's values causes people to examine their own. This somewhat introspective essay should be logically organized with a clear thesis statement.

"View From the Summit" by Edmund Hillary
"The Dream Comes True" from *The Tiger of the Snows* by Tenzing Norgay

Selection Test (p. 4)

Critical Reading/Vocabulary and Grammar

1. a 2. a 3. c 4. c 5. a 6. d 7. b 8. b 9. c
10. b 11. c 12. d 13. a 14. d 15. d 16. d
17. c 18. b 19. a 20. d

Questions are classified in these categories:
  Comprehension 2(A), 7(A), 9(E)
  Interpretation 1(A), 3(C), 6(E), 8(C), 12(A)
  Literary Analysis 5(A), 10(E), 11(C), 14(C)
  Reading Strategy 4(C), 13(A), 15(A)
  Vocabulary 17(A), 18(A), 20(E)
  Grammar Skill 16(A), 19(E)
  E = Easy, A = Average, C = Challenging

Essay Questions

Guidelines for student response:

21. (Easy) Students should note that Hillary is primarily concerned with documenting his achievement. He describes the view, but it is, in part, with an eye toward his next adventure. Norgay describes the view quite thoroughly and speaks of his great love for mountains. Conclusions about the men may include that Hillary is more concerned with personal achievement than with the grand view. Norgay seems to revere the mountains and to appreciate their beauty more than Hillary.

22. (Average) Some students may refer to Hillary's longer sentences and his use of more difficult words as examples of his ability to detail his climb more vividly. Other students may have found Hillary's account somewhat tedious because of that level of detail. Norgay's account is

"View From the Summit"
by Edmund Hillary
"The Dream Comes True"
from *The Tiger of the Snows*
by Tenzing Norgay *(continued)*

likely to strike students as quite readable and still engaging, though it lacks the detail of Hillary's.

23. (Challenging) Students should note that Hillary refers to Norgay's "impressive strength." Hillary also notes that Norgay sometimes takes the lead, usually at Hillary's direction. Beyond that, Hillary consistently represents himself as the leader, decision maker, and problem solver. Norgay seems to be just tagging along. Students should acknowledge that there is no way of knowing exactly what roles they played during the climb. However, given Norgay's account, Hillary's representation of their roles is certainly questionable.

"The Monkey's Paw" by W.W. Jacobs
"The Bridegroom"
by Alexander Pushkin

Selection Test (p. 7)

Critical Reading/Vocabulary and Grammar

1. d 2. b 3. b 4. c 5. a 6. b 7. a 8. c 9. d
10. a 11. d 12. c 13. a 14. b 15. d 16. b
17. d 18. a 19. c 20. b

Questions are classified in these categories:
Comprehension 1(A), 6(A), 8(A), 10(A), 11(A), 14(A)
Interpretation 2(C), 7(C), 9(C), 12(E), 13(C)
Literary Analysis 4(A), 5(E), 15(E)
Reading Strategy 3(A)
Vocabulary 17(A), 18(E)
Grammar Skill 16(A), 19(A), 20(C)
E = Easy, A = Average, C = Challenging

Essay Questions

Guidelines for student response:

21. (Easy) Students must identify two examples of foreshadowing, such as the sergeant major's discussion of fate, the first man's wish for death, the sergeant major's warning of the consequences, and the image of the monkey face in the fire.

Students must also fully explain what specific future event is foreshadowed by each of their two examples.

22. (Average) Students are likely to predict that had Natasha married the groom, her fate would have been the same as that of the young girl in the hut. Students must identify evidence to support whatever prediction they make.

23. (Challenging) Students should recognize that Mr. White realizes his son has returned not as an alive human being but as a corpse from the grave. Students may predict that had Mrs. White opened the door to welcome her son, the sight of him might have destroyed her sanity. Students should support their explanations with details from the story.

from **"A Walk to the Jetty"** from
Annie John by Jamaica Kincaid

Selection Test (p. 10)

Critical Reading/Vocabulary and Grammar

1. a 2. c 3. b 4. b 5. d 6. c 7. a 8. d 9. d
10. d 11. a 12. b 13. c 14. a 15. b 16. c
17. b

Questions are classified in these categories:
Comprehension 1(A), 7(C)
Interpretation 3(A), 4(A), 10(C), 12(C)
Literary Analysis 5(A), 6(A), 8(E)
Reading Strategy 2(C), 9(C), 11(A)
Vocabulary 16(E), 17(E)
Grammar Skill 13(A), 14(A), 15(C)
E = Easy, A = Average, C = Challenging

Essay Questions

Guidelines for student response:

18. (Easy) Students should note that "dustheap" indicates or connotes debris—items of no value or worth. Annie feels strongly that a number of her past experiences are of no value to her. Students might note that Annie's apprenticeship, which included more sweeping and fetching than sewing, did not teach Annie any valuable life or work skills. Students should also note that the scorn with which Miss Dulcie treats Annie is meant to make Annie feel worthless.

19. (Average) Students may indicate that Annie's fond experiences at the library have most prepared her for leaving home. Students should note it was at the library that Annie learned about the outside world and about the impact that ideas—such as pasteurization—have upon people's lives. Students may also note that Annie found words engaging, "just the way they looked on the page was interesting to me," long before she could read.

20. (Challenging) Students should note generally that Annie's childhood experiences have helped her become an independent thinking person who feels stifled by island life and by her mother's love and who yearns for a larger experience. Students must support their inferences with specific details. Most students will probably cite Annie's longest, most detailed flashback—that of her first walk down the road unaccompanied by someone to hold her hand. Students may see this flashback as an early metaphor for Annie's departure at the jetty. Annie has fears as she did in childhood, but she is not afraid. Although her mother's love is overbearing and stifling at times, it is her mother's love that encourages Annie to go on that first walk by herself.

"The Masque of the Red Death"
by Edgar Allan Poe

Selection Test (p. 13)

Critical Reading/Vocabulary and Grammar

1. b 2. d 3. c 4. c 5. a 6. d 7. a 8. d 9. c
10. b 11. d 12. b 13. c 14. a 15. c 16. d
17. b

Questions are classified in these categories:
   Comprehension 1(E), 10(A), 12(A)
   Interpretation 3(C), 4(A), 11(A)
   Literary Analysis 2(A), 6(A), 7(C)
   Reading Strategy 5(A), 8(C), 9(E)
   Vocabulary 13(E), 15(A), 17(A)
   Grammar Skill 14(E), 16(A)
   E = Easy, A = Average, C = Challenging

Essay Questions

Guidelines for student response:

18. (Easy) Students may focus on symbols of death, such as the ebony clock, the black

room with red windows situated at the western end of the wing, and the tomb-like setting of the abbey. Students should explain that such symbols underscore the story's mood and theme.

19. (Average) Students might criticize Prospero's actions on the grounds of class—wealthy Prospero invites his friends to join him in safety after "his dominions were half depopulated." Students might defend Prospero's actions by recognizing in themselves a desire to avoid death; Prospero's actions cannot be condemned simply because they are unusual.

20. (Challenging) Students should recognize that these details reveal Prospero's obsession with obscuring the everyday and plague-ravaged world beyond the abbey walls. Such details also create the story's uneasy mood and underscore the story's theme.

"Fear" by Gabriela Mistral
"The street" by Octavio Paz
"Spring and All"
by William Carlos Williams

Selection Test (p. 16)

Critical Reading/Vocabulary and Grammar

1. c 2. d 3. a 4. c 5. d 6. b 7. a 8. c 9. b
10. b 11. b 12. c 13. d 14. b 15. d

Questions are classified in these categories:
   Comprehension 1(E), 5(A)
   Interpretation 3(A), 7(E), 11(C)
   Literary Analysis 2(A), 4(E), 10(C)
   Reading Strategy 6(A), 8(C), 9(C)
   Vocabulary 14(A), 15(A)
   Grammar Skill 12(A), 13(E)
   E = Easy, A = Average, C = Challenging

Essay Questions

Guidelines for student response:

16. (Easy) Student essays should note the lack of precise imagery in "Fear" and how its vague descriptions are in keeping with the narrator's own vague and unnamed fears. They should contrast this vagueness with the rich imagery of "Spring and All," which uses series of adjectives that appeal to the senses to create a vivid portrait of a harsh early-spring landscape.

"Fear" by Gabriela Mistral
"The street" by Octavio Paz
"Spring and All"
by William Carlos Williams (*continued*)

17. (Average) Students' essays should respond in a way that includes a comparison to or contrast with the tenacity of the life outside. The hospital serves as a reminder of illness and death, and the vegetation outside looks dead at the outset. Life may be ending in the hospital, but it is beginning again outside. Births also take place in hospitals, and the line "They enter the world naked" can also apply to people, as can several lines thereafter. Students' essays should focus on the ways that they see the plant life depicted in the rest of the poem as similar or dissimilar to the concept of human life represented by the hospital.

18. (Challenging) Students' essays should reflect an understanding that the poem's events mirror the mental activity of the speaker. Students might speculate how fear can lead the mind to become unfocused or scattered. They might note that fear permeates the unconscious and can be reflected in our dreams. Fear also can lead us to paranoid thoughts and imagined assumptions. Mental activity of this nature is inescapable, and the speaker becomes trapped in his own psychological maze.

"Two Friends" by Guy de Maupassant
"Damon and Pythias"
retold by William Russell

Selection Test (p. 19)

Critical Reading/Vocabulary and Grammar

1. b 2. d 3. b 4. c 5. d 6. d 7. b 8. a 9. d
10. c 11. b 12. a 13. c 14. b 15. a

Questions are classified in these categories:
Comprehension 1(A), 4(A), 8(A)
Interpretation 2(A), 5(C), 11(E)
Literary Analysis 7(C), 9(A), 10(C)
Reading Strategy 3(C), 6(E)
Vocabulary 12(A), 14(A)
Grammar Skill 13(A), 15(A)
E = Easy, A = Average, C = Challenging

Essay Questions

Guidelines for student response:

16. (Easy) Students should recognize the fact that Dionysius sets Damon and Pythias free because he hopes that they will be his friends and allow him to be a friend to them. Throughout the myth, Dionysius envies the friendship that Damon and Pythias share. He has been unable to develop any great friendships because of his selfishness and his streak of cruelty. Although his reasons for releasing the pair can be seen as selfish, he at least shows that he recognizes the value of friendship and the fact that he must be a friend to have friends.

17. (Average) Students should understand that Damon agrees to wait in prison for Pythias because he is unselfishly trying to help his friend. He also has complete trust in Pythias and feels certain that Pythias will return. Pythias would never consider sacrificing his friend's life for his own, despite the fact that he is being treated unfairly by Dionysius. Damon and Pythias show that they are honest and loyal, and that they value their friendship above all other things.

18. (Challenging) Students should name at least some of the following background details of war: Paris blockaded and in its "death agony"; abandoned villages and the presence of military outposts; the characters' constant awareness of the proximity of the Prussians; the descriptions of the Prussians' ruthless destruction of Paris; the sound of cannons; and the sight of "powdersmoke." These details show that the war is a constant presence and that Morissot and Sauvage are in danger, even though they try to find a brief respite from the fighting by enjoying a day of fishing together.

Unit Test (p. 22)

Critical Reading/Vocabulary and Grammar

1. c 2. a 3. c 4. b 5. c 6. d 7. a 8. d 9. c
10. a 11. b 12. c 13. b 14. b 15. d 16. b
17. a 18. c 19. c 20. d

Questions are classified in these categories:
Comprehension 1(E)
Interpretation 2(A), 9(A), 10(E)
Literary Analysis 3(C), 6(C), 8(A)
Reading Strategy 4(A), 5(A), 7(A)
Vocabulary 11(A), 15(A), 16(A), 17(C), 18(C)
Grammar Skill 12(A), 13(A), 14(A), 19(C), 20(C)
E = Easy, A = Average, C = Challenging

Essay Questions

Guidelines for student response:

21. (Easy) Students should focus on one selection that they consider to be the most exciting, and support their choices by citing details from the text. For example, students might refer to Tom Benecke's frightening experience on the ledge of a building in the story "Contents of the Dead Man's Pocket" or to the experiences faced by Sir Edmund Hillary or Tenzing Norgay during the climb up Mount Everest.

22. (Average) Students' essays should focus on the specific details of a moment of suspense in one story or poem. They should identify what specific words, phrases, and actions create tension. For example, students might focus on details in the final scene of the "The Monkey's Paw," during which Mrs. White is trying to respond to the knocking on the door and Mr. White is frantically trying to wish the knocking away. Readers wonder if Mrs. White will open the door, if the intruder is in fact her son, or if Mr. White will find the paw and make his final wish.

23. (Average) Students should focus on the experience and thoughts of one character from a selection in the unit. They should

examine what happens to the character and how the experience changes his or her outlook on life or forces the character to re-examine his or her life. For example, students might describe Annie's story in "A Walk to the Jetty," in which she is leaving the island on which she was raised. In the moments before she leaves, she reflects on her life and the people she has known.

24. (Average) Students' responses should point to specific details and actions that suggest the personality traits of two characters in a selection. They should also describe how the selection's specific situation helps to bring out these personality traits. For example, students might describe the bravery and cleverness of the woman in "The Bridegroom," the defiance and patriotism of Morissot and Sauvage in "Two Friends," or the loyalty and trust exhibited by Damon and Pythias.

25. (Challenging) Students may compare and contrast any two selections in the unit. They should provide concrete details to support the statements they make. They should explain the different ways the unit's theme is addressed in both selections and what the selections have in common. For example, students might compare the eerie scenarios of "The Monkey's Paw" and "The Masque of Red Death" and how both of these selections deal with fate and danger; or they might compare Annie's life-changing decision to leave Antigua in "A Walk to the Jetty" with Sir Edmund Hillary's life-changing decision to climb Mount Everest.

Unit 2:   Striving for Success

from *In Commemoration: One Million Volumes* by Rudolfo A. Anaya

Selection Test (p. 26)

Critical Reading/Vocabulary and Grammar

1. c 2. c 3. c 4. b 5. b 6. d 7. c 8. c 9. d
10. a 11. a 12. d 13. b 14. c 15. b 16. d
17. b 18. c 19. d 20. c

Questions are classified in these categories:
Comprehension 1(C), 3(A), 4(C), 5(E), 6(A), 8(A)

Interpretation 2(A), 7(A), 9(C), 10(A)
Literary Analysis 12(A), 15(A)
Reading Strategy 11(A), 13(E), 14(E)
Vocabulary 16(A), 17(A), 18(E)
Grammar Skill 19(E), 20(A)
E = Easy, A = Average, C = Challenging

Essay Questions

Guidelines for student response:

21. (Easy) Students could identify three distinct elements in Anaya's essay. First, the

from _In Commemoration: One Million Volumes_ by Rudolfo A. Anaya _(continued)_

library is not only a deep part of his personal history, but also a bridge linking his origins to the larger world of his writing. His many references to his childhood and to his native culture reinforce that link. Second, he says that the library is "the collective memory of all mankind." It is the "storehouse" of all knowledge, which is free from censorship and dedicated to the preservation of the history and literature of all cultures. Third, the library should be a place for people; a civic center where ideas and events are discussed in a civil manner, the cultural center of a city. Anaya closes his essay with the statement that the library should be a "warm place that serves the needs and aspirations of its people." Student responses should evidence understanding of at least two of these elements.

22. (Average) Students should indicate in their essays that Anaya's references to his native culture provide sensory images that allow the Spanish history to come alive. They also serve as a reminder of the author's own personal journey from isolation to education, and suggest a model of multicultural pluralism and harmony. The many references to Spanish and his uses of the language both provide authenticity to Anaya's reminiscences, and make his childhood appear vivid. These references also show how far he has come from that childhood and suggest the library's pivotal role in his personal development. They also preserve his cultural heritage and the diversity he hopes to see preserved in the library.

23. (Challenging) Students may make a wide range of predictions about the library's role in the future. However, their essays should indicate that they have considered the two primary functions of the library as Anaya articulates them in his essay: the library as an archive of "the collective memory of all mankind" and a place where issues should be "discussed and debated and researched." Students may note the trend in libraries to become community computer centers with specialized tools, software, and search capabilities.

Some libraries are staffed with Internet experts. Many libraries have a variety of community service functions, from voter registration to concert series, and these trends may continue regardless of the technology. All of these changes serve the two main functions Anaya proposes, and student essays should relate their predictions to these functions.

"How Much Land Does a Man Need?"
by Leo Tolstoy

Selection Test (p. 29)

Critical Reading/Vocabulary and Grammar
1. b 2. d 3. a 4. c 5. b 6. d 7. b 8. a 9. a
10. d 11. c 12. b 13. d 14. c 15. d 16. c
17. a 18. b 19. b 20. b

Questions are classified in these categories:
  Comprehension 2(A), 3(E), 5(C)
  Interpretation 7(C), 9(C), 10(A), 11(C), 15(C)
  Literary Analysis 1(E), 4(A), 14(E)
  Reading Strategy 6(A), 8(C), 12(A), 13(E)
  Vocabulary 16(A), 17(A), 20(E)
  Grammar Skill 18(A), 19(A)
  E = Easy, A = Average, C = Challenging

Essay Questions
Guidelines for student response:

21. (Easy) Students should say that Pahom is a boastful and greedy peasant. He reveals his boastful nature at the beginning of the parable by claiming that if he had enough land he wouldn't even fear the Devil. Students should also note that Pahom's greedy nature helps to predict his actions; he is never satisfied with his acquisitions and always wants more. Eventually, it is Pahom's greed that leads him to the steppe to acquire more land. It is here that Pahom meets the Bashkirs, the Devil in the form of the Bashkir chief, and his own death.

22. (Average) Students should indicate that Tolstoy's parable teaches a lesson about the difference between need and greed. The Devil represents evil and all temptations thereof. The peasant Pahom, through his boastful and greedy nature, represents flawed humanity. Pahom's character traits, particularly his greed, make him weak in the face of the great

temptation for more land. The Devil's actions are motivated by his desire to use Pahom's weaknesses against him. Pahom's actions are motivated by his greed and by his foolish belief that all his problems would be solved if only he had enough land.

23. (Challenging) Students should say that Tolstoy regarded property ownership as evil or immoral. Some students may quote the last line of the parable, "Six feet from his head to his toes was all he needed," as Tolstoy's concise reply to the question of how much land a man needs. To support Tolstoy's position, students might note Pahom's greed in acquiring more land and the ultimate sacrifice of his life for yet another parcel of land. Students might also note the carefree life of the Bashkirs, whose attitude toward land ownership parallels Tolstoy's. To refute Tolstoy's position, students might point as well to the carefree life of the Bashkirs, whose attitude toward owning land could also be interpreted as lazy and unproductive. Students might also note that land ownership represents the ability to control one's destiny and that the outcome of Pahom's experience is due to his greed and not the ownership of land.

"Success is counted sweetest" and "I dwell in Possibility—" by Emily Dickinson
"Uncoiling" by Pat Mora
"Columbus Dying" by Vassar Miller

Selection Test (p. 32)

Critical Reading/Vocabulary and Grammar

1. b 2. c 3. a 4. a 5. c 6. b 7. d 8. c 9. b
10. a 11. b 12. c 13. b 14. a 15. d 16. b
17. b 18. d 19. c 20. c

Questions are classified in these categories:
    Comprehension 1(E), 2(A), 6(A)
    Interpretation 5(C), 7(C), 8(A)
    Literary Analysis 4(E), 9(A), 12(C)
    Reading Strategy 3(A), 10(A), 11(A), 13(A)
    Vocabulary 14(C), 17(A), 18(A), 19(A)
    Grammar Skill 15(A), 16(E), 20(E)
    E = Easy, A = Average, C = Challenging

Essay Questions

Guidelines for student response:

21. (Easy) Students should correctly identify the theme of the poem they choose. Students might support their choice of "Success is counted sweetest" by pointing out the speaker's sympathy toward the dying, defeated man. "I dwell in Possibility—" might be supported by the hopeful, inspiring images of the house with many windows and doors, high ceilings, and limitless possibilities.

22. (Average) Arguments in support of the statement might point out the bitter irony of "Success is counted sweetest"—the person who most values success is the one who never realizes it—or the empty satisfaction Columbus feels in the moments before his death. Opposing arguments might point to the boundless optimism expressed by the speaker of "I dwell in Possibility—."

23. (Challenging) Students should recognize the contrast between the strong, wild wind, personified as a woman, and the "pale women" who "scurry" and "sing lace lullabies." These domestic and traditional images can be compared to the liberated woman who "tosses her hair dark with rain" and throws her head back and roars. As a counterargument students might point out that this image of a wild, angry woman suggests the stereotypical image of a woman scorned.

from *My Left Foot* by Christy Brown

Selection Test (p. 35)

Critical Reading/Vocabulary and Grammar

1. b 2. a 3. c 4. a 5. c 6. d 7. d 8. b 9. c
10. b 11. a 12. c 13. a 14. c 15. c 16. d
17. c 18. a 19. d 20. b

Questions are classified in these categories:
    Comprehension 1(E), 4(A), 6(A)
    Interpretation 7(C), 8(A), 9(A), 12(C), 13(C)
    Literary Analysis 3(A), 10(E), 11(A)
    Reading Strategy 2(A), 5(E), 14(A)
    Vocabulary 16(E), 17(A), 18(C)
    Grammar Skill 15(C), 19(A), 20(E)
    E = Easy, A = Average, C = Challenging

from *My Left Foot*
by Christy Brown *(continued)*

Essay Questions

Guidelines for student response:

21. (Easy) Students should conclude that the author's purpose was to show how isolated he felt even in the midst of his large family. He emphasizes the loneliness and isolation by restating the idea in six different ways. He was "lonely," "imprisoned," "unable to communicate," "cut off," "separated," "beyond the sphere of their lives and activities." Furthermore, he draws a vivid picture with the phrase "as though a glass wall stood between my existence and theirs." His desire to "run about and play" humanizes him so that he seems just like any other little boy. For a moment the reader forgets his physical limits, until the word "bondage" appears at the end of the sentence.

22. (Average) Students should acknowledge that details such as the description of his birth, his symptoms, his mother's conviction and patience, and his inability to respond to and communicate with his mother add to the impact of the significant moment because they are all in contrast to the ability that Christy displays in the significant moment. Even the quietness and appearance of the kitchen add to the impact of the significant moment because the description draws the reader into the room, waiting with the family to see what, if anything, will happen next. Pieces of information such as the doctors' opinions serve as a kind of expert testimony, leading readers to fear that the doctors are right and the mother is wrong. Students must identify the significant moment as the successful completion of the letter *A*, thus indicating to his family for the first time that he had intelligence.

23. (Challenging) Students will assign the qualities of strength, courage, persistence, stubbornness, and determination to Christy's mother. She strives for success by loving Christy and deciding to treat him just like her other children. When faced with failure or frustration, Christy's mother maintains her faith and certainty that Christy can think. Students may also cite his mother's endless patience, her soft-spoken encouragement prior to the significant moment, and her fierce refusal to accept the doctors' opinions that Christy has no intelligence.

"A Visit to Grandmother"
by William Melvin Kelley

Selection Test (p. 38)

Critical Reading/Vocabulary and Grammar

1. c 2. d 3. a 4. b 5. d 6. d 7. c 8. d 9. a
10. c 11. a 12. c 13. a 14. b 15. c 16. b
17. a 18. b 19. b 20. d

Questions are classified in these categories:
Comprehension 4(E), 5(E)
Interpretation 1(A), 3(C), 6(C), 9(E), 10(C), 12(A), 14(A), 16(C)
Literary Analysis 2(A), 8(A), 13(C)
Reading Strategy 7(A), 11(A), 15(E)
Vocabulary 17(E)
Grammar Skill 18(A), 19(E), 20(A)
E = Easy, A = Average, C = Challenging

Essay Questions

Guidelines for student response:

21. (Easy) Students should understand that the problem between Charles and his mother and brother exists because Charles grew up believing that his mother did not love him. He felt that she seemed to take more of an interest in his brother GL and that she often overlooked GL's mistakes. Charles's mother, on the other hand, says that she had to spend more time with GL because he needed more guidance than Charles. Charles was a mature child who had a bright future ahead of him, while GL was immature and not as smart as Charles. Charles views GL as irresponsible and dishonest, but he also views him with some jealousy. The reason for this jealousy is Charles's wish to be loved by his mother in the way he believes GL is loved.

22. (Average) Students should understand that Chig sees these things in his father's face because his father is dealing with painful childhood memories for the first time in years. Charles feels strongly that

he was not loved by his mother growing up and that his brother GL unfairly took all of his mother's love and attention. Charles feels fear and uncertainty because he knows that he is about to face his mother and his childhood problem as an adult. He feels sadness for himself, because of the pain of his childhood. He feels hatred because he believes he was cheated and treated unfairly by his family.

23. (Challenging) Students might say that Chig's grandmother is a strong, opinionated woman who takes her job as a parent seriously. She feels both proud and protective of her children. His grandmother's strong reaction to the appearance of Chig and his father, her way of sharing the story about GL's horse and buggy, and her shocked reaction to Charles's accusation reveal these details about her character. Charles is an intelligent, responsible, sensitive, and angry character. Charles's feelings toward his mother and brother, his reaction to his mother's story, his angry words to his mother, and his mother's perception of him reveal these details about his character. GL is wild and irresponsible—a person who does not think clearly about what he is doing and the consequences of his actions. Charles's and his grandmother's descriptions of GL and the horse and buggy incident reveal these details about his character.

"Mowing" and "After Apple-Picking"
by Robert Frost
"Style" and "At Harvesttime"
by Maya Angelou

Selection Test (p. 41)

Critical Reading/Vocabulary and Grammar

1. c 2. d 3. a 4. d 5. c 6. b 7. c 8. a 9. d 10. a 11. b 12. c 13. d 14. d 15. b 16. d 17. b 18. d 19. d 20. b

Questions are classified in these categories:
Comprehension 1(E), 5(A), 11(E)
Interpretation 3(E), 6(A), 8(C), 14(E)
Literary Analysis 2(A), 9(A), 12(A)
Reading Strategy 4(A), 7(C),10(A), 13(C)
Vocabulary 16(A), 18(A), 19(C), 20(A)
Grammar Skill 15(A), 17(C)
E = Easy, A = Average, C = Challenging

Essay Questions
Guidelines for student response:

21. (Easy) Students should notice that in both pieces, Angelou encourages people to take responsibility for their own actions, to be confident and forceful, and to show tolerance when dealing with others. In both passages, Angelou is trying to express to people that they have the ability to turn negative situations into positive ones.

22. (Average) Students should understand that both speakers work hard at their difficult jobs and take their work seriously. The speaker in "Mowing" is expressing his feelings of respect for the land and the work he is able to do. He is feeling content and at peace with the steady routine and the solitude of his work. On the other hand, the speaker in "After Apple-Picking" has just finished a difficult task and is feeling exhausted and preoccupied with the details of his work.

23. (Challenging) Students should list the images of the whispering scythe, the hay, the feeble-pointed spikes of flowers, and the green snake from "Mowing." These images create the calm, tranquil mood of the poem and relate to the idea that working the land is a noble profession. Students should list the images of the apples, their wafting aroma, and the ladder poking into the trees that appear in "After Apple-Picking." These images show the details and difficulties of the apple farmer's job. He thinks of these as he is trying to drift off to sleep, which shows how he is affected by the magnitude of the task he has just completed. Students should list Angelou's images of seeds and arable soil, which she uses to symbolize more general life experiences. She compares the difficult task of cultivating seeds to cultivating a peaceful and productive existence.

"The Apple Tree"
by Katherine Mansfield

Selection Test (p. 44)

Critical Reading/Vocabulary and Grammar

1. c 2. a 3. d 4. b 5. a 6. b 7. b 8. c 9. b
10. a 11. b 12. c 13. c 14. d 15. d 16. d
17. a 18. c 19. d 20. d

Questions are classified in these categories:
Comprehension 1(A), 2(A), 7(E)
Interpretation 3(E), 4(C), 5(A), 6(A), 8(A)
Literary Analysis 11(A), 13(C), 14(A)
Reading Strategy 9(C), 10(A), 12(E)
Vocabulary 15(A), 16(E), 19(C)
Grammar Skill 17(A), 18(E), 20(C)
E = Easy, A = Average, C = Challenging

Essay Questions

Guidelines for student response:

21. (Easy) Students' questions should have to do with the reasons behind events and/or characters' actions. For example, a question might be "Why did Father tell the children not to touch the tree?" To answer that question, students might point to Father's sudden interest in the apparent value of the tree and to the "delight" he feels based on his friend's comments. Father is so taken with the tree that he feels the need to assert his authority and keep the children away from it. Asking and answering this question helps readers to understand Father's motives, shedding light on his actions later in the story.

22. (Average) Students may say that Father's very high hopes and expectations hint that something may go wrong. The narrator says that he would rather his house burned down than have something happen to that tree. The allusion to the Forbidden Tree in the Garden of Eden also provides a hint. There were unhappy consequences for the people who ate of *that* tree; perhaps there will be similar consequences for the people who eat of *this* tree. Students may also identify the color of the flesh of the apple as a hint that something is amiss. Finally, Father's instruction not to bolt the apple may be viewed as a hint, though ironically so, since the apple did not warrant bolting.

23. (Challenging) Students should cite the "Forbidden Tree" as parallel to the "Forbidden Fruit" of the biblical version. In both stories, people are warned not to touch or eat from the tree or the fruit. In both stories, someone does eventually eat from the tree. In the biblical story, Adam and Eve are warned that they will die if they eat the fruit of the tree. A snake, representing "evil," tempts Eve and tells her that she will not die. In Mansfield's story, the consequences of touching the tree are a "good sound whipping," and there is no character tempting anyone to eat from the tree. Mansfield's characters partake of the tree only to be disappointed by the fruit. However, Adam and Eve find the fruit very desirable. The allusion in Mansfield's story helps readers to form expectations. Any reader who is familiar with the Adam and Eve story suspects that there will be some kind of unpleasant circumstance resulting from touching the tree or eating its fruit.

"Africa" by David Diop
"Old Song" Traditional
"All" by Bei Dao
"Also All" by Shu Ting
from *The Analects* by Confucius

Selection Test (p. 47)

Critical Reading/Vocabulary and Grammar

1. b 2. d 3. a 4. c 5. c 6. b 7. a 8. b 9. b
10. d 11. a 12. c 13. c 14. b 15. a 16. b
17. d 18. c 19. d 20. c

Questions are classified in these categories:
Comprehension 1(E), 3(C), 12(A), 13(C)
Interpretation 2(A), 4(C), 8(E), 14(A)
Literary Analysis 6(A), 7(E), 10(E), 16(A)
Reading Strategy 5(A), 9(A), 11(E), 15(C)
Vocabulary 17(A), 20(C)
Grammar Skill 18(A), 19(E)
E = Easy, A = Average, C = Challenging

Essay Questions

Guidelines for student response:

21. (Easy) Student responses should make a distinction between the kind of self-knowledge that Confucius refers to and the kind of knowledge that simply com-

prises a large array of facts and skills. Having an adequate understanding of oneself is necessary in order to make an accurate estimate of what one really knows. Students can cite examples from life of lost opportunities because people were not aware of what they actually knew. Conversely, people have failed because they either overestimated their abilities or pretended to know more than they did. In terms of specific fields of knowledge, students might point out that the vast amount of information available makes it impossible for a single human being to know everything. Therefore, recognizing what one doesn't know but knowing when and where to seek information is an indispensable quality in society.

22. (Average) The selections are similar in that they both regard personal conduct, advise conducting oneself in a modest way, and focus on self-knowledge as the arbiter of conduct, rather than recognition from the exterior world. Confucius' ideas are detailed, but are generally consistent with the traditions expressed in "Old Song." The selections differ in that *The Analects*, though aphoristic, is intended as teaching material, advising specific behaviors, and knowledge for prospective rulers through its proverbs. "Old Song" depends upon its universal appeal, placing life in the context of passing generations, as in the line "Many heroes are not yet born/many have already died." It, therefore, offers a code, which is not dependent on the success of an individual life. They also differ in that "Old Song" offers a more modest prospect in its final line, "To be alive to hear this song is a victory." *The Analects* seems more absolute, comparing the successful student of the Master to a Pole Star.

23. (Challenging) Students may agree or disagree with Bei Dao's statement. Their responses should clearly express a thesis statement early in the essay, and have identifiable reasons for the position they have taken. Those who agree with the statement might note that human beings remain the same, even though technology has changed the world. Human relationships, ambitions, feelings, codes of con-

duct, and questions about existence remain constant throughout recorded history. Those who disagree with Bei Dao's statement may cite revolutionary ways in which the world and existence may have changed, citing mass media, instantaneous and constant exchange of information, world economies, and an ever-expanding shared culture that may have produced a different concept of humanity and its place.

Unit Test (p. 50)

Critical Reading/Vocabulary and Grammar

1. b 2. a 3. b 4. c 5. b 6. d 7. a 8. b 9. d
10. c 11. d 12. c 13. a 14. b 15. b 16. c
17. b 18. c 19. a 20. d

Questions are classified in these categories:
Comprehension 1(E)
Interpretation 3(A), 8(A), 9(A)
Literary Analysis 4(E), 6(A), 10(A)
Reading Strategy 2(C), 5(C), 7(C)
Vocabulary 11(A), 12(C), 16(A), 17(A), 20(A)
Grammar Skill 13(C), 14(A), 15(E), 18(A), 19(E)
E = Easy, A = Average, C = Challenging

Essay Questions

Guidelines for student response:

21. (Easy) Students' essays should focus on the characters, details, events, and main idea of the selection they choose. They should explain why a particular selection speaks to them, and what specific details they find inspiring. Students might write about Rudolfo Anaya's dedication to learning and how books and stories help him to achieve his goals, the challenges faced by Christy Brown and his mother's unwillingness to give up on him, the satisfaction with hard work expressed in "Mowing," and "After Apple-Picking," or the wise advice conveyed in the poem "Style."

22. (Average) Students should focus on two selections that deal specifically with failure or disappointment. In their essays, they should give specific details from the selections. They should also analyze what lessons can be learned from the failures or disappointments described in stories, or from the messages of certain poems.

For example, some students might write about the death of Pahom in "How Much Land Does a Man Need," which is a direct result of his greed; the message that success is most appreciated by those who don't experience it in "Success is counted sweetest"; or the misunderstanding that occurs in "A Visit to Grandmother," which is the result of a lack of communication.

23. (Average) Students' essays should describe the personality of one character from the unit. Students should identify specific character traits and then explain how specific thoughts, words, actions, and interactions with other characters reveal these traits. For example, they might describe Pahom's thoughts of wealth and the way he is driven to continue walking despite his exhaustion in "How Much Land Does a Man Need," or they might describe Charles Dunford's discomfort and obvious sensitivity and anger when he is in the home of his mother.

24. (Average) Students should describe how relationships among family members shape certain characters in the unit. For exam-

ple, students might cite some of the following examples: In "One Million Volumes," the author writes about how his mother always encouraged him to learn and become as wise as his grandfather was. In *My Left Foot*, Christy Brown's mother believed in him even when doctors told her that her son's life was hopeless. In "A Visit to Grandmother," Charles Dunford suffers anger and sadness throughout much of his life because of his belief that his mother loved his brother more than she loved him. This belief drove him to move far away from his family and to overachieve.

25. (Challenging) Students' responses should point to three specific selections in the unit. They should be able to identify a specific tone in each of the three selections and then describe which words and phrases help to create this tone. For example, students might describe the peaceful tone of "Mowing," which is emphasized by descriptions of the whispering scythe and of the long hours the speaker spends in the hay field; or the assertive tone of "Style," which is emphasized by the speaker's instructions on life and the value of style.

Unit 3:   Clashing Forces

"Through the Tunnel"
by Doris Lessing

Selection Test (p. 54)

Critical Reading/Vocabulary and Grammar

1. b 2. a 3. a 4. b 5. d 6. d 7. b 8. a 9. c
10. c 11. d 12. c 13. b 14. a 15. d 16. b
17. c 18. b 19. d 20. b

Questions are classified in these categories:
   Comprehension 2(A), 8(E), 9(E)
   Interpretation 1(A), 5(C), 13(E), 14(E)
   Literary Analysis 3(A), 6(A)
   Reading Strategy 4(A), 7(C), 10(A), 11(A), 12(A)
   Vocabulary 15(C), 16(A), 18(A)
   Grammar Skill 17(C), 19(A), 20(A)
   E = Easy, A = Average, C = Challenging

Essay Questions

Guidelines for student response:

21. (Easy) Students should clearly state their opinion on the worthiness of risking one's safety to meet a challenge. Those who agree with the statement might cite the positive changes Jerry undergoes as he trains to swim the tunnel and his feelings of satisfaction at having met his goal. Those who disagree might cite the possibility of drowning, developing nosebleeds, and hurting himself in some other way, which could cause a serious or fatal injury.

22. (Average) Jerry is in conflict with his fears about swimming the tunnel and his desire to be like the older boys. He imagines that octopuses lurk in the tunnel and at one point decides to postpone his swim until

the following year. However, his desire to meet the challenge outweighs his fears and he methodically trains for his swim despite nosebleeds and dizzy spells. Students should summarize Jerry's feat and acknowledge that Jerry resolves the conflict by overcoming his fears.

23. (Challenging) Students should note that, initially, Jerry has many childlike qualities. He pouts and demands attention from his mother, while at the same time wanting to separate himself from her. He wants the admiration of older boys but resorts to foolish antics when faced with failure. Students should recognize that Jerry's decision to swim the tunnel is the mark of his maturation—he starts developing more mature qualities such as self-control and patience. Students should recognize that by the story's end Jerry is more confident, self-possessed, and differentiated from his mother.

"The Dog That Bit People"
by James Thurber

Selection Test (p. 57)

Critical Reading/Vocabulary and Grammar

1. d 2. b 3. b 4. c 5. b 6. a 7. d 8. d 9. a
10. c 11. a 12. b 13. a 14. a 15. b 16. c
17. d 18. c 19. d 20. c

Questions are classified in these categories:
    Comprehension 5(E), 7(A), 9(E), 13(A)
    Interpretation 1(E), 2(A), 3(A), 14(E)
    Literary Analysis 4(E), 6(A), 10(C)
    Reading Strategy 8(A), 11(E), 12(C)
    Vocabulary 15(A), 18(C), 19(C)
    Grammar Skill 16(A), 17(A), 20(A)
    E = Easy, A = Average, C = Challenging

Essay Questions

Guidelines for student response:

21. (Easy) Students should choose scenes rich in sensory detail, such as Roy's confrontation with Muggs in the dining room, the author's "foolhardy" encounter with the dog, or Muggs' reaction to the thunder machine. All examples should be supported with appropriate sensory details, such as "scattering dishes," the author's "hoisting" of the dog by the tail, and the "vigorous" shaking of the thunder machine.

22. (Average) Students might focus on Thurber's extensive use of exaggeration. Examples include quotations such as "They acted like pet mice, almost like mice somebody had trained" and "He sent it right back, probably because he suspected it was trick candy." Other exaggerations include Uncle Horatio's reaction to the news that Muggs eats off the table. Students should note that Thurber's use of exaggeration adds energy to the story and distracts from the more ordinary details of the life of a troublesome pet.

23. (Challenging) Students might note that the essay reveals a family that seems generally happy and communicative. Students might interpret Mother's approach to the problem of Muggs as either soft-heartedness or an inability to face difficult decisions, such as getting rid of Muggs. Mother chooses to avoid conflict and seems to placate those people whom she knows have been offended by Muggs' behavior. The author and Roy seem to deal more directly with Muggs, but only through shows of physical anger or domination.

"Conscientious Objector"
by Edna St. Vincent Millay
"A Man" by Nina Cassian
"The Weary Blues"
by Langston Hughes
"Jazz Fantasia" by Carl Sandburg

Selection Test (p. 60)

Critical Reading/Vocabulary and Grammar

1. d 2. b 3. a 4. b 5. d 6. a 7. b 8. d 9. b
10. c 11. d 12. b 13. c 14. a 15. b 16. c
17. d 18. b 19. a 20. c

Questions are classified in these categories:
    Comprehension 1(E), 5(A), 9(C)
    Interpretation 2(A), 3(A), 7(C), 13(A)
    Literary Analysis 6(A), 11(E), 12(C), 15(A)
    Reading Strategy 4(C), 8(A), 10(E), 14(A)
    Vocabulary 16(A), 18(C), 19(E)
    Grammar Skill 17(A), 20(E)
    E = Easy, A = Average, C = Challenging

"Conscientious Objector"
by Edna St. Vincent Millay
"A Man" by Nina Cassian
"The Weary Blues"
by Langston Hughes
"Jazz Fantasia" by Carl Sandburg *(continued)*

Essay Questions

Guidelines for student response:

21. (Easy) In their essays students should articulate that a good attitude is essential for achievement. Students should illustrate the principle through examples drawn either from their own lives or from the lives of others. Examples might include the role of determination in accomplishing a difficult task, the presence of constancy or perseverance in the face of adversity, or the part that enthusiasm plays in the success of a public or private figure. In each case, a valid relationship between attitude and accomplishment should be discussed.

22. (Average) The conscientious objector of the title is one who will not give in or surrender in spirit or in action to unpleasant fates. Students' responses should indicate that they understand the way St. Vincent Millay personifies death throughout the poem in order to make it an adversary. As a militant agent of destruction, with "business in Cuba, business in the Balkans," death becomes an embattled figure at war with life. St. Vincent Millay uses martial imagery to characterize the struggle by having death saddle and ride a horse, conduct military campaigns around the world, terrorize victims with a "whip" of fear, and use bribery all in the effort to find the route to victory. Although St. Vincent Millay acknowledges that death cannot be stopped, just as a conscientious objector cannot stop a war alone, she nevertheless refuses to participate. The list of things she "shall not" do is similar to the list of things one might enumerate in refusing to engage in warfare.

23. (Challenging) Students should structure their responses to note differences in setting, action, images, ideas, and tone between the two poems, and give examples of those differences. The primary difference between "The Weary Blues" and

"Jazz Fantasia" is the scope of the portrait. Hughes' poem is a single setting, a dark club, with a single performer, which becomes an intimate look at one man's feelings and music. Sandburg takes a comprehensive approach, addressing his poem to all jazz players, and moves the setting of his images to many places, which include treetops, city streets with fleeing cars, backstairs at a brawl, and a Mississippi riverboat. The music is replicated by Hughes's use of rhythm and rhyme and Sandburg's catalog of instrumental sounds. Hughes creates a sense of the man's weariness by images that focus on the musician's hands, piano, voice, and specific lyrics. Sandburg's emphasis is on the power and the emotions that jazz evokes. His sharp images of many types of life convey a tone of deep feeling and vibrancy.

"Like the Sun" by R. K. Narayan
"Tell all the Truth but tell it slant—"
by Emily Dickinson

Selection Test (p. 63)

Critical Reading/Vocabulary and Grammar

1. b 2. c 3. d 4. c 5. d 6. d 7. b 8. d 9. c
10. a 11. c 12. c 13. a 14. b 15. d 16. a
17. b 18. b 19. d 20. a

Questions are classified in these categories:
Comprehension 1(E), 13(E), 14(A)
Interpretation 2(A), 5(C), 6(A), 7(A), 11(C), 12(A), 15(C)
Literary Analysis 3(A), 9(A)
Reading Strategy 4(A), 8(C), 10(A)
Vocabulary 16(A), 18(A), 19(A)
Grammar Skill 17(A), 20(E)
E = Easy, A = Average, C = Challenging

Essay Questions

Guidelines for student response:

21. (Easy) According to Sekhar, truth is like bright sun because it is often painful for people to face the truth, in the same way that it is painful for them to look directly into bright sunlight. Because people have trouble speaking and hearing the truth, they go through life lying to themselves and others or they continually try to temper the truth so as not to shock or anger

one another. He believes that his experiment is crucial because he feels that without truth, life is not worth living.

22. (Average) "Like the Sun" presents a number of examples of irony of situation. Sekhar violates his wife's expectations when he criticizes the meal she prepares. She expects a compliment on her cooking, whether or not it is good. When Sekhar is at work, he does not give the expected response to news that a colleague has died. He is the only person who is honest in saying that the man was "a mean and selfish brute." Sekhar then becomes a victim of irony himself when the headmaster, Sekhar's boss, unexpectedly asks him to critique his musical ability. Sekhar had not expected to be tested in such a difficult situation. After Sekhar decides to stand firm in his decision to be honest and tells the headmaster to give up on music, the headmaster surprises him by following his advice. Although the headmaster at first seems accepting of Sekhar's advice, he shows his obvious annoyance by demanding that Sekhar finish correcting one hundred test papers by the next day. The end of the story is ironic because it expresses the idea that although telling the truth is admirable, it is also a luxury. Sekhar learns that people who want to be successful and live peacefully with others must often temper, or adjust, the truth.

23. (Challenging) Students should note that both pieces express the importance of living a truthful life. In "Like the Sun," Sekhar expresses concern that people are so afraid of truth that they are never able to be completely honest with one another, and that without truth "life is not worth living." Dickinson says that people should "Tell all the truth. . ." and uses words like *superb* and *dazzle* in describing truth. Dickinson, however, recognizes that for truth to be genuinely accepted and understood, it must be told at a "slant" and it must "dazzle gradually"—meaning that truth must be introduced gradually and with kindness, or people will be blinded by its light and unable to comprehend or accept it. Sekhar, on the other hand,

makes a vow one morning to tell nothing but the absolute truth. In doing this, he shocks and angers people with his brutal honesty. Although he does not seem to regret his experiment, it is clear that his harsh honesty works against him in certain situations. If he had read the Dickinson poem before his day of truth, he might have been inclined to introduce truth more gradually into his life. He might have considered the possibility that truth delivered with kindness might be more effective in the long run.

"Hearts and Hands" by O. Henry
"The Fish" by Elizabeth Bishop

Selection Test (p. 66)

Critical Reading/Vocabulary and Grammar

1. c 2. c 3. d 4. b 5. c 6. c 7. b 8. d 9. a
10. b 11. b 12. d 13. a 14. d 15. a 16. c
17. c 18. d 19. a 20. b

Questions are classified in these categories:
Comprehension 5(A), 8(E), 13(A)
Interpretation 4(C), 6(C), 9(E), 15(A)
Literary Analysis 2(C), 7(A), 12(A), 14(A)
Reading Strategy 1(C), 3(A), 10(E), 11(A)
Vocabulary 16(C), 17(A), 19(E)
Grammar Skill 18(E), 20(A)
E = Easy, A = Average, C = Challenging

Essay Questions

Guidelines for student response:

21. (Easy) Students should indicate that the speaker in "The Fish" views the fish not as a meal but as a worthy opponent and one who deserves to continue to live. The fact that the fish has fought and won so many other battles causes the speaker to feel that he does not have the right to kill the fish. The marshal in "Hearts and Hands" shows compassion by representing himself as the criminal, and saving Mr. Easton the embarrassment of admitting to an old acquaintance that he, in fact, has become a criminal since last they met. The marshal understands that although Mr. Easton is his prisoner, he deserves the right to retain his dignity. Students should identify compassion as a necessary human quality

"Hearts and Hands" by O. Henry
"The Fish" by Elizabeth Bishop *(continued)*
that causes people to treat each other
fairly, respectfully, and with dignity. Students' examples may involve compassionate treatment of older relatives, animals,
fellow students, and so on.

22. (Average) Some of the clues that foreshadow the ending: the marshal's appearance is a sign that he is a Western law
officer; Mr. Easton is not alert like a law
officer should be and has to rouse himself
when spoken to; and the position of the
handcuffs, which cause Easton to grasp
Miss Fairchild with his *left* hand. The
crime of counterfeiting points ironically to
the situation and its outcome. For instance, Mr. Easton's discussion of his
need for money lends credence to the possibility of his being a counterfeiter, as
does the marshal's statement that "Mr.
Easton knows his business"—i.e., the
business of counterfeiting. Also, Mr. Easton will not soon be in Washington because he will be in prison for seven years,
and Mr. Easton says he "must go on to
Leavenworth," a destination about which
he has no choice.

23. (Challenging) Students will likely state
that the "handsome" and "frank" appearance of Mr. Easton contrasted with the
glum, heavily built, roughly dressed appearance of the marshal lead the reader to
believe that the marshal, rather that Easton, is the prisoner. O. Henry is hoping
readers will assume that criminals are
sloppy, ill-dressed, nicotine addicts,
whereas law officers are handsome, polite,
and gallant. Popular situation comedies
exploit the use of stereotypes. Teenagers
are depicted as vain, rebellious, and too
interested in the opposite sex. Women
work at the office and at home but generally still run the household and serve as
primary caregivers for children. Fathers or
husbands are depicted as inept at home,
although their intentions are usually
good. They generally are less sensitive
than female characters, very interested in
sports, and work long hours at the office.
Students should discuss the disadvantage
of having movies and television perpetuate

stereotypes. The media does influence
how people think, act, and treat one another. Very often people are given the
message to judge others on their appearances, not on their merits.

from *Desert Exile* by Yoshiko Uchida
"Speech on Japanese American Internment . . ." by Gerald Ford

Selection Test (p. 69)

Critical Reading/Vocabulary and Grammar
1. a 2. b 3. a 4. c 5. c 6. d 7. b 8. b 9. c
10. a 11. d 12. d 13. d 14. a 15. c 16. a
17. b 18. c 19. b 20. d

Questions are classified in these categories:
Comprehension 1(A), 4(E), 8(C), 10(A)
Interpretation 5(C), 6(A), 7(E), 12(C), 14(A)
Literary Analysis 2(E), 3(A), 13(A)
Reading Strategy 9(A), 11(C), 15(E)
Vocabulary 16(A), 17(E), 20(A)
Grammar Skill 18(A), 19(E)
E = Easy, A = Average, C = Challenging

Essay Questions
Guidelines for student response:
21. (Easy) Students are likely to say that the
government did not respect Japanese
Americans. Because they "looked different" or "looked like the enemy," they were
easy to isolate from the rest of the American population. The government felt
Japanese Americans were such a threat
that they hurried them into ill-prepared,
crowded camps. This paranoia, shared by
many Americans at the time, is based on
the stereotype that existed of the well-
trained, militaristic Japanese soldier, our
enemy during World War II.

22. (Average) Students should acknowledge
that the Uchida account provides extensive, detailed background information
about the consequences of Executive
Order 9066. Understanding how the
Japanese Americans were treated makes
Ford's concession and apology appear to
be appropriate, even though it took a long
time to acknowledge. Students may suggest that Ford's speech camouflages the
hurt and humiliation that Japanese Americans suffered at the hands of the govern-

ment. They may cite the poor living conditions, the ill-prepared food and inadequate shelter, and the suspension of liberty as facts from *Desert Exile* that shaped their opinions.

23. (Challenging) At the very least, students should state that evacuating the Japanese Americans based on unfounded suspicions was unfair. They were denied their freedom of speech (to some extent) and freedom of assembly, they were relieved of their own property, and they were unjustly accused without being given the chance to establish their innocence. They had no trial, no jury, and no counsel. Students should understand that once the civil liberties of one group of people are violated, a precedent is set that may lead to the violation of another group's rights. This is why *all* citizens' rights must be protected.

"The Cabuliwallah"
by Rabindranath Tagore

Selection Test (p. 72)

Critical Reading/Vocabulary and Grammar

1. c 2. b 3. c 4. d 5. a 6. b 7. c 8. d 9. a
10. b 11. b 12. a 13. c 14. c 15. b 16. c
17. c 18. b 19. b 20. d

Questions are classified in these categories:
Comprehension 2(E), 7(A), 13(A)
Interpretation 1(A), 4(A), 9(C), 10(C), 14(C)
Literary Analysis 5(A), 6(C), 11(C)
Reading Strategy 3(E), 8(E), 12(A)
Vocabulary 15(E), 17(A), 18(A)
Grammar Skill 16(A), 19(E), 20(A)
E = Easy, A = Average, C = Challenging

Essay Questions

Guidelines for student response:

21. (Easy) Students will probably focus on three sensory details that evoke an image of Mini or of the Cabuliwallah. Students must identify the sense or senses that their chosen details engage. Three details evoking a playful, fun-loving image of Mini include: "her face would ripple with laughter" (sight); ". . . was playing softly, drumming on her knees" (sound); ". . . putting her hand into mine" (touch). Three details evoking an image of the Cabuliwallah as a kind, merry, poor peddler include: "He wore the loose, soiled clothing of his people, and a tall turban" (sight); "He would reply in the nasal accents of a mountaineer: 'An elephant!'" (sound); "With great care he unfolded this and smoothed it out with both hands on my table" (touch).

22. (Average) Students should say that before his arrest, the Cabuliwallah enjoyed a fun, lively, and childlike relationship with Mini. Together they chattered away, and shared and laughed at old jokes. Mini delighted in his visits. The Cabuliwallah, as he later tells Mini's father, brought Mini fruits and thought of his own daughter far away in Afghanistan. Students should note that after the Cabuliwallah is released from prison, he expects to revive his old friendship with Mini. Some students may even note that the Cabuliwallah naively or nostalgically expects to find Mini still a child, just as she was eight years ago. In contrast, Mini has grown up and in her new adult wisdom knows that the old friendship cannot be revived. Sadly, the Cabuliwallah tries to engage her with their old "father-in-law's house" joke, but Mini now knows the double meaning of the phrase. More advanced students will note that the Cabuliwallah finally realizes, through the drastic change in his relationship with Mini, how his close relationship with his own daughter may be lost, too.

23. (Challenging) Students should note the following series of events leading to the Cabuliwallah's arrest. Rahmun, the Cabuliwallah, tries to collect from the neighbor the money owed to him for a Rampuri shawl, but the neighbor falsely denies having bought the shawl. Rahmun is angered by the neighbor's false denial, and the men quarrel. In anger, Rahmun strikes the neighbor, who strikes him back, and Rahmun's clothes become bloodied. Rahmun calls the neighbor names, the police are called, and Rahmun is arrested and accused of murderous assault. Students might infer that the knife belongs to the Cabuliwallah because of his occupation as a fruit seller. Students might also note that the Cabuliwallah's

"The Cabuliwallah"
by Rabindranath Tagore *(continued)*

anger is justified although, if indeed he did strike the neighbor, his assault was not. Furthermore, students might note that because of his low position within India's caste system, the Cabuliwallah would not be believed over the neighbor. The narrator refers to the neighbor as "a certain neighbor," which indicates the narrator's low opinion of him.

Unit Test (p. 75)

Critical Reading/Vocabulary and Grammar
1. b 2. a 3. c 4. b 5. a 6. b 7. a 8. b 9. c
10. c 11. a 12. c 13. b 14. a 15. d 16. c
17. a 18. c 19. c 20. d

Questions are classified in these categories:
  Comprehension 6(E)
  Interpretation 3(A), 4(A), 5(E), 7(A)
  Literary Analysis 9(C), 10(C)
  Reading Strategy 1(E), 2(A), 8(C)
  Vocabulary 11(E), 15(A), 16(A), 17(A), 18(A)
  Grammar Skill 12(A), 13(C), 14(C), 19(A),
    20(A)
  E = Easy, A = Average, C = Challenging

Essay Questions
Guidelines for student response:

21. (Easy) Students should identify a specific struggle experienced by one character in the unit and should provide details about the struggle and how the character copes. Students should explain why they identify with the struggle they choose and why they like or dislike the way in which a character handles his or her struggle. For example, in "Through the Tunnel," students might identify with Jerry's wish to grow up and prove himself. They might admire his decision to swim through the tunnel, or they might feel he took an unnecessary risk.

22. (Average) Students should reveal an understanding of the word *justice* and how the selection they choose deals with a struggle for justice, supporting their ideas with specific examples. For example, some students might discuss the struggle faced by Japanese-American political prisoners in the selection from *Desert Exile* and the way in which Gerald Ford tries to resolve this issue in his remarks. Other students might discuss the injustice of taking the life of a fish in the poem "The Fish" and how the struggle within the speaker results in the compassionate release of the fish.

23. (Average) Students should focus on the internal struggle of a character or speaker in the unit, such as the struggle faced by Jerry in "Through the Tunnel" when he is trying to decide how to prove himself and whether or not he should swim through the tunnel. Students might also choose to describe the struggle of the main character in "Like the Sun," who wants to live a truthful life.

24. (Average) Students should present specific images from any of the selections in the unit. They might describe the details of the underwater tunnel in "Through the Tunnel," the comic details of Thurber's relationship with his dog in "The Dog That Bit People," the vivid details of the fish in "The Fish," or the details of the world of the Cabuliwallah.

25. (Challenging) Students should understand that Thurber's story is written to entertain. Details that show the behavior of the dog and people's response to the dog add to the humor of the selection. *Desert Exile* is a personal record of one person's experience as a political prisoner. Details that convey the suffering and injustices of the period reveal the writer's purpose. Ford's remarks were written as an official acknowlegement of the injustice of the camps. Students should list specific details from the selections that reveal these different purposes.

Unit 4: Turning Points

from *Speak, Memory* by Vladimir Nabokov

Selection Test (p. 79)

Critical Reading/Vocabulary and Grammar

1. b 2. b 3. d 4. a 5. c 6. b 7. d 8. b 9. c
10. a 11. c 12. b 13. d 14. c 15. c 16. a
17. c 18. b 19. d 20. b

Questions are classified in these categories:
Comprehension 2(A), 3(E), 7(E)
Interpretation 8(A), 10(C), 11(E), 13(A)
Literary Analysis 1(A), 12(E), 14(E)
Reading Strategy 4(A), 5(C), 6(C), 9(C)
Vocabulary 15(E), 16(A), 17(C)
Grammar Skill 18(A), 19(A), 20(C)
E = Easy, A = Average, C = Challenging

Essay Questions

Guidelines for student response:

21. (Easy) Students should note that evidence
that Nabokov's first reading experiences
held great meaning for him throughout
his adult life is found in the vivid descriptions of his characters, all of which seem
to be described by a devoted, eager, bright
young boy. The quiet, loving time spent
with his mother, who often read to him at
bedtime, is reflected in the sensory detail
that is characteristic of his work.

22. (Average) Whichever passage students
choose to discuss, they must identify and
explain the sensory details used. Many
students may select Nabokov's description
of the schoolroom, which uses details that
engage the reader's senses of sight, smell,
touch, and hearing.

23. (Challenging) Most students will recognize
that Nabokov has a cynical, bitter attitude
toward the Russian Revolution, which he
shows to the reader by using before and
after descriptions. Students should note
that the impact on Nabokov of his father's
assassination and his family's forced exile
profoundly influenced his attitude.

"Games at Twilight" by Anita Desai

Selection Test (p. 82)

Critical Reading/Vocabulary and Grammar

1. c 2. b 3. a 4. b 5. d 6. b 7. d 8. a 9. b
10. a 11. c 12. c 13. b 14. a 15. b 16. d
17. c 18. a 19. b 20. c

Questions are classified in these categories:
Comprehension 7(C), 10(A), 13(A), 14(A)
Interpretation 1(E), 2(C), 3(E), 9(A), 11(A)
Literary Analysis 4(E), 5(C), 12(A)
Reading Strategy 6(C), 8(A)
Vocabulary 16(C), 17(E), 19(E)
Grammar Skill 15(A), 18(C), 20(A)
E = Easy, A = Average, C = Challenging

Essay Questions

Guidelines for student response:

21. (Easy) Students should recognize that
Ravi feels it would be thrilling to be the
winner in "a circle of older, bigger, luckier
children" and, especially, to gain victory
over his imposing older brother. Out-
smarting the other children would earn
him their respect and admiration. Unfor-
tunately his plan backfires. He stays in
the shed too long, is forgotten and, ultimately, humiliated.

22. (Average) Students should recognize that
the use of dialogue adds variety and interest to writing, moves the plot forward, and
makes the story seem real and personal.
It also reveals information about the per-
sonalities and motivations of the characters. Students should give specific examples of motivation and character traits
revealed for Ravi, Mira, and Raghu. For
example, Raghu's dialogue reveals that he
can be short-tempered and intimidating.

"Games at Twilight"
by Anita Desai (*continued*)

23. (Challenging) Students should describe Ravi's dilemma about whether or not to stay in the shed, his motivation to outsmart the older children, the pros and cons of staying put, allowing himself to be caught, or making a run for the den, and the humiliation of being forgotten and denied the thrill of victory. Students should conclude that Ravi did not make the best possible decision. He should have come out of the shed sooner and made a run for the den. His decision caused him to miss out on a lot of fun, and resulted in his feeling angry and upset.

"The Bridge" by Leopold Staff
"The Old Stoic" by Emily Brontë
"I Am Not One of Those Who Left the Land" by Anna Akhmatova
"Speech During the Invasion of Constantinople" by Empress Theodora

Selection Test (p. 85)

Critical Reading/Vocabulary and Grammar
1. b 2. d 3. c 4. b 5. d 6. b 7. c 8. a 9. b 10. d 11. a 12. b 13. c 14. d 15. a 16. a 17. a 18. b 19. d 20. b

Questions are classified in these categories:
  Comprehension 1(E), 10(A)
  Interpretation 2(A), 5(E), 6(C), 11(A), 15(A)
  Literary Analysis 3(C), 7(A), 9(E), 12(A)
  Reading Strategy 4(A), 8(E), 13(C), 14(A)
  Vocabulary 16(A), 18(C), 19(A)
  Grammar Skill 17(E), 20(A)
  E = Easy, A = Average, C = Challenging

Essay Questions
Guidelines for student response:

21. (Easy) Students' essays should focus on the decisions and values revealed in the selection they choose. Brontë chooses personal liberty; she values independence, dismisses riches, scorns love, and regards fame to be a dream. Empress Theodora chooses to fight; life is meaningless to her without power. Anna Akhmatova chooses to endure foreign rule, physical suffering, and loss of home and friends; she values her land. Leopold Staff chooses to go forward, however unsurely; he values perseverence.

22. (Average) Student essays should focus primarily on the differing tones of the poems. Both poets are uncomfortable with easy responses to challenges. "The Old Stoic" celebrates the courage to cry out for independent life and thought. The poem is a ringing defense of what many would consider nonconformist values in society. Brontë is disdainful of the conventional values of life; her poem dismisses them in favor of personal liberty. The tone of the poem, with its regular meter and rhetorical flourish, is a battle cry for independence. Leopold Staff is uncertain about whether he can "cross that bridge." He lacks Brontë's decisiveness. For him, courage may be going forward in the face of uncertainty.

23. (Challenging) Students should express a clear thesis statement that identifies possible reasons. Dramatic events often hinge on a single decision, as in the single act by Empress Theodora that saves Justinian's reign. Dramatic situations often strip issues to their essences, as in "I Am Not One of Those Who Left the Land." The destruction of war leaves nothing to live for but patriotism. Although the circumstances behind Brontë's credo are not given, the ringing dismissal of conventional values in favor of independence carries the drama of rebellion. In "The Bridge," Staff suspends easy answers in favor of a true-to-life representation of uncertainty, often the psychological condition of dramatic events. Because dramatic situations are by their nature not routine, they offer example and illustration of fundamental ideas and actions.

"The Good Deed" by Pearl S. Buck

Selection Test (p. 88)

Critical Reading/Vocabulary and Grammar
1. b 2. d 3. c 4. a 5. b 6. c 7. c 8. b 9. b
10. a 11. b 12. c 13. b 14. d 15. a 16. a
17. d 18. a 19. d 20. b

Questions are classified in these categories:
Comprehension 1(E), 4(A), 7(E)
Interpretation 2(A), 6(A), 9(C), 10(A), 13(C)
Literary Analysis 12(E), 14(C)
Reading Strategy 3(A), 5(A), 8(A), 11(C), 15(A)
Vocabulary 16(C), 17(A), 20(A)
Grammar Skill 18(A), 19(A)
E = Easy, A = Average, C = Challenging

Essay Questions

Guidelines for student response:

21. (Easy) Students should note that old Mrs. Pan's good deed—introducing Lili to young Mr. Lim—may be described as central to the story. Other good deeds include Mr. Pan's bringing his mother to the United States, young Mrs. Pan's kind and patient treatment of old Mrs. Pan, Lili's giving of her time to meet with old Mrs. Pan, Mr. Lim's kind treatment of old Mrs. Pan, and young Mr. Lim's kindness toward Lili. Students might say that Mr. Pan and his wife are motivated by love and concern for old Mrs. Pan, that Lili is motivated by her compassionate nature and her genuine interest in Chinese culture, that old Mr. Lim is motivated by his general good nature and the fact that old Mrs. Pan amuses him, and that young Mr. Lim is motivated by his good nature and his interest in Lili.

22. (Average) Students should understand that old Mrs. Pan fits the definition of a dynamic character because she changes during the course of the story. In the beginning of the story she has a negative attitude toward American culture. This attitude is reflected in her refusal to eat or leave her room. After meeting Lili, Mrs. Pan begins to change. Driven by a wish to find Lili a suitable husband, Mrs. Pan begins to venture out of her room and meet with people. By the end of the story she is speaking sharply to people and trying to take an active role in shaping Lili's future. Mrs. Pan's change is brought on because she becomes involved in something that is important and familiar to her.

23. (Challenging) Students should understand that the American tradition of marriage is one that involves mutual love and freedom in choosing a marriage partner. The Chinese tradition is one that involves arranged marriages between partners who do not necessarily love each other. Although the typical American marriage is said to be based on love and free choice, it is often the man who asks the woman to marry, and some women who want to marry are not asked. In China most people get married, but many marriages are based on the needs of a community, rather than on love and mutual consent. Both traditions come together in the marriage of old Mrs. Pan's son, who ultimately marries for love but who, out of respect for tradition, allows his elders to feel as if they are arranging his marriage.

"Thoughts of Hanoi"
by Nguyen Thi Vinh
"Pride" by Dahlia Ravikovitch
"Auto Wreck" by Karl Shapiro
"Before the Law" by Franz Kafka

Selection Test (p. 91)

Critical Reading/Vocabulary and Grammar
1. d 2. a 3. c 4. d 5. a 6. b 7. b 8. a 9. d
10. c 11. c 12. c 13. b 14. c 15. a 16. a
17. a 18. c 19. a 20. b

Questions are classified in these categories:
Comprehension 1(E), 7(E), 10(A), 13(A)
Interpretation 2(C), 5(A), 8(A), 12(A), 14(C)
Literary Analysis 3(A), 4(C), 15(C)
Reading Strategy 6(C), 9(A), 11(C)
Vocabulary 17(E), 20(C)
Grammar Skill 16(C), 18(E), 19(A)
E = Easy, A = Average, C = Challenging

Essay Questions

Guidelines for student response:

21. (Easy) Students should note that, according to the poet, death should be caused by war or suicide or cancer or by old age, not by a crashing of metal in the middle of the street. The poet's theme is that

"Thoughts of Hanoi"
by Nguyen Thi Vinh
"Pride" by Dahlia Ravikovitch
"Auto Wreck" by Karl Shapiro
"Before the Law" by Franz Kafka *(continued)*

death by auto wreck is beyond explanation or sense and is, therefore, all the more horrible.

22. (Average) Students should identify the message of each poem and support their points with examples from the poems. In "Thoughts of Hanoi," the message is that friendships or relationships are stronger than political differences. The speaker recalls the past he shared with the person he is addressing, noting the "frontier of hatred" that separates them, but concluding that their shared roots are stronger. In "Pride," the message is that people hide hurts and troubles until some event causes them to be uncovered. The poet supports her message with images of rocks as they are tossed by waves, baked and frozen by heat and cold, lying in wait for years, and finally rubbed against by a little seal.

23. (Challenging) Students may identify "the Law" as government, justice, rights, perhaps even freedom. The man is "from the country" and stands for common, ordinary, if somewhat unimaginative, people. Students may identify the doorkeeper as a symbol for the means of access to "the Law," as the barrier between people and their access to the Law, or perhaps as the excuse people have for not gaining access. The country man is not able to gain access because he hasn't the imagination to be bold, to assert himself, to take a chance on entering and encountering the other doorkeepers.

Unit Test (p. 94)

Critical Reading/Vocabulary and Grammar

1. b 2. d 3. a 4. d 5. b 6. a 7. c 8. d 9. b
10. c 11. a 12. a 13. b 14. c 15. c 16. d
17. b 18. d 19. c 20. b

Questions are classified in these categories:
Comprehension 8(A), 9(E)
Interpretation 7(E), 10(A)
Literary Analysis 1(A), 3(C), 4(E), 6(A)
Reading Strategy 2(C), 5(A)

Vocabulary 15(A), 16(A), 17(C), 18(C), 19(A), 20(A)
Grammar Skill 11(E), 12(A), 13(A), 14(C)

Essay Questions

Guidelines for student response:

21. (Easy) Students should discuss Ravi's personality on the basis of the actions, behavior, thoughts, and feelings described in the text. They might focus on his ingenuity, courage, stubbornness, and determination. Some students may feel that Ravi's age was a factor in his inability to determine the best course of action. Some may feel he was distracted by fantasies of his own glory.

22. (Average) Students should clearly and thoroughly explain the possible consequences of each course of action relating to the person's decision. For example, had Empress Theodora decided to flee with Emperor Justinian, she probably would have lived her life away from her homeland or even have been killed by the Roman rebels. By deciding as she did, she and her husband remained in power in Rome (although they could have died at the hands of rebels there). Students should make a clear judgment about Empress Theodora's decision.

23. (Average) Students should correctly identify the dramatic situation—impending death ("The Old Stoic"), a serious automobile accident ("Auto Wreck"), the denial of justice to a citizen ("Before the Law")—and focus on how characters are affected by it. They may mention that the speaker of Brontë's poem has found a way to accept the inevitability of death; that the auto passengers in Shapiro's poem are touched and haunted by unanswerable questions about responsibility and fate; or that the protagonist of Kafka's parable spends—perhaps *wastes*—his entire life waiting to be granted access to justice.

24. (Average) Students should note the similarity between Ravi's realization that he should long ago have made a run for the den and the man's realization that he should have attempted to gain admittance to the Law himself instead of begging someone else to grant it for him. In both cases, the protagonists displayed dogged

determination, however, the failure to pursue the right course of action prevented them from achieving their goals. Students should also note that a major distinction between the two turning points is that Ravi's occurred in his youth and may well be a useful learning experience, while the man's occurred just before he died.

25. (Challenging) Students may focus on the speakers of "The Bridge" or "I Am Not One of Those Who Left the Land," or on Empress Theodora in "Speech During the Invasion of Constantinople." Students should examine a symbolic action—for instance, the decision to stay and defend the palace and its symbolic meaning involving courage and nobility—and discuss how this act could make the rulers' remaining tenure more secure and highly esteemed.

Unit 5:   Expanding Horizons

"The Widow and the Parrot"
by Virginia Woolf

Selection Test (p. 98)

Critical Reading/Vocabulary and Grammar

1. b 2. a 3. c 4. d 5. a 6. b 7. b 8. c 9. a
10. a 11. c 12. c 13. d 14. d 15. b 16. d
17. d 18. c 19. a 20. b

Questions are classified in these categories:
   Comprehension 2(A), 8(A), 10(A), 14(E)
   Interpretation 1(E), 3(C), 7(C), 9(A)
   Literary Analysis 5(A), 12(E), 13(A)
   Reading Strategy 4(C), 6(E), 11(A)
   Vocabulary 15(C), 19(A), 20(E)
   Grammar Skill 16(A), 17(C), 18(A)
   E = Easy, A = Average, C = Challenging

Essay Questions

Guidelines for student response:

21. (Easy) Students should describe how drawing inferences helped them better understand the story. For example, by closely observing the words and actions of the characters, they could draw conclusions about the meaning of a particular passage. When the parrot leads Mrs. Gage to the burnt house and begins pecking at the miser's hiding place, for instance, you can infer that he wants to help her.

22. (Average) Students might focus on the following actions: Mrs. Gage's empathy motivates her to show kindness to the parrot, and as a result, the parrot shows its gratitude by leading her to the gold; Joseph Brand's miserliness motivates him to hide his fortune, which results in Mrs. Gage's despair; the parrot's desire to repay Mrs. Gage's kindness leads it to set fire to the house, which results in a blazing light that rescues Mrs. Gage.

23. (Challenging) Students should recognize that, on the whole, Mrs. Gage's interactions with animals are more positive than her interactions with people. Positive interactions with animals include: Mrs. Gage's self-sacrificing behavior toward her dog Shag and her concern for Shag while she's away; her kindness to James the parrot, whom others regard as pesky; her belief in the parrot's intelligence. Negative interactions with humans include: Brand's lifelong disregard for Mrs. Gage; the solicitors' lack of concern for Mrs. Gage's impoverished state. Students might conclude that the story stresses the importance of showing kindness for its own sake.

"Civil Peace" by Chinua Achebe

Selection Test (p. 101)

Critical Reading/Vocabulary and Grammar

1. d 2. a 3. c 4. c 5. b 6. a 7. a 8. d 9. b
10. b 11. b 12. a 13. d 14. c 15. b 16. d
17. c 18. b 19. c 20. d

Questions are classified in these categories:
   Comprehension 2(C), 10(E), 13(A), 14(C)
   Interpretation 1(A), 5(A), 9(E), 12(A)
   Literary Analysis 3(E), 6(A), 11(A)
   Reading Strategy 4(A), 7(A), 8(E)
   Vocabulary 15(A), 17(C), 20(A)
   Grammar Skill 16(C), 18(E), 19(A)
   E = Easy, A = Average, C = Challenging

"Civil Peace" by Chinua Achebe *(continued)*

Essay Questions

Guidelines for student response:

21. (Easy) Students must compare and contrast their own experiences with three of Jonathan's, which might include: Jonathan's ingenuity in finding jobs for himself; his returning to Enugu to find his house relatively unscathed after the war; his fear of losing his egg-rasher or being attacked by the crowd outside the Treasury; his fear for himself and his family when the thieves come in the middle of the night.

22. (Average) Students should note that Jonathan relies on the proverb in good times and in bad; it applies when he receives the fortune of the egg-rasher as well as when it is stolen from him. Rather than providing an easy explanation for events, the proverb acts as a source of spiritual strength in the face of the devastating loss of family and material possessions.

23. (Challenging) Students might point out that the story begins and ends with statements about Jonathan's optimism. In the beginning, he is described as counting himself lucky even though one of his children died in the war. At the story's end, he reminds others, as well as himself, that the loss of the egg-rasher is nothing compared to other losses suffered in war. Jonathan has a remarkable ability to find the positive in difficult situations—scrounging for work, waiting in government lines, bargaining with mercenaries. Therefore, students might conclude that he is optimistic in spite of his circumstances.

"The Bean Eaters"
by Gwendolyn Brooks

"How to React to Familiar Faces"
by Umberto Eco

Selection Test (p. 104)

Critical Reading/Vocabulary and Grammar
1. c 2. b 3. a 4. d 5. a 6. c 7. d 8. a 9. a
10. b 11. c 12. b 13. d 14. a 15. b 16. a
17. b 18. c 19. d 20. d

Questions are classified in these categories:
Comprehension 2(C), 8(E), 10(A)
Interpretation 4(A), 6(C), 12(C), 13(A)
Literary Analysis 3(E), 9(C), 11(A)
Reading Strategy 1(C), 5(A), 7(A), 14(E)
Vocabulary 15(E), 17(A), 20(A)
Grammar Skill 16(A), 18(A), 19(E)
E = Easy, A = Average, C = Challenging

Essay Questions

Guidelines for student response:

21. (Easy) Students should focus on the first stanza for the setting of the intimate tone. The simple description of how the two people eat dinner allows readers to imagine being in the room. The sad part of the poem occurs when the people recall happier times from the past, with pangs ("twinges") of regret. The respectful tone is evident throughout. The two people are "Mostly Good," and they continue to be that way, though they have "lived their day."

22. (Average) Students should recognize that the informal tone comes largely from the use of everyday language constructed in fairly simple sentences. Because Eco chooses personal details to illustrate his points, the essay is more informal than if he chose to cite statistics or other people's experiences.

23. (Challenging) Students should recognize that Eco implies that the mass media work hard to make their characters and stories appear real so that people will believe in them. He is hinting that the profusion and availability of media cause some people to lose sight of reality because they are so involved in the imaginary worlds of the characters in movies and television shows.

"A Picture From the Past: Emily Dickinson" by Reynolds Price

"What Makes a Degas a Degas?"
by Richard Mühlberger

Selection Test (p. 107)

Critical Reading/Vocabulary and Grammar
1. b 2. c 3. a 4. b 5. d 6. b 7. c 8. c 9. d
10. a 11. b 12. a 13. c 14. d 15. d 16. d
17. c 18. b 19. b 20. c

Questions are classified in these categories:
Comprehension 1(A), 7(E), 8(A)
Interpretation 2(A), 4(C), 9(E), 14(C), 15(C)
Literary Analysis 3(E), 12(A), 13(A)
Reading Strategy 5(E), 6(A), 10(C), 11(C)
Vocabulary 16(C), 17(A), 19(A)
Grammar Skill 18(A), 20(E)
E = Easy, A = Average, C = Challenging

Essay Questions

Guidelines for student response:

21. (Easy) Students should note that Price suggests that Dickinson was a homely, sensible young woman who lived a lonely life ("sensible rough-knuckled hands" and "a sensible cook"). He uses Dickinson's physical characteristics as seen in the portrait ("lopsided face," "unmatched eyebrows," and "unpainted bruised lips") to point up her homely appearance. Students may agree or disagree with Price's interpretation.

22. (Average) In explaining the sense of immediacy created in Degas' paintings, students should identify the following elements: cutoff figures create a candid effect; tipped elements give the viewer the sense of viewing the painting from above; patches of brilliant color suggest the feeling of movement; large open spaces move the viewer's eye deep into the picture. Collectively, these elements create for the viewer a sense of immediacy, of "being there."

23. (Challenging) Most students will note that what makes a Degas a Degas is the overall element of innovation. Degas' innovation can be seen in a number of elements: the simulated matte finish of pastels, the sketchy charcoal outlines of figures, the extension of color from foreground to backgrounds creating the impression of spontaneous execution. Students should also note Degas' prevailing theme is the ballet.

"The Orphan Boy and the Elk Dog," a Blackfeet Myth

Selection Test (p. 110)

Critical Reading/Vocabulary and Grammar
1. b 2. c 3. a 4. b 5. d 6. b 7. d 8. c 9. b
10. c 11. c 12. a 13. b 14. b 15. a 16. b
17. c 18. a 19. b 20. d

Questions are classified in these categories:
Comprehension 1(E), 3(A), 6(A), 8(E), 11(A), 15(A)
Interpretation 4(A), 9(C), 12(A), 13(A), 14(C)
Literary Analysis 5(A), 10(A)
Reading Strategy 2(E), 7(C)
Vocabulary 17(A), 18(A), 20(A)
Grammar Skill 16(A), 19(A)
E = Easy, A = Average, C = Challenging

Essay Questions

Guidelines for student response:

21. (Easy) Students should understand that the journey to find Elk Dogs becomes important to Long Arrow because he sees it as a chance to prove his worth to his people. Because of this strong desire to be respected by people in his village, he feels pride, excitement, and anticipation as he returns with Elk Dogs.

22. (Average) Students might describe Long Arrow as strong, brave, smart, determined, and considerate. At the beginning of the story, he is wise enough to know that he must follow the camp in order to survive. His bravery, intelligence, and determination help him to face the many obstacles on his journey and to deal effectively with the spirit people.

23. (Challenging) Students should note that a myth is a traditional story that explains the world view of a people. This story is a myth that explains how the Blackfeet came to have use of the horse, an essential part of their culture. It features larger-than-life characters and reveals many important details about the Blackfeet: They were hunters, they were often forced to move in search of buffalo, and before the arrival of horses their lives were much more difficult. The reader also learns about the traits the Blackfeet valued.

"The Street of the Cañon" from Mexican Village by Josephina Niggli

Selection Test (p. 113)

Critical Reading/Vocabulary and Grammar
1. b 2. c 3. b 4. c 5. c 6. c 7. d 8. b 9. d
10. d 11. b 12. a 13. a 14. b 15. a 16. d
17. d 18. a 19. c 20. a

"The Street of the Cañon" *from* **Mexican Village** by Josephina Niggli *(continued)*

Questions are classified in these categories:

Comprehension 2(E), 3(A), 4(E), 5(E), 10(A), 15(A)

Interpretation 8(A), 9(A), 13(A), 14(A), 16(C)

Literary Analysis 7(C), 12(C)

Reading Strategy 1(A), 6(C), 11(A)

Vocabulary 17(A), 19(A)

Grammar Skill 18(A), 20(A)

E = Easy, A = Average, C = Challenging

Essay Questions

Guidelines for student response:

21. (Easy) Students should understand that the author uses third-person omniscient point of view to present the perspectives of all the characters, particularly Pepe and Sarita. While Sarita explains the fight between the two villages, readers get Pepe's thoughts about the fight. While Pepe's thoughts are revealed as he slips into the party and asks Sarita to dance, Sarita's thoughts are revealed after he leaves.

22. (Average) Pepe appears at the party in San Juan Iglesias because he is trying to prove that people from Hidalgo and San Juan Iglesias are not so different from one another that they cannot socialize. People generalize about other people and build hatred in their minds. Pepe sets out to prove to the people in San Juan Iglesias that he can appear at their party and not stand out as their enemy.

23. (Challenging) Students should understand that Sarita has conflicting feelings toward Pepe Gonzalez. Even as she expresses hate for people from Hidalgo, she expresses admiration for the courage and bravery of Pepe. At the end of the story, when she figures out the truth about the stranger, she is amazed that she feels no anger. Pepe affects Sarita's beliefs by showing her that people are not always who they seem to be.

"A Storm in the Mountains" by Alexander Solzhenitsyn
"In the Orchard" by Henrik Ibsen
"A Tree Telling of Orpheus" by Denise Levertov

Selection Test (p. 116)

Critical Reading/Vocabulary and Grammar

1. d 2. b 3. c 4. c 5. d 6. a 7. b 8. a 9. d
10. c 11. a 12. c 13. c 14. a 15. c 16. a
17. b 18. a 19. b 20. d

Questions are classified in these categories:

Comprehension 5(A), 11(C), 13(E)

Interpretation 2(E), 4(C), 6(A), 9(C), 12(A)

Literary Analysis 3(E), 8(A), 15(C)

Reading Strategy 1(A), 7(E), 10(C), 14(A)

Vocabulary 17(E), 18(A), 20(A)

Grammar Skill 16(A), 19(E)

E = Easy, A = Average, C = Challenging

Essay Questions

Guidelines for student response:

21. (Easy) Students should write essays that discuss the general nature of storms and use Solzhenitsyn's text to illustrate their points. In Solzhenitsyn's description, the onlookers are unable to escape the power of the storm, and are thus reduced to mere objects in it, like the crags and the pines. They are isolated and rendered helpless by darkness, blinded by lightning, and deafened by thunder so that their normal perceptions are at the storm's mercy. There is nothing they can do but watch and wait. Thus they feel themselves witness to events that occur regardless of human presence, just as storms occurred in the primal world.

22. (Average) Student responses should answer both parts of the question. Ibsen's theme is that the present moment should be fully appreciated and not lost in the pursuit of daily tasks and goals. Nature is an effective setting for this theme because the pleasures of the natural world can be

described in sensual detail in a way that connects to readers' experience.

23. (Challenging) Student essays should focus on the intimacy and reality created by the use of a first-person speaker. This perspective creates an intimate relationship with the readers by speaking directly to them. Reading the story, we respond to the tree's description of a white dawn as we would to a description by a human.

Unit Test (p. 119)

Critical Reading/Vocabulary and Grammar
1. d 2. b 3. a 4. a 5. c 6. a 7. b 8. c 9. d
10. d 11. c 12. a 13. b 14. a 15. d 16. b
17. c 18. c 19. a 20. b

Questions are classified in these categories:
Comprehension 3(C), 8(A)
Interpretation 4(A), 9(E)
Literary Analysis 1(A), 5(A), 7(A)
Reading Strategy 2(A), 6(C), 10(C)
Vocabulary 15(C), 16(C), 17(A), 18(E), 20(C)
Grammar Skill 11(A), 12(A), 13(A), 14(C), 19(C)

Essay Questions
Guidelines for student response:

21. (Easy) Students should clearly identify the dramatic event (for instance, war in Nigeria or the birthday party in the Niggli story) and explain the way in which the event causes a character's horizons to expand. For example, in the war Jonathan Iwegbu loses a child, a job, money, and all of his possessions except his humble home and a bicycle. These losses give Jonathan a new understanding of his family's paramount importance to him; in turn, this understanding helps him survive a harrowing robbery and start over again.

22. (Average) Students should focus on a single selection and clearly explain how a character's understanding of the world is enriched by some aspect of nature. For instance, students might discuss how the violence and theatricality of the storm in the Solzhenitsyn work humble and fill the speaker with awe; the natural event seems to shed light on the speaker's understanding of human beings' place in the natural order of things.

23. (Average) Students might discuss the importance of memory to the two characters in "The Bean Eaters." Despite the number of years that may have passed in the lives of these two "common people," they apparently take great pleasure not only in the act of remembering, but also in the mementos of their shared lives.

24. (Average) Students might focus their attention on how profound stress, anxiety, and loss can—in time—bring growth and expanded horizons to an individual. For example, the extraordinary losses incurred by the protagonist of "Civil Peace" ultimately give him a deeper, simpler way of looking at the world. This new perspective clarifies for him the importance of love and family and the secondary importance of worldly goods and possessions.

25. (Challenging) Students might focus on visual art or music as they relate to the two selections. Alternatively, students might allude to other art forms that relate to their own prior knowledge and experience. In any case, students should attempt to make a clear explanation of how the originality of art can inspire an individual to reconsider ways of approaching the most basic aspects of life.

Unit 6: Short Stories

"The Open Window" by Saki

Selection Test (p. 123)

Critical Reading/Vocabulary and Grammar
1. b 2. d 3. a 4. d 5. b 6. b 7. d 8. b 9. a
10. c 11. d 12. c 13. b 14. d 15. b 16. c
17. a 18. c 19. a 20. c

Questions are classified in these categories:
Comprehension 1(E), 3(A), 5(E), 6(A)
Interpretation 2(A), 4(A), 9(E), 12(C), 14(C), 15(A), 16(C)
Literary Analysis 8(C), 10(A), 13(A)
Reading Strategy 7(C), 11(A)
Vocabulary 18(E), 20(A)
Grammar Skill 17(A), 19(A)
E = Easy, A = Average, C = Challenging

Essay Questions

Guidelines for student response:

21. (Easy) Students should understand that Framton expects to meet nice, polite people and to have a chance to rest and relax. His expectations are violated by Vera who is able to manipulate him politely into leaving. He is so absorbed with his own problems and worries that he is unable to look beyond Vera's conventionally polite behavior. Framton's actions show that he is self-absorbed and gullible.

22. (Average) Students should describe the exposition as the point in the story during which readers meet Framton and Vera and learn why he is at the unfamiliar home; the inciting incident as Vera's question about how well Framton knows her aunt, which prompts the story she tells about the open window; the central conflict as Vera's problem of trying to figure out a way to get rid of Framton; and the resolution as the point at which the hunting party returns and Framton leaves. Students should understand that the reader cannot be sure whether or not Vera is being truthful until the end of the story.

23. (Challenging) Students should understand that while Framton and Mrs. Sappleton are caught up in polite social conventions, Vera secretly operates outside of these conventions. Framton is nervously trying to make a good impression while also trying to judge people based on his sister's letters and his own observations about "nice behavior." He is so absorbed in himself that he cannot view his situation objectively. Mrs. Sappleton, too, is caught up in social convention and is easily tricked by her niece's final story about the dogs.

"Leiningen Versus the Ants" by Carl Stephenson

Selection Test (p. 126)

Critical Reading/Vocabulary and Grammar
1. d 2. c 3. b 4. a 5. c 6. a 7. d 8. c 9. a
10. b 11. b 12. c 13. b 14. a 15. b 16. c
17. c 18. b 19. d 20. b

Questions are classified in these categories:
Comprehension 3(A), 9(E), 10(A)
Interpretation 2(A), 6(E), 11(C), 12(A), 14(C)
Literary Analysis 1(C), 5(E), 7(A)
Reading Strategy 4(E), 8(E), 13(A)
Vocabulary 15(A), 17(C), 19(C)
Grammar Skill 16(A), 18(A), 20(A)
E = Easy, A = Average, C = Challenging

Essay Questions

Guidelines for student response:

21. (Easy) Students should recognize that "Leiningen Versus the Ants" presents a conflict early on and builds through a series of complications until the climax. Familiarity with other suspense stories might lead students to predict that Leiningen will save the day as well as himself. Students may be surprised by the failure of some efforts against the ants.

22. (Average) Students should note that the external conflict of the ant attack on the plantation sets the stage for the story's action and drives many of the other external conflicts. However, students should also recognize that Leiningen's internal conflicts factor greatly into the story. Students should conclude that Leiningen's decision to risk his own life and his strug-

gle to gain safety are the defining moments in the story.

23. (Challenging) Students might characterize Leiningen positively as a strong, intelligent, resourceful, and determined individual. However, his stubbornness and pride create serious problems. While his strong characteristics allow him to battle the ants and win, his pride and stubbornness cause several men to die and Leiningen himself to be injured.

"By the Waters of Babylon"
by Stephen Vincent Benét

Selection Test (p. 129)

Critical Reading/Vocabulary and Grammar
1. b 2. c 3. d 4. a 5. b 6. a 7. d 8. b 9. a
10. c 11. d 12. b 13. c 14. b 15. c 16. b
17. c 18. d 19. b 20. c

Questions are classified in these categories:
Comprehension 1(A), 2(C), 3(A), 4(E), 11(A)
Interpretation 7(A), 10(A), 12(A), 14(C)
Literary Analysis 6(E), 13(A)
Reading Strategy 5(A), 8(A), 9(E)
Vocabulary 15(A), 18(E), 19(E)
Grammar Skill 16(E), 17(C), 20(A)
E = Easy, A = Average, C = Challenging

Essay Questions
Guidelines for student response:

21. (Easy) Students should note that the first-person point of view creates a personal tone and a suspenseful mood. Seeing events unfold through John's eyes makes readers feel part of the action and leaves them wondering what will happen next. Insight into John's thoughts increases the intimacy of the tone and tension of the mood.

22. (Average) Students should recognize that the first-person point of view limits the reader's knowledge of important details, such as setting and plot background. The "I" narrator creates a personal, intimate tone. Contrasting points might include: a third-person limited narrator would make the reader feel more detached from story events or a third-person omniscient point of view would provide too much information and diminish the story's suspense.

23. (Challenging) Students might contend that Benét's outlook is generally optimistic. Although modern civilization has come to an end, it is not clear why or how it ended. The fact that John has awe and respect for the monuments of modern technology implies that Benét respects them as well. On the other hand, students could argue that the story is a denouncement of technology because the Great Burning seems to have been caused by chemical warfare. Additionally, time and nature eventually conquer even the greatest technological accomplishments of humankind.

"A Problem" by Anton Chekhov
"Luck" by Mark Twain

Selection Test (p. 132)

Critical Reading/Vocabulary and Grammar
1. c 2. b 3. d 4. b 5. c 6. b 7. a 8. d 9. b
10. b 11. c 12. d 13. a 14. b 15. c 16. a
17. d 18. a 19. b 20. c

Questions are classified in these categories:
Comprehension 1(E), 9(A), 10(C)
Interpretation 2(C), 3(C), 6(E), 8(A), 11(E)
Literary Analysis 7(A), 13(A), 14(A)
Reading Strategy 4(C), 5(A), 12(E)
Vocabulary 15(E), 17(A), 18(E)
Grammar Skill 16(A), 19(C), 20(A)
E = Easy, A = Average, C = Challenging

Essay Questions
Guidelines for student response:

21. (Easy) Students should note that Sasha's behavior causes a serious dilemma revolving around the family's honor. It will remain untarnished if the family pays his debt. If they allow Sasha to face his punishment, the family honor will be tarnished, for Sasha will be a criminal in the eyes of the law. Students should note that Sasha is indifferent to the family dilemma.

22. (Average) Students must note that static characters do not change throughout the course of a story. Neither Scoresby nor Uskov learn from their experiences; Scoresby remains a lucky fool and Sasha remains an indifferent ne'er-do-well. Students may choose to contrast the static character of Scoresby with the dynamic

"A Problem" by Anton Chekhov
"Luck" by Mark Twain *(continued)*

character of the clergyman, who changed his opinion of Scoresby; he once thought of him as naive and sweet and now considers him an absolute fool.

23. (Challenging) Students should note that Scoresby is described as good, sweet, lovable, and guileless. He is also described as dimwitted, ignorant and foolish. The fact that he accepts his promotions seemingly without question suggests that he is not aware that he is ill-equipped to hold those positions, nor is he aware that only dumb luck is responsible for his success. Given all this, he probably feels proud and deserving of his success, though somewhat baffled by it. Some students might identify with Scoresby's run of good luck, though in a similar situation they may feel "fraudulent" and undeserving.

"There Will Come Soft Rains"
by Ray Bradbury
"The Garden of Stubborn Cats"
by Italo Calvino

Selection Test (p. 135)

Critical Reading/Vocabulary and Grammar
1. b 2. d 3. a 4. b 5. a 6. c 7. c 8. a 9. c
10. b 11. b 12. a 13. d 14. b 15. a 16. d
17. c 18. d 19. c 20. d

Questions are classified in these categories:
Comprehension 1(E), 3(C), 7(A)
Interpretation 5(E), 9(C), 11(A), 15(C)
Literary Analysis 2(A), 4(A), 6(A), 8(C), 14(E)
Reading Strategy 10(A), 12(E), 13(C)
Vocabulary 16(A), 18(A), 19(E)
Grammar Skill 17(E), 20(A)
E = Easy, A = Average, C = Challenging

Essay Questions

Guidelines for student response:

21. (Easy) Students should recognize that the Teasdale poem reflects the theme of the story. The poem's message is that nature would not care if "mankind perished utterly." In the story, the prophecy of the poem comes true. Dawn comes and the sun rises as the story ends, and no human is left "to know that we were gone."

22. (Average) Students should recognize that the theme of the story is a warning about the effects of modern invention, specifically nuclear weaponry. Modern devices are used in this story to make the point about man's fragility. By setting the story in the future, Bradbury creates a cautionary tale. He presents the double edge of technology and issues a warning about its effects.

23. (Challenging) Both stories have elements of a fable. "There Will Come Soft Rains" is a simple story with a clear message about the dangers of nuclear war; it uses animal-like machines to make its point about the consequences of modern life. "In the Garden of Stubborn Cats" is almost a classic fable written from the perspective of animals.

"The Princess and All the Kingdom"
by Pär Lagerkvist
"The Censors" by Luisa Valenzuela

Selection Test (p. 138)

Critical Reading/Vocabulary and Grammar
1. b 2. a 3. c 4. d 5. d 6. b 7. c 8. c 9. b
10. c 11. a 12. b 13. d 14. a 15. a 16. c
17. c 18. b 19. d 20. d

Questions are classified in these categories:
Comprehension 1(A), 3(E), 8(E)
Interpretation 4(A), 5(A), 9(C), 11(A)
Literary Analysis 6(C), 12(A), 13(A)
Reading Strategy 2(A), 7(C), 10(A), 14(C)
Vocabulary 15(A), 16(E), 18(E)
Grammar Skill 17(E), 19(A), 20(C)
E = Easy, A = Average, C = Challenging

Essay Questions

Guidelines for student response:

21. (Easy) Students may say that the story is pessimistic because all of the prince's hopes are dashed by the unexpected news of his burden of responsibility. Those who believe the story is optimistic may cite the prince's acceptance of the crown, his sincerity, and his pure ambitions. Lagerkvist's general outlook is that we must take the bad with the good and pay the price for our actions or ambitions.

22. (Average) Students should recognize that the "system" in the story is a government using its power intrusively to censor cor-

respondence. The acquisition, use, and misuse of power is one of the story's universal themes.

23. (Challenging) Students should state that Lagerkvist reveals his message directly through the chancellor's words. They should also note that he uses a fairy tale format to teach that happiness has a price. For Valenzuela's story, students should note that the message is revealed indirectly through the plot and outcome of the story. Her message is that power is uncontrollable: The main character becomes so absorbed in the system that he condemns himself to execution. Because the views are universal literary themes, most students will conclude that they are founded in reality.

Unit Test (p. 141)

Critical Reading/Vocabulary and Grammar

1. a 2. c 3. d 4. b 5. c 6. b 7. c 8. a 9. a
10. d 11. d 12. a 13. b 14. b 15. c 16. a
17. d 18. b 19. a 20. c

Questions are classified in these categories:
Comprehension 1(A), 7(E)
Interpretation 2(C)
Literary Analysis 3(A), 5(A), 8(A), 10(A)
Reading Strategy 4(C), 6(A), 9(E)
Vocabulary 11(A), 12(A), 13(A), 18(A), 19(A), 20(C)
Grammar Skill 14(C), 15(C), 16(C), 17(A)

Essay Questions

Guidelines for student response:

21. (Easy) Students should make certain that the story they choose contains both types of characters. After identifying examples, students should explain why their two choices are static and dynamic characters, respectively. For example, in "A Problem," Ivan Markovitch is static, for he does not change or grow during the course of the story; he merely attempts to defend and support his nephew. On the other hand, Sasha Uskov is dynamic because his initial indifference and weariness about life is transformed first into rage and finally into criminal thinking.

22. (Average) Students should identify a specific literary element in a selection and explain how it figures centrally in the overall effect of the story. For instance, in "There Will Come Soft Rains," Ray Bradbury's use of setting is the single most important element in understanding the story's ideas. (In fact, this story has no characters and almost no plot.) The setting—both its time frame and its numerous details illustrating future domestic life—provides the reader with vivid proof of the fragility of human life, the destructiveness of war, and the potentially empty promise of progress.

23. (Average) Students should note the essential similarity between the two stories—the central subject matter of destroyed civilization. To convey the idea that human life is fragile, Bradbury relies on details of a highly mechanized future (and the specific geography of a single house), whereas Benét uses the lens of religion and a spiritual journey and the geography of a city. Bradbury looks forward, whereas Benét places the reader in a position to look back at our own times.

24. (Average) Students should make clear and thorough analyses of a story's plot structure. For instance, the exposition in "The Princess and All the Kingdom" conveys information about the prince's valor and skill in battle. The inciting incident (which could be identified either as the princess and prince's wedding or as the presentation of the city keys to the prince by the aged chancellor) introduces the central conflict—the prince's exclusive interest in a happy life with the princess versus his responsibility to his new kingdom. The rising action occurs in the animated argument between chancellor and prince. The climax occurs when the prince threatens violence and the chancellor gently crowns him and dubs him king. The resolution occurs in the final sentence, as the new king accepts his lot.

25. (Challenging) Students should identify the theme of a work and discuss the way in which the author conveys that theme. For example, in "The Censors," Valenzuela conveys his ideas about the importance of resisting tyranny and securing personal and political freedom for people. His plot—involving Juan's misguided attempts to protect Mariana—highlights the idea that human beings must exert extraordinary concentration and self-control to avoid inadvertently joining the enemy.

Unit 7: Nonfiction

"The Marginal World"
by Rachel Carson

Selection Test (p. 145)

Critical Reading/Vocabulary and Grammar
1. b 2. a 3. a 4. c 5. c 6. a 7. d 8. b 9. d
10. c 11. b 12. c 13. a 14. d 15. a 16. c
17. b 18. d 19. c 20. b

Questions are classified in these categories:
Comprehension 1(A), 4(E), 8(C)
Interpretation 7(A), 9(C), 10(A), 11(A)
Literary Analysis 3(C), 12(E), 13(A)
Reading Strategy 2(A), 5(C), 6(C), 14(C)
Vocabulary 15(E), 16(A), 20(E)
Grammar Skill 17(E); 18(A), 19(A)
E = Easy, A = Average, C = Challenging

Essay Questions

Guidelines for student response:

21. (Easy) Students should cite the different places that Carson writes about and provide examples that show how she describes each setting in detail. They should note that her approach allows her to recreate a particular time of day, evoke a particular mood, and focus on the intriguing and awe-inspiring aspects of each location, offering readers "proof" that "the edge of the sea is a strange and beautiful place."

22. (Average) Whichever passages students cite, they should in some way understand that Carson's creation of the sense of a primeval world serves the purpose of supporting one of her main points: "Underlying the beauty of the spectacle there is meaning and significance."

23. (Challenging) Students should note that what these three places share is the sense of mystery, beauty, tenacity, mutability, and adaptability that Carson finds in all elements of the "marginal world" between land and sea. For Carson, "underlying the beauty of the spectacle there is meaning and significance." These three places differ, however, in their specific details of mystery, beauty, and tenacity.

from *The Way to Rainy Mountain*
by N. Scott Momaday
from "Nobel Lecture"
by Alexander Solzhenitsyn
"Keep Memory Alive" by Elie Wiesel

Selection Test (p. 148)

Critical Reading/Vocabulary and Grammar
1. d 2. d 3. a 4. b 5. b 6. d 7. b 8. a 9. d
10. b 11. b 12. d 13. c 14. a 15. c 16. b
17. d 18. a 19. d 20. d

Questions are classified in these categories:
Comprehension 1(A), 7(E), 12(A), 15(E)
Interpretation 2(E), 3(C), 6(C), 8(A), 9(A), 10(E), 13(C)
Literary Analysis 4(C), 16(C)
Reading Strategy 5(A), 11(A), 14(A)
Vocabulary 18(A), 19(C)
Grammar Skill 17(E), 20(A)
E = Easy, A = Average, C = Challenging

Essay Questions

Guidelines for student response:

21. (Easy) Students should note that Momaday uses personal experiences to reflect on the passing of an entire culture, a device that is characteristic of reflective essays. The loss of his grandmother serves as a means of reflecting on the loss of an entire culture.

22. (Average) Students should recognize that Wiesel believes that if we forget the Holocaust, it will happen again. Remembering not only prevents a repeat of events, it also honors those who died between 1933 and 1945.

23. (Challenging) Students should acknowledge that Solzhenitsyn's experience under a repressive government is the source for this piece. In it, he emphasizes the relationship between violence and lying. Neither is necessary because we can live by truth. And writers, as both speakers and audience, are the transmitters of truth.

"A Child's Christmas in Wales" by Dylan Thomas
"Marian Anderson: Famous Concert Singer" by Langston Hughes

Selection Test (p. 151)

Critical Reading/Vocabulary and Grammar

1. c 2. b 3. c 4. d 5. a 6. d 7. c 8. b 9. c
10. d 11. b 12. b 13. c 14. b 15. d 16. a
17. b 18. d 19. c 20. a

Questions are classified in these categories:
  Comprehension 1(E), 9(E), 10(A), 13(A)
  Interpretation 4(C), 6(A), 7(C), 12(A), 16(A)
  Literary Analysis 2(A), 5(A), 11(A), 14(A)
  Reading Strategy 3(A), 8(E), 15(C)
  Vocabulary 18(A), 20(A)
  Grammar Skill 17(A), 19(A)
  E = Easy, A = Average, C = Challenging

Essay Questions

Guidelines for student response:

21. (Easy) Students may say that Thomas remembers his childhood with warmth and fondness. Detailed descriptions of throwing snowballs, enjoying the snow with his best friends, receiving and opening presents, and watching how the holidays affect his relatives reveal this attitude. The passage of time has caused many of Thomas's Christmas memories to blend together and become exaggerated and larger-than-life. He conveys in his autobiographical piece the innocence and excitement of a child at an exciting time of year.

22. (Average) Students should understand that Langston Hughes has great admiration and respect for Marian Anderson as a singer and a person. In his essay, he highlights her musical talent, her ability to work hard to overcome hardships, her willingness to live simply and unpretentiously, and her generosity toward others. Langston Hughes emphasizes that she not only contributed to the world of music with her beautiful voice, but also broke racial stereotypes and paved the way for other Americans of color.

23. (Challenging) Students should understand that the autobiographical "A Child's Christmas in Wales" reveals many personal details about Thomas's thoughts and childhood perceptions that would be missing in a biographical essay. The biographical "Marian Anderson: Famous Concert Singer" presents facts about Marian Anderson's life. Hughes is able to see Anderson's contributions from the historical perspective of the biographer rather than the more personal perspective of the autobiographers.

"Flood" by Annie Dillard

Selection Test (p. 154)

Critical Reading/Vocabulary and Grammar

1. a 2. a 3. c 4. b 5. d 6. d 7. c 8. b 9. c
10. c 11. b 12. a 13. c 14. b 15. c 16. b
17. b 18. a 19. b 20. d

Questions are classified in these categories:
  Comprehension 1(E), 3(E), 4(E), 12(E)
  Interpretation 6(C), 9(C), 11(A), 13(A), 15(C), 16(A)
  Literary Analysis 5(A), 8(A), 10(C)
  Reading Strategy 2(A), 7(A), 14(C)
  Vocabulary 17(A), 19(A)
  Grammar Skill 18(A), 20(A)
  E = Easy, A = Average, C = Challenging

Essay Questions

Guidelines for student response:

21. (Easy) Students should understand that "Flood" is a good example of a descriptive essay because it is rich in imagery. Dillard presents detailed images that help the reader to understand what it is like to be in the presence of a flood. Students may cite these passages: comparison of the rising creek to a blacksnake caught in a kitchen drawer; how the familiar creek appears to have been usurped by a larger creek; the roar of the wind and the rushing water; the images of people and items floating in the swiftly moving water; the image of "the whole world" being in a flood and sliding like sand down a chute; the image of the water crashing against the bridge.

22. (Average) Students should be able to recall that the destructive flood takes place in the month of June, during the solstice, and that it is the result of a tropical storm.

"Flood" by Annie Dillard *(continued)*

Tinker Creek rises its banks, crashes across a bridge that sat far above it, and carries away mud, personal possessions, splintered wood, and animals. The author's personal impressions include her description of the rushing water as violent, dragon-like, and snapping the bridge "like a fist"; her description of the land as a painted scroll; her descriptions of her feelings of dizziness and being mauled; her descriptions of her thoughts about animals such as the snapping turtle; and her description of the "whole earth" sliding like sand down a chute. These impressions reveal Dillard's fascination with the flood and its power. The scene makes her feel fearful, overwhelmed, amazed.

23. (Challenging) Students should understand that the essay expresses the idea that the balance between order and chaos in nature is delicate and can shift at any moment. The writer addresses this theme when she describes the "air of menace" and the ominous feelings of the damp air after a driving rain. She knows after witnessing the flood that people can never assume that everything is always going to be predictable and calm. She also addresses this theme by describing how quickly the creek rises up and takes over her area. The rushing water, which only the day before was a peaceful creek, is suddenly capable of destroying everything in its path. The writer learns from the flood that the forces of nature are more powerful than people imagine.

"Star Wars—A Trip to a Far Galaxy That's Fun and Funny . . ." by Vincent Canby
"Star Wars: Breakthrough Film Still Has the Force" by Roger Ebert

Selection Test (p. 157)

Critical Reading/Vocabulary and Grammar

1. a 2. c 3. b 4. d 5. d 6. a 7. b 8. a 9. b
10. c 11. c 12. c 13. b 14. a 15. a 16. c
17. d 18. a 19. d 20. d

Questions are classified in these categories:
    Comprehension 1(E), 5(A), 9(C), 13(E)
    Interpretation 3(C), 6(A), 8(E), 10(C), 14(C), 15(A)

Literary Analysis 2(A), 11(A), 19(A)
Reading Strategy 4(A), 7(E), 12(E), 23(C)
Vocabulary 16(C), 18(C)
Grammar Skill 17(C), 20(A)
E = Easy, A = Average, C = Challenging

Essay Questions

Guidelines for student response:

21. (Easy) Students should recognize that the two essays have different purposes. Canby's review intends to inform his readers about the plot of *Star Wars* and encourage them to go see it; Ebert's review defines the role of *Star Wars* in the history of cinema. Canby mentions the movie's reference to similar tales; Ebert's critique compares the movie to classics of fiction and cinema. Canby focuses on the pleasure of watching the movie; Ebert describes how it changed all movies that came after it. Canby evaluates the movie for the average moviegoer; Ebert evaluates the movie in terms of its artistic quality and contributions to movie-making in general.

22. (Average) Student responses should express a clear understanding of the critical review as an artistic form of communication in itself. Writers of reviews evaluate works of art and provide information that helps readers to make a choice about seeing or reading the works. Both Canby and Ebert comment on *Star Wars* in ways the average moviegoer is not trained to do. Their reviews reflect the experience of having seen many films and read many books on movie history. Even if we disagree with their evaluations, reading them helps us to form or examine our own opinions.

23. (Challenging) Students should recognize that Ebert uses other works of art to prove his argument that *Star Wars* deserves to be viewed as a masterpiece. If *Birth of a Nation* and *Citizen Kane* broke new ground in photography, editing, special effects, and storytelling, so does *Star Wars*; if *2001: A Space Odyssey* was a brilliant technical accomplishment, so was *Star Wars*; if *Don Quixote, Huckleberry Finn,* and *The Odyssey* are great because each tells the eternal tale of a simple character on a quest for the meaning of life, *Star Wars* is great for the same reason.

"Mothers & Daughters"
by Tillie Olsen and Estelle Jussim

Selection Test (p. 160)

Critical Reading/Vocabulary and Grammar

1. c 2. a 3. c 4. a 5. d 6. a 7. a 8. b 9. b
10. d 11. a 12. b 13. d 14. c 15. d 16. c
17. b 18. d 19. b 20. c

Questions are classified in these categories:
Comprehension 2(A), 5(E), 6(E)
Interpretation 1(C), 4(C), 13(A), 14(C)
Literary Analysis 3(E), 10(C), 11(A)
Reading Strategy 7(A), 8(E), 9(A), 12(A)
Vocabulary 16(E), 18(A), 19(A)
Grammar Skill 15(A), 17(E), 20(A)
E = Easy, A = Average, C = Challenging

Essay Questions

Guidelines for student response:

21. (Easy) Students should provide accurate examples and reasonable interpretations of facial expressions, body language, connection or estrangement between the subjects, background, and other significant visual details.

22. (Average) Students must choose two different photographs that represent contrasting emotions. Students should identify key phrases in Olsen's writing that helps them uncover meaning. Students should also demonstrate an ability to interpret body language, facial expression, proximity of figures, and other visual details.

23. (Challenging) Students should understand that the metaphor implies that while mothers have great hopes for their daughters, they cannot control the paths their daughters will take. In creating something of possibility, the mother/photographer must accept that her creation might be successful in a way she did not intend and may not understand. Students might note that Sohier concedes the mother/photographer is not always the best interpreter of her creation. In a way, her text might be limiting the way in which the viewer approaches her photograph, of which, she admits, she may not be the best interpreter.

"Imitating Nature's Mineral Artistry" by Paul O'Neil
"Work That Counts"
by Ernesto Ruelas Inzunza

Selection Test (p. 163)

Critical Reading/Vocabulary and Grammar

1. a 2. d 3. d 4. b 5. d 6. a 7. c 8. c 9. d
10. a 11. c 12. b 13. c 14. b 15. a 16. b
17. a 18. d 19. c 20. c

Questions are classified in these categories:
Comprehension 1(E), 2(A), 3(C), 9(C), 12(A)
Interpretation 4(C), 6(A), 8(E), 10(C)
Literary Analysis 7(A), 11(C), 13(A)
Reading Strategy 5(E), 14(C)
Vocabulary 17(A), 18(A), 19(E)
Grammar Skill 15(E), 16(A), 20(A)
E = Easy, A = Average, C = Challenging

Essay Questions

Guidelines for student response:

21. (Easy) Students should acknowledge that Inzunza was writing for a general audience, not a scientific one. The use of the first-person makes the article accessible to a general audience. It also helps engage readers and draws them into the experience of seeing the River of Raptors. The nondescriptive language of the article is what distinguishes it from a first-person account. The article contains facts and statistics presented clearly and directly. It does not contain the author's impressions or opinions. Students may cite the use of defined terms, the logical presentation of information, and the inclusion of facts (not opinions) as characteristics of a technical article such as Inzunza's.

22. (Average) Students should recognize that the interconnectedness of nature makes the study of all living things important. Learning about animal and bird populations and how they move reveals information about their food sources and habitats. That, in turn, can reveal how these populations are being affected by human activities. A decrease in the bird count could indicate that the birds are not migrating, are dying, or have taken a different route (though this last is unlikely). An

"Imitating Nature's Mineral Artistry"
by Paul O'Neil
"Work That Counts"
by Ernesto Ruelas Inzunza *(continued)*
increase in the bird count could indicate that the birds' natural or human predators are less abundant or that their habitat is somehow more protected than it once was. In any case, variations in the bird count should be a sign to bird-watchers like Inzunza that something—whether caused by nature or humans—is happening and might need to be studied.

23. (Challenging) Students should make a choice of synthetic or natural and state a good reason. Some students may conclude that because natural and synthetic gems are made of identical materials, it does not matter what one owns. In terms of the appeal of synthesizing gems, students may cite humans' fascination with gems dating from ancient times. Synthesizing is just a continuation of that fascination. By pursuing this type of synthesis, perhaps scientists will be led to other knowledge that will benefit humans in some way. Some students may feel that synthesizing gems is just another way to market unneeded luxury items to people who may or may not be able to afford them.

Unit Test (p. 166)

Critical Reading/Vocabulary and Grammar
1. d 2. a 3. b 4. c 5. a 6. b 7. c 8. c 9. d 10. a 11. b 12. d 13. c 14. a 15. a 16. d 17. b 18. c 19. b 20. c

Questions are classified in these categories:
Comprehension 1(A), 5(A)
Interpretation 4(C), 9(C)
Literary Analysis 2(A), 6(E), 8(E)
Reading Strategy 3(A), 7(C), 10(A)
Vocabulary 11(C), 12(A), 13(E), 16(A), 17(A)
Grammar Skill 14(A), 15(A), 18(C), 19(A), 20(A)

Essay Questions
Guidelines for student response:

21. (Easy) Students' essays should contain clear explanations of how written and visual elements reinforce each other and help readers appreciate more deeply the subject matter. For instance, the list of emotions in Olsen's third paragraph can help a reader focus on meaningful details in the three female subjects of "August, New Mexico, 1979"; conversely, this photograph gives hard, clear form to the meaning of text such as "holding, embracing, touching; or in terrible isolation."

22. (Average) Students should analyze the biographical or autobiographical essay for its author's use of impressions and facts. For example, Langston Hughes uses facts almost exclusively in his account of Marian Anderson's life. One of the few impressions included in this excerpt begins its second section: "When Marian Anderson again returned to America, she was a seasoned artist."

23. (Average) Students' essays should clearly compare and contrast a technical article with an example of another type of nonfiction. For example, whereas Annie Dillard uses dozens of sensory details to help general readers vividly imagine a flooded landscape, Paul O'Neil relies on definitions, examples, explanations of processes and properties, illustrations, and technical language to convey information about gemstones to a general audience.

24. (Average) Students' essays should note similarities as well as differences between the two persuasive essays. For example, both Solzhenitsyn and Wiesel wish to persuade their audiences to embrace a political idea. Yet the Russian writer uses a bold, exhortative tone to convey to an audience of writers his central message—let writers worldwide seize their considerable power "to help mankind see itself accurately." On the other hand, Wiesel uses a softer, more personal tone to convey to a more general audience his central message—"if we forget" history's horrors, then "we are guilty, we are accomplices."

25. (Challenging) Students should analyze a reviewer's use of literary devices associated with expository and/or persuasive writing. For example, Vincent Canby explains and interprets various ideas from *Star Wars*, classifies characteristics of the film, and gives many illustrations to support his assertions. Canby's use of these literary devices places his critical review closer to an expository than to a persuasive essay.

268 Formal Assessment

Unit 8: Drama

Antigone, Prologue through Scene 2, by Sophocles

Selection Test (p. 170)

Critical Reading/Vocabulary and Grammar

1. d 2. b 3. a 4. c 5. d 6. c 7. c 8. c 9. a
10. b 11. d 12. b 13. c 14. a 15. a 16. b
17. d 18. a 19. b 20. c

Questions are classified in these categories:
  Comprehension 1(A), 5(E), 10(C)
  Interpretation 3(C), 6(E), 8(A), 12(A), 13(C)
  Literary Analysis 7(E), 11(C), 14(A)
  Reading Strategy 2(A), 4(E), 9(A)
  Vocabulary 15(E), 16(A), 17(A)
  Grammar Skill 18(A), 19(A), 20(C)
  E = Easy, A = Average, C = Challenging

Essay Questions

Guidelines for student response:

21. (Easy) Students should understand that Antigone is the protagonist who is in conflict with the antagonist Creon. Students should recognize that the clash between Antigone's individualism and sense of duty to a higher authority and Creon's desire for obedience from his subjects and his adherence to the letter of the law fuel the play's conflict.

22. (Average) Students might agree that Antigone's words and actions reveal that she is motivated by loyalty to her brother and adherence to higher laws. Indeed, she risks her own life to defy Creon's orders, a high price to pay for mere pride. However, students might also point out that Antigone's pride fuels the conflict between her and Creon. Rather than trying to reason with Creon after her arrest, she seems to take pleasure in her defiance and wishes to be a pure voice of dissent, refusing to accept Ismene's change of heart.

23. (Challenging) Students should recognize that Creon needs to establish himself as a firm ruler in the wake of the recent assault and his assumption of the throne. Students might note Creon's emotional appeal to his audience; he reminds them of their devotion to previous rulers and of his blood connection to them. He establishes the dichotomy between loyal men and traitors and enforces it with loaded language such as *heroes, slavery*, and *friendship.* Creon's pride rings throughout his speech; he continually uses the pronoun *I* and refers to his wisdom, principles, and values. Students might conclude that the speech conveys Creon's defensiveness rather than his strength.

Antigone, Scenes 3 through 5, by Sophocles

Selection Test (p. 173)

Critical Reading/Vocabulary and Grammar

1. a 2. b 3. a 4. c 5. c 6. d 7. d 8. b 9. a
10. d 11. b 12. b 13. c 14. c 15. a 16. d
17. b 18. c 19. b 20. a

Questions are classified in these categories:
  Comprehension 4(E), 10(A), 12(A), 13(A)
  Interpretation 1(A), 2(A), 7(A), 14(C)
  Literary Analysis 5(A), 9(A), 11(E)
  Reading Strategy 3(E), 6(C), 8(A)
  Vocabulary 15(C), 17(A), 20(C)
  Grammar Skill 16(E), 18(A), 19(A)
  E = Easy, A = Average, C = Challenging

Essay Questions

Guidelines for student response:

21. (Easy) Students should choose one character and make reasonable connections between the character's actions and words and their own experiences. For example, students who identify with Antigone might strongly relate to her moral dilemma. Students might recall experiences from their own lives and draw comparisons. Students should conclude that identifying with the character makes the character's motivation clearer and gives greater meaning to the play.

22. (Average) Students who believe Antigone is the tragic character might provide evidence such as Antigone's unyielding determination to defy Creon, a prideful action that leads to her death. Students who view Creon as the tragic character might point out that Creon suffers more tragic losses than Antigone—he loses his son, his wife, and probably the respect of his people. His stubbornness in the face of

Antigone, Scenes 3 through 5,
   by Sophocles (continued)
reason is a deep flaw that he admits and corrects too late.

23. (Challenging) Students should conclude that the play's theme of unchecked pride and its tragic consequences reflects a timeless human dilemma. The imbalance of political power, inequality of the sexes, and struggle between parent and child featured in the tragedy are all themes that resonate in the modern era.

The Tragedy of Julius Caesar, Act I, by William Shakespeare

Selection Test (p. 176)

Critical Reading/Vocabulary and Grammar

1. b 2. a 3. c 4. d 5. a 6. c 7. c 8. d 9. b 10. c 11. a 12. d 13. d 14. c 15. a 16. d 17. a 18. b 19. b 20. c

Questions are classified in these categories:
   Comprehension 1(E), 2(C), 9(E), 13(E)
   Interpretation 6(A), 7(A), 8(C), 12(A), 14(C), 15(C)
   Literary Analysis 3(A), 5(A)
   Reading Strategy 4(E), 10(C), 11(A)
   Vocabulary 17(A), 18(A)
   Grammar Skill 16(C), 19(C), 20(E)
   E = Easy, A = Average, C = Challenging

Essay Questions

Guidelines for student response:

21. (Easy) Students may cite the following events or phenomena: the soothsayer's prediction, the thunderstorm, the slave's burning hand, the lion that Casca meets, the "hundred ghastly women" claiming to have seen men walking about enveloped in fire, and the owl that Casca saw at midday in the marketplace. They may note that these unusual occurrences seem to indicate a great change. Taken individually, the portents help to build suspense and speculation as to why Caesar should beware the ides of March. Students may mention that the particularly violent storm may be caused by unhappy gods. Are they unhappy because of events that happened or that are *about* to happen? The other instances that Casca cites were unusual but perhaps explicable in one way or another. Taken together, though, they create anxiety among both characters and readers/audience members.

22. (Average) Students should recognize that the characters in Act I, Scene i, are representatives of groups of people—commoners who are supportive of Caesar, and tribunes who disapprove of Caesar's popularity. The tribunes Flavius and Marullus show readers, through both words and actions, that there exists a faction that does not wholly support Caesar. This is important to the play and foreshadows the conspiracy that will soon begin. The fact that Caesar is celebrating a triumph serves further to introduce the situation. Readers learn not only that Caesar is supported by the commoners, but that he is a successful military general. The fact that he is an effective military leader helps shape readers' reactions to the conspiracy against Caesar. The exposition also establishes the physical setting—the streets of Rome. And it establishes the time setting—February 15. This becomes important immediately in Scene ii, when Caesar is warned about the ides of March, just a month away.

23. (Challenging) Students should acknowledge that kingship would extend one person's influence or power in a way that is undemocratic. The American governmental system revolves around the people's right to choose. "Kingship" connotes ideas of power that are not compatible with democracy. Also, there are notions of "inherited power" with kingship that do not fit with democratic systems. Romans would have reacted to the idea of a king for some of the same reasons. Final decisions about government, justice, tax collection, law-making, warfare, and so on would all rest with one person. In terms of evidence, Cassius refers to Caesar's behavior as godlike or arrogant and likens Roman citizens to slaves under Caesar's rule, as well as to sheep under a wolf's care.

The Tragedy of Julius Caesar, Act II, by William Shakespeare

Selection Test (p. 179)

Critical Reading/Vocabulary and Grammar

1. c 2. a 3. d 4. c 5. b 6. a 7. c 8. a 9. d
10. d 11. a 12. c 13. a 14. d 15. a 16. d
17. b 18. b 19. c 20. b

Questions are classified in these categories:
Comprehension 1(A), 2(E), 8(A)
Interpretation 4(A), 7(E), 9(E), 10(C), 12(E), 14(C), 15(C)
Literary Analysis 5(A), 11(E)
Reading Strategy 3(A), 6(C), 13(E)
Vocabulary 16(A), 18(C), 19(E)
Grammar Skill 17(E), 20(A)
E = Easy, A = Average, C = Challenging

Essay Questions

Guidelines for student response:

21. (Easy) Students may note that Brutus embodies the essential conflict of the play, and that his principle of protecting the Republic from the risks of dictatorship outweighs his personal kindness and noble nature. Essays should include some or all of these details: Brutus is not ambitious and thinks only of the good of the country. He values his friends closely, as indicated in his speeches. In his soliloquy at the beginning of Act II, Brutus makes the case that Caesar wants to be crowned, and if he becomes emperor, there will be nothing to stop him from any abuse.

22. (Average) Students should note the meteor showers, the thunder and lightning, the dreams and portents mentioned by Calpurnia as the major omens of Act II. They may point out that the omens serve three purposes in the play. They serve to foreshadow difficult times, first for Caesar and eventually for all. Second, they connect with Roman religion, which believed in omens. Students may cite the odd events such as a lioness giving birth in the street, opening graves, gruesome dreams, meteor showers, and fierce storms that increase the pressure on the characters. Third, they apply an element of suspense because the characters have the option of heeding the omens. Essays may provide this example: Caesar ignores the soothsayer, but he listens to Calpurnia until Decius reinterprets the bloody dream. The possibility that they may heed warnings suggests the possibility that the characters could control or avoid their fates.

23. (Challenging) Essays should note that the conspirators choose to leave Antony alive because they fear killing him would make their "course seem too bloody." Their concern that public opinion would turn against them is consistent with the high purpose Brutus serves in rebelling. The essential element of Brutus' character that animates the play is his nobility. He is Caesar's personal friend; he likes Antony. He is a respected member of society. Unlike Cassius, he does not act against Caesar because of any personal animosity or ambition, but takes seriously the principles that he feels Caesar's rise have put at risk. He is noble and high-minded, so a merciful and "civilized" approach, even in so extreme a case, seems the best course to him. He also trusts that if the conspirators act from the high principles Brutus values, the public will understand and agree. He underestimates the threat posed by Antony, which Cassius recognizes; because he is so focused on his own high cause, he assumes Antony can "do no more than Caesar's arm, when Caesar's head is off." Brutus would do none of this bloody business if he didn't feel he had to, and he wants to do as little of it as possible.

The Tragedy of Julius Caesar, Act III, by William Shakespeare

Selection Test (p. 182)

Critical Reading/Vocabulary and Grammar

1. b 2. a 3. c 4. a 5. b 6. d 7. b 8. a 9. b
10. d 11. c 12. b 13. c 14. d 15. a 16. d
17. b 18. a 19. d 20. c

Questions are classified in these categories:
Comprehension 1(A), 3(A), 8(A), 13(E)
Interpretation 2(A), 6(C), 12(C), 14(A), 15(E)
Literary Analysis 5(E), 7(E), 10(A), 11(C)
Reading Strategy 4(C), 9(A), 16(A)
Vocabulary 18(A), 20(E)
Grammar Skill 17(A), 19(E)
E = Easy, A = Average, C = Challenging

The Tragedy of Julius Caesar,
Act III, by William Shakespeare *(continued)*

Essay Questions

Guidelines for student response:

21. (Easy) Students should recognize that Antony is playing to these men who obviously hold power, since they planned and carried out an assassination. Antony's message is that he bows to their greater judgment, and if he, too, must be killed because they deem him too powerful, then he willingly submits to their decision, since they undoubtedly act for the good of all. Antony's tone is just short of fawning; it is certainly ingratiating. Antony hopes to endear himself to the conspirators. His motives involve ensuring his own safety and gaining some measure of advantage in the situation. The speech is delivered *to* the conspirators, of course, because Antony could not accomplish his purpose—gaining the good will of the conspirators—without addressing these ideas directly to them.

22. (Average) Students should recognize that Antony's roles are those of friend to conspirators and champion of Caesar. He appears to make an agreement with the conspirators to ensure his own safety, most importantly, and to find out what their motives are. Given his close relationship with Caesar, Antony *must* take this step to make sure the conspirators are not out to get him as well. Willingly offering his life to Brutus is a test to see how Brutus will react. In fact, he reveals in his funeral oration and in the two-line statement afterward that he is in fact still Caesar's man and has purposely set the crowd against the conspirators. Antony switches from one role to the other very carefully at the beginning of his funeral oration. While apparently honoring Brutus and his judgment, he actually discredits Brutus by crying Caesar's praises, though very cleverly. Scene iii very briefly demonstrates that Antony's speech has done its job. The crowd has indeed gone after the conspirators and is out of control in its desire to avenge Caesar's death.

23. (Challenging) Sample paraphrase: Here is where Cassius' dagger slashed, and see what a tear the dagger of spiteful Casca

made. Through here Caesar's friend Brutus stabbed, and as he pulled the dagger away the blood ran out as if out of a door to see if it was actually Brutus who had knocked so unkindly. For Brutus was dear to Caesar, the gods may judge. Brutus' cut was the most cruel of all, for Caesar felt betrayed when he saw Brutus, and this betrayal is what hurt, more than the wound. He was heartbroken, and died at the base of the bloody statue, with his cloak covering over his face. Students should recognize that Antony is personalizing the assassination to make it more horrible to the crowd. He cannot possibly know who made which wound, but he nonetheless labels several of them with individual assassins' names. Caesar's body is no longer a corpse, it is a living testament of betrayal and broken friendship. Antony dwells on Brutus' relationship with Caesar because he knows Brutus was the leader of the conspiracy and Antony needs, especially, to turn the crowd against him. Antony goes so far as to claim that it was not the daggers that killed Caesar, but the betrayal of his and Brutus' friendship. In this, the third section of his oration, Antony already knows that the crowd is coming around to his way of seeing things. The appeal to emotion and passion he uses here cements the crowd's allegiance *to* Antony and Caesar and *against* the conspirators.

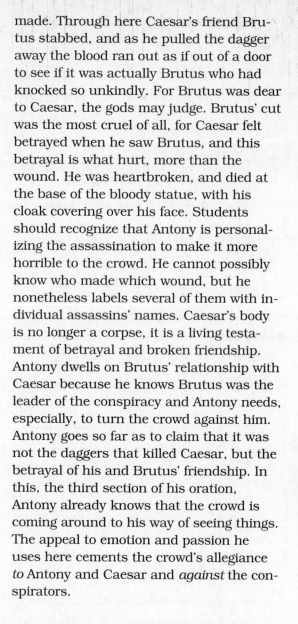

The Tragedy of Julius Caesar,
Act IV, by William Shakespeare

Selection Test (p. 185)

Critical Reading/Vocabulary and Grammar
1. b 2. d 3. c 4. a 5. b 6. d 7. b 8. c 9. a 10. a 11. c 12. c 13. a 14. c 15. b 16. c 17. d 18. c 19. b 20. d

Questions are classified in these categories:
   Comprehension 1(E), 7(E), 11(E), 14(A)
   Interpretation 3(A), 5(A), 6(A), 8(C), 10(C), 15(C)
   Literary Analysis 4(A), 9(C)
   Reading Strategy 2(A), 12(E), 13(C)
   Vocabulary 16(A), 18(A), 20(A)
   Grammar Skill 17(A), 19(A)
   E = Easy, A = Average, C = Challenging

Essay Questions

Guidelines for student response:

21. (Easy) Students should understand that the conflict between Antony and Brutus and Cassius is about power. Brutus and Cassius killed Julius Caesar, a leader of whom Antony was a loyal follower. Antony is driven by his wish to avenge the murder of Julius Caesar and to secure his own power. He is a difficult enemy to have because he is manipulative and calculating, and he will stop at nothing to get what he wants. He demonstrates these qualities at the beginning of Act IV when he talks with his men about which Romans must die, and again when he talks about changing Caesar's will.

22. (Average) Students should say that Brutus' wife dies, he loses respect for Cassius, and his friendship with Cassius begins to deteriorate. He faces the threat of Antony's army and is unable to gather an army nearly as strong. He faces defeat, the loss of Rome, and possibly death. He is also visited by the ghost of Julius Caesar, who stirs his feelings of guilt over the killing. Brutus handles the difficult events of Act IV with stoicism—he does not allow emotion to cloud his judgment or stand in the way of his responsibilities. Given the events of Act IV, students might say that the future for Brutus seems grim.

23. (Challenging) Both Antony and Brutus tend to keep emotion from interfering with their professional roles, but Antony is calculating, mercenary, and hypocritical while Brutus is sincere and strives to be virtuous. Antony demonstrates his traits at the beginning of Act IV when he talks about different ways in which he can secure his power, the people who must die, and the ways to change Julius Caesar's generous will. Brutus demonstrates his traits when he criticizes Cassius for being dishonest, when he talks about his reasons for killing Julius Caesar, and with his kind treatment of his men. Antony appears to have no feeling, and Brutus seems to struggle with keeping emotions down so that he can concentrate on important matters. Unlike Brutus and Antony, Cassius is an emotional character—he is shocked when Brutus seems to express no emotion over the death of his wife. Like Antony, he is eager for personal power and is often dishonest. Brutus accuses him of accepting bribes and forgetting the ideals for which they killed Caesar. Like Brutus, Cassius at times shows signs of having a conscience.

The Tragedy of Julius Caesar, Act V, by William Shakespeare

Selection Test (p. 188)

Critical Reading/Vocabulary and Grammar
1. b 2. a 3. c 4. c 5. d 6. c 7. b 8. a 9. a
10. b 11. d 12. b 13. d 14. a 15. c 16. c
17. d 18. a 19. d 20. c

Questions are classified in these categories:
Comprehension 4(E), 6(E), 8(A), 11(A)
Interpretation 1(E), 5(E), 7(C), 9(C), 10(A), 12(C), 16(C)
Literary Analysis 14(A), 15(A)
Reading Strategy 2(A), 3(A), 13(A)
Vocabulary 18(A), 20(A)
Grammar Skill 17(E), 19(E)
E = Easy, A = Average, C = Challenging

Essay Questions

Guidelines for student response:

21. (Easy) After the murder of Julius Caesar, Antony wants only revenge against Brutus. He sees him as one of the greedy conspirators who is envious of Caesar's power and popularity. By the end of Act V, Antony considers Brutus "the noblest Roman of them all." He realizes that although Brutus' actions may have been wrong, his intentions are virtuous and sincere. Antony understands that Brutus honestly believed that killing Caesar was best for the Roman people. Unlike the others, who wanted Caesar's power, Brutus was a gentle man who wanted to do what he thought was best.

22. (Average) Students should say that Caesar's death produces a variety of effects. The strongest effect of Caesar's death is the tension between Antony and the conspirators. Antony becomes driven by the idea that he must have revenge and strengthen his own power, and he

The Tragedy of Julius Caesar,
Act V, by William Shakespeare *(continued)*

succeeds in turning the people of Rome against the conspirators. In trying to unite against the threat of Antony and his strong army, Brutus and Cassius begin to experience conflict in their own relationship. Brutus begins to lose respect for Cassius, who abuses his power following the death of Caesar. They also begin to disagree on many issues. The deterioration of Brutus' trust in Cassius causes Brutus to begin to doubt whether killing Caesar was truly the right thing to do. When he is visited by Caesar's ghost, his anxiety about the murder and about the impending battle grows. In Act V, when a battle finally results from the growing tension between Antony and Brutus and Cassius, both Cassius and Brutus kill themselves. Cassius makes an error in judgment and kills himself out of guilt. Brutus kills himself so he won't be captured and brought back to Rome in complete dishonor. The tragic events of Act V occur because killing Caesar was an evil act, and no good can come of such an act.

23. (Challenging) Students might say that Brutus' heroic qualities include his loyalty, his love for his country, and his high ideals. He exhibits these qualities when he discusses his reasons for killing Caesar, when he gives his funeral speech for Caesar, and when he speaks as he is dying. Students should say that his tragic flaw is his trusting nature and his ability to be swayed by other people. This flaw becomes obvious when he allows Cassius to talk him into killing Caesar and he cannot see that Cassius has other motives. He is also tricked into trusting Antony immediately following Caesar's death. Brutus' death is tragic because he is a kind, noble man who tries to live according to his beliefs. Unlike many of the other people around him, he makes mistakes but always has the best intentions.

Unit Test (p.191)

Critical Reading/Vocabulary and Grammar
1. c 2. b 3. a 4. c 5. c 6. a 7. b 8. d 9. a
10. c 11. a 12. c 13. b 14. d 15. c 16. d
17. b 18. b 19. b 20. c

Questions are classified in these categories:
Comprehension 1(E)
Interpretation 4(A), 6(A), 8(A), 22(A), 24(A)
Literary Analysis 2(A), 7(A), 10(A)
Reading Strategy 3(E), 5(C), 9(A)
Vocabulary 13(A), 14(E), 17(A), 19(C), 20(C)
Grammar Skill 11(A), 12(A), 15(C), 16(E), 18(C)
E = Easy, A = Average, C = Challenging

Essay Questions
Guidelines for student response:
21. (Easy) Students should articulate what they found most sympathetic and interesting about the character they choose and then support their essay with details of the character's thoughts, words, and actions. For example, if students focus on the character of Brutus, they might highlight his sincerity and his loyalty, describing some of his interactions with other characters and his reasons for killing Caesar.

22. (Average) Students should understand that most of the actions of Antony and Octavius are rooted in rational thought, while Brutus and Cassius are often moved and misguided by their emotions. Students might mention that these differences are revealed after the death of Caesar, when the two groups are planning their strategies. Antony is so rational and void of emotion that he is even planning to kill certain relatives in order to secure his power. Meanwhile, Brutus and Cassius have petty arguments and begin to show disunity.

23. (Average) Students might focus on the external conflict between Antony and the conspirators, or the external conflict between Brutus and Cassius that develops after Caesar's death. Students are likely to describe the internal struggle of Brutus after the death of Caesar or the internal struggle of Cassius when he believes he is responsible for the death of Titinius.

24. (Average) Students' essays should identify Brutus's wish to avoid the shame of capture as an immediate cause of his suicide. Other events that lead to his final, desperate moments include: Caesar's murder; Brutus' placing of his trust in Cassius; and Brutus' decision to advance on Antony's army. Students should say

that an immediate effect of his death is Antony's awareness that Brutus was the "noblest Roman of all," and his promise to bury Brutus with honor. Students might speculate that because of the death of Brutus Antony is secure in his leadership.

25. (Challenging) Students might say that Caesar's heroic qualities include his leadership skills and his ability to gain popularity. These qualities are revealed when he returns from a successful battle to celebrations in Rome. His tragic flaw is his pride, which prevents him from listening to warnings about his life being in danger. Brutus's heroic qualities include his loyalty, his love for his country, and his high ideals. He exhibits these qualities when he discusses his reasons for killing Caesar, when he gives his funeral speech for Caesar, and when he speaks as he is dying. Students should say that his tragic flaw is his trusting nature which allows him to be swayed by other people. Students should understand that Brutus does not display the same pride and leadership skills that Caesar displays.

Unit 9: Poetry

"The Stolen Child"
by William Butler Yeats

Selection Test (p. 195)

Critical Reading/Vocabulary and Grammar
1. c 2. b 3. d 4. d 5. a 6. b 7. c 8. a 9. b 10. a 11. d 12. c 13. d 14. c 15. b 16. a 17. c 18. c 19. c 20. d

Questions are classified in these categories:
Comprehension 1(E), 8(A), 12(C)
Interpretation 4(A), 5(C), 9(A), 11(E), 15(C)
Literary Analysis 2(A), 6(E), 10(C), 14(A)
Reading Strategy 3(E), 7(A), 13(C)
Vocabulary 18(E), 19(A), 20(A)
Grammar Skill 16(E), 17(E)
E = Easy, A = Average, C = Challenging

Essay Questions

Guidelines for student response:

21. (Easy) Student essays should show that they recognize that the child may weep no more, but neither will he see home nor hear its harmonies again. Students may use examples of similar sorts of loss and gain from their lives. One cannot be hurt by one's friends if one has no friends, but neither can one have the pleasures friendship offers. One cannot lose if one does not participate, but neither can one win. The joy of love may equal the pain of its loss, and life itself, as the poem suggests, is precious because it is finite.

22. (Average) Student essays should point to images of nature that Yeats uses to describe both the supernatural world of the fairies and the world from which the child is taken. Descriptions of natural settings of cliffs, lakes, woods, and birds are all easily recognizable in the human world of the reader. We don't really believe in fairies, and we do not think someone is whispering to trout, but we see the ponds and ferns. Simple concrete images, from large natural ones to small domestic ones, reveal what is being stolen from the child.

23. (Challenging) Yeats uses the fairy to articulate both the pleasures and pain of being human. From the first, when the fairy describes a world shared by both humans and fairies, this speaker claims a position beyond human pain. He tries to lure the child because "the world's more full of weeping than you can understand." Readers know the stakes of life, though the child may not, so they understand that the fairy is trying to trick the child out of his human destiny. He details the fairy life in mystical ways, although still in a recognizable natural setting, and he reveals that his intention is to take the child from human troubles. But human troubles also include human pleasures, and as the child is lost to the world, the fairy points out what is lost to the child as well: peaceful evenings and small pleasures. The pretended point of view of a fairy allows us to step back from humanity and assess the reward as well as the price of being human. A fairy, if such a thing existed, would not understand the loss.

"In Flanders Fields" by John McCrae
"The Kraken" by Alfred,
Lord Tennyson
"Reapers" by Jean Toomer
"Meeting at Night"
by Robert Browning
"Prayer of First Dancers"
Traditional Navajo Chant

Selection Test (p. 198)

Critical Reading/Vocabulary and Grammar

1. c 2. a 3. d 4. c 5. b 6. a 7. b 8. d 9. a
10. c 11. a 12. c 13. a 14. b 15. c 16. d
17. c 18. a 19. d 20. b

Questions are classified in these categories:
Comprehension 1(E), 4(E), 6(A), 8(E), 10(A)
Interpretation 2(A), 9(C), 12(C), 14(A), 15(C)
Literary Analysis 5(A), 11(A), 13(A)
Reading Strategy 3(C), 7(A), 16(A)
Vocabulary 18(A), 20(A)
Grammar Skill 17(A), 19(A)
E = Easy, A = Average, C = Challenging

Essay Questions

Guidelines for student response:

21. (Easy) Students should understand that the speaker has been on a journey at sea. He brings his boat to shore, and readers can sense his relief as he leaves the gray sea and starts walking on the "warm sea-scented beach." He approaches a farm house and taps on the window, eager to see someone inside. The speaker's feelings on meeting the person inside the farm house are revealed by his description of their two beating hearts, which overpower voices expressing joy and fear. The meeting is obviously a joyful and long-awaited one.

22. (Average) In "In Flanders Fields," soldiers who have been killed in battle challenge people still living to continue their fight. They say that if people who are living do not "carry the torch" and complete what has been started, they are unable to rest peacefully. The poem "The Kraken" is a legend about a sea monster that has been passed down. The poem presents a new perspective on this legend and predicts for readers what could happen to the leg-

endary Kraken. "Prayer of First Dancers" is a ceremonial chant that has been passed down among the Navajo people. In this piece, reverence for nature and tradition is shared among the Navajo.

23. (Challenging) In "In Flanders Fields," a regular repetition is reflective of the endless rows of grave markers in Flanders fields. The rhythm of the poem is disrupted when the speaker describes the sound of gunfire, the abrupt end to the soldiers' lives, and the possibility of never being able to sleep if the fight is not continued. These disruptions in the rhythm of the poem draw attention to these lines. In "The Kraken," Tennyson's use of repeated sounds and rhythms gives the poem a musical quality, reflective of an entertaining poem about a legend. In "Reapers," the repetition of the *s* sound at the beginning of the poem suggests the steady movement of the scythes over the fields. The rhythm of this poem also reflects the repetitive movements of the reapers. "Meeting at Night" features a repetition of consonant sounds that gives the poem a musical quality, reflective of the poem's happy ending. The fact that "Prayer of First Dancers" is a ceremonial chant is emphasized by the repetition of words and phrases important and sacred to the Navajo people.

"The Wind—tapped like a tired Man"
by Emily Dickinson
"A Pace Like That"
by Yehuda Amichai
"Metaphor" by Eve Merriam
"Right Hand" by Philip Fried

Selection Test (p. 201)

Critical Reading/Vocabulary and Grammar

1. b 2. d 3. c 4. a 5. b 6. c 7. c 8. a 9. b
10. a 11. c 12. b 13. d 14. c 15. b 16. b
17. d 18. c 19. a 20. c

Questions are classified in these categories:
Comprehension 1(E), 6(E), 12(A)
Interpretation 3(A), 5(C), 7(C), 10(E), 14(C), 15(C)
Literary Analysis 2(A), 9(E), 13(A)

Reading Strategy 4(A), 8(A), 11(A)
Vocabulary 16(A), 18(A), 20(A)
Grammar Skill 17(A), 19(A)
E = Easy, A = Average, C = Challenging

Essay Questions

Guidelines for student response:

21. (Easy) The poem "Metaphor" presents a metaphor in which morning is compared to a blank sheet of paper. Merriam describes how each morning presents a blank sheet of paper on which a person can "write" the events and experiences of the day. Each night, the paper holding the day's experiences is folded up and filed away. With this metaphor, Eve Merriam is saying that each morning presents a new beginning. In "Right Hand," Philip Fried uses Grandfather's hand as a metaphor for Grandfather's whole person. As he uses his hand each day to iron trousers and shirts, his hand becomes expressive and self-assured, telling stories and poems in Yiddish of his life and heritage. When Grandfather needs to form English words, he places the hand in his pocket. With this metaphor, the speaker illustrates the personality of Grandfather, the importance of his native culture, and his experience living in a new culture and trying to learn a different language.

22. (Average) The speaker in "A Pace Like That" is tired of living life in haste and wants a quieter, slower existence. He wants to approach life slowly and carefully, to think more about his own actions and thoughts and less about what other people say. The speaker in "The Wind—tapped like a tired Man" seems to have a similar approach to life. She takes the time to notice and respond to a simple gust of wind blowing through her home. When the wind leaves, she focuses on her aloneness.

23. (Challenging) In "The Wind—tapped like a tired Man," the speaker takes the time to focus on an aspect of nature—the wind. She chooses to allow the wind into her home and becomes fascinated by its sound and movements. Her solitude allows her to appreciate this moment with the wind, which she sees as having a per-

sonality and a will all its own. In "A Pace Like That," the speaker makes the choice to approach life at a slower pace so that he can appreciate the quiet beauty of the world around him and reflect on his own life. In "Metaphor," the speaker chooses to treat each morning as a positive new beginning—a chance to have a fresh start and live life to the fullest. In "The Hand," the speaker expresses his respect for his grandfather and his grandfather's experiences. The poem shows that Grandfather values his heritage and hard work.

"La Belle Dame sans Merci"
by John Keats
"Danny Deever" by Rudyard Kipling

Selection Test (p. 204)

Critical Reading/Vocabulary and Grammar

1. c 2. b 3. c 4. d 5. c 6. b 7. d 8. b 9. a
10. d 11. d 12. d 13. a 14. c 15. b 16. b
17. c 18. b 19. a 20. a

Questions are classified in these categories:
Comprehension 4(A), 6(C), 10(A), 14(A)
Interpretation 1(C), 3(A), 7(C), 8(A), 12(E), 15(C)
Literary Analysis 2(E), 5(C), 13(A), 16(A)
Reading Strategy 9(A), 11(C)
Vocabulary 17(E), 18(E)
Grammar Skill 19(A), 20(A)
E = Easy, A = Average, C = Challenging

Essay Questions

Guidelines for student response:

21. (Easy) Student essays should reflect an understanding that the clues they get come from the three speakers of the poem. Files-on-Parade primarily asks questions, and his puzzlement at the change of routine and his wonder at the nearness of the condemned man reveal his inexperience. The Color-Sergeant bluntly says he dreads what he must watch, and although he describes it grimly, he's tough enough to deal with it. The third speaker, the unnamed soldier who reports the conversations of the other two, explains Deever's crimes and the rituals of military justice.

"La Belle Dame sans Merci" by John Keats
"Danny Deever" by Rudyard Kipling
(continued)

22. (Average) Student essays should indicate that they understand that Keats is lamenting the temporary nature of love. The knight has made a total and absolute commitment to the lady, and he awakes to find her gone forever beyond his reach. He is left with nothing. She may be an elf or apparition, but what she represents— the romantic tradition of courtly love to the knight, and romance and the moment at large to Keats—is gone from life. The pitilessness exists not so much in the lady as in the impossibility of fulfillment.

23. (Challenging) The unnamed speaker in "Danny Deever" functions as a supplier of information that cannot easily come in dialogue. He identifies, for example, the other two speakers, and after each of their exchanges voices a refrain. This narrator also speaks in the idiom of the soldiers, so readers presume he shares inside military knowledge. He moves the action forward so that the other two can comment upon it. In each of the refrain sections, the plot progresses. In the first, Deever is described; in the second, he is brought out; and in the third, his crime is explained. After Deever's death, the unnamed narrator says "they're marchin' us away," so we presume he is a soldier who has, like the readers, witnessed the execution as well as the exchange between the two other speakers.

"The Guitar"
by Federico García Lorca
"Making a Fist"
by Naomi Shihab Nye
"Jade Flower Palace" by Tu Fu
"The Moon at the Fortified Pass"
by Li Po
"What Are Friends For"
by Rosellen Brown
"Some Like Poetry"
by Wisława Szymborska

Selection Test (p. 207)

Critical Reading/Vocabulary and Grammar
1. c 2. d 3. b 4. c 5. a 6. d 7. b 8. b 9. c
10. a 11. b 12. c 13. d 14. d 15. a 16. b
17. c 18. a 19. b 20. d

Questions are classified in these categories:
Comprehension 1(A), 4(E), 7(A), 9(E)
Interpretation 5(A), 6(C), 10(E), 11(A), 14(C)
Literary Analysis 2(A), 12(C), 15(C)
Reading Strategy 3(A), 8(A), 13(E)
Vocabulary 16(A), 17(C), 18(A)
Grammar Skill 19(A), 20(A)
E = Easy, A = Average, C = Challenging

Essay Questions
Guidelines for student response:

21. (Easy) Students may choose "The Guitar" and "Jade Flower Palace." Supporting examples will illustrate lack of end line punctuation. Students should draw the conclusion that reading in sentences helps them understand whole ideas in a poem.

22. (Average) Students should clearly identify the poem's theme and chief emotion. For example, students should note that "The Moon at the Fortified Pass," whose theme is war, creates a strong feeling of melancholy and longing. Poetic devices might include imagery, as in "Jade Flower Palace" or "Making a Fist"; figures of speech, such as the simile, metaphor, and personification in "The Guitar"; and diction, such as *infinite, wistful,* and *toss and sigh* in "The Moon at the Fortified Pass."

23. (Challenging) Students should recognize that even though the poems do not follow

a regular rhythm, the words and images still create a musical effect. For example, in "The Guitar," repetition of lines such as "Now begins the cry / Of the guitar" and "Impossible / To still it" are like a chorus in a song. Students should also note that, like music, the poems create an overall mood that is not explicitly stated; rather, the mood is created by key "notes" or images such as the "wistful eyes" in "The Moon at the Fortified Pass" or clutching onto poetry as a "saving bannister" in "Some Like Poetry."

Sonnet 18 by William Shakespeare
"The Waking" by Theodore Roethke
Tanka by Ki no Tsurayuki and Priest Jakuren
Haiku by Matsuo Bashō and Kobayashi Issa

Selection Test (p. 210)

Critical Reading/Vocabulary and Grammar
1. c 2. d 3. d 4. b 5. b 6. a 7. a 8. d 9. a 10. c 11. b 12. a 13. b 14. c 15. d 16. b 17. c 18. d 19. a 20. c

Questions are classified in these categories:
Comprehension 1(E), 2(A), 6(E), 9(E)
Interpretation 4(C), 5(A), 12(A), 13(C)
Literary Analysis 3(A), 8(E), 14(C)
Reading Strategy 7(C), 10(C), 11(A), 15(A)
Vocabulary 16(A), 17(E)
Grammar Skill 18(C), 19(A), 20(A)
E = Easy, A = Average, C = Challenging

Essay Questions
Guidelines for student response:

21. (Easy) Students should describe imagery in sensory terms. For instance, they might describe feeling the cold, blowing wind and hearing the mournful cry of the plovers in Tsurayuki's tanka. Students must use these sensory descriptions to analyze each poem's meaning. Students might explain that the imagery in the tanka contrasts with the speaker's feelings for the girl he loves and that it implies that his love is not returned. The haiku's imagery might reflect the poet's goal of praising nature's peaceful, calming beauty.

22. (Average) Students must identify the poetic form of the poem they choose. They should provide examples of how the poem fits the given form. Moreover, they should analyze the poem's effectiveness in relating the poet's message or impression. For example, students might prefer Sonnet 18, both because of its challenging form and its appealing imagery and message.

23. (Challenging) Students should identify Sonnet 18 as a Shakespearean sonnet and "The Waking" as a villanelle. In analyzing Sonnet 18, students might note that the rhyming words in the rhyme scheme support the content: shines/declines, dimmed/untrimmed, fade/shade, and see/thee—the closing couplet rhyme emphasizing the poem's focus. In analyzing "The Waking," students might note that the repetition of the lines *I wake to sleep, and take my waking slow* and *I learn by going where I have to go* underscore the poem's theme.

Unit Test (p.213)

Critical Reading/Vocabulary and Grammar
1. a 2. c 3. b 4. d 5. b 6. c 7. b 8. a 9. c 10. b 11. c 12. b 13. c 14. b 15. c 16. d 17. d 18. a 19. d 20. a

Questions are classified in these categories:
Comprehension 1(E)
Interpretation 2(A), 6(A), 8(A)
Literary Analysis 3(A), 5(A), 10(A)
Reading Strategy 4(4), 7(A), 9(A)
Vocabulary 11(A), 12(C), 15(A), 17(E), 18(E)
Grammar Skill 13(E), 14(E), 16(C), 19(A), 20(A)
E = Easy, A = Average, C = Challenging

Essay Questions
Guidelines for student response:

21. (Easy) Students might describe the image of the cypress-mountain in Priest Jakuren's tanka, explaining that the poem reminds them of feelings of loneliness. Other students might mention the vivid images of the Kraken in Tennyson's poem, explaining how these images helped them to view a sea monster in a unique way.

22. (Average) Students should focus on the specific details of two nature poems. They

should be able to explain why each poet's perspective is unique. For example, students might describe Emily Dickinson's depiction of the wind as a flustered man who is visiting her home, Shakespeare's comparison of a temperate spring day to the person he loves, or the images of dawn, clouds, rain, and corn in "Prayer of First Dancers."

23. (Average) Students should be able to write specifically about one selection in the unit. They should be able to identify and define the musical device or devices in the poem and explain what effect they create. For example, students might note alliteration in the poem "Reapers," which echoes the swish of the reaper's blade

24. (Average) Students' essays should focus on two poems from the unit that deal with the theme of making a choice or adopting a particular attitude toward life. Students should be able to identify specific details in each piece they choose and explain why

they feel the piece is effective. For example, some students might write about the poem "A Pace Like That," which expresses the attitude that a slower pace is needed in life. The poet expresses this theme by having the speaker describe the growth of a lemon tree, which he could not do when he was living his life at a hectic pace. He also illustrates the pace at which he wants to live with images of a child learning to read or a person slowly deciphering ancient text on a tombstone.

25. (Challenging) Students should understand that a lyric poem focuses closely on a single incident or experience, exploring a single effect. Lyric poetry also reveals the feelings of the poem's speaker. A narrative poem tells a story and is usually longer than other types of poems. Like a story, a narrative poem often features characters, setting, conflict, and a series of events leading to a conclusion. A dramatic poem is a poem in which one or more characters tells a story through dialogue.

Unit 10:   Epics and Legends

from *Don Quixote*
by Miguel de Cervantes

Selection Test (p. 217)

Critical Reading/Vocabulary and Grammar

1. d 2. a 3. c 4. b 5. a 6. d 7. c 8. c 9. b
10. a 11. a 12. d 13. a 14. d 15. b 16. b
17. c 18. b 19. d 20. c

Questions are classified in these categories:
Comprehension 2(A), 3(E), 5(C), 6(A), 13(A)
Interpretation 4(C), 8(C), 10(E), 12(A), 14(A)
Literary Analysis 7(E), 9(C), 10(E)
Reading Strategy 1(E), 11(C), 15(A)
Vocabulary 16(E), 17(A), 18(C)
Grammar Skill 19(A), 20(A)
E = Easy, A = Average, C = Challenging

Essay Questions

Guidelines for student response:

21. (Easy) Students should list two or three qualities of Quixote's character and point

to evidence of those qualities in the text. For example, Quixote devotes his life to what he believes and abandons all for his ideals. He is heroic because his old-fashioned virtues of nobility and service, though of little practical use, are worth the struggle.

22. (Average) Students should identify two or three points of contrast between Don Quixote and Sancho Panza that serve as examples of the conflict between the modern, pragmatic world and the hopelessly romantic world. Examples include differences in speech: Quixote is almost always speaking in formal imitation of the reading material that inspires him, while Sancho is direct, realistic, and blunt. The two also differ in the focus of their lives: Quixote never loses his vision of idealism and Sancho is usually looking for his next meal.

23. (Challenging) The narrator represents himself as a person who is merely reporting a story. He acknowledges that it is a story, and increases that sense by noting that some details are uncertain. This guise as a reporter allows him to comment ironically without seeming to be critical. Thus he can indulge in parody without seeming vicious, mock Quixote without cruelty, comment on modern life without seeming cynical, and contrast Quixote to the real world without making him seem insane.

"Morte d'Arthur" by Alfred, Lord Tennyson
"Arthur Becomes King of Britain" from *The Once and Future King* by T. H. White

Selection Test (p. 220)

Critical Reading/Vocabulary and Grammar
1. d 2. c 3. d 4. b 5. b 6. c 7. a 8. b 9. d
10. a 11. b 12. c 13. c 14. a 15. d 16. c
17. b 18. c 19. a 20. d

Questions are classified in these categories:
Comprehension 1(E), 4(A), 6(A), 10(E), 11(A)
Interpretation 2(C), 3(A), 12(A), 14(C), 16(C)
Literary Analysis 5(A), 9(E), 13(A)
Reading Strategy 7(A), 8(C), 15(C)
Vocabulary 19(E), 20(C)
Grammar Skill 17(A), 18(E)
E = Easy, A = Average, C = Challenging

Essay Questions
Guidelines for student response:
21. (Easy) Students should acknowledge that Kay is depicted as excitable, even a bit flighty. Wart seems a little more down to earth. He is truly sad to see his teacher Merlyn depart. Kay, on the other hand, is too self-absorbed to pay much attention. Kay at first lies about acquiring the sword. Then, when confronted directly, he admits the truth. Kay shows respect to Wart when it's apparent that Wart is destined to be king.

22. (Average) Students should recall that Bedivere hides the sword in the grasses along the lake. Later, he decides that it would be better to save this relic for future generations. He also thinks that Arthur doesn't really know what he's asking and, at any rate, Arthur is dying and will never know if Bedivere throws the sword away. Students may support Bedivere or not. Some may say he should have obeyed the king, especially since it was his dying request. Others may say that it was prudent of Bedivere to want to retain a valuable and important symbol of the kingdom. Students' explanations of what they would have done in Bedivere's place must be supported by reasons for their actions.

23. (Challenging) Students may define the statement as using energy and strength for good rather than for destruction. Students may note that Tennyson's Arthur does not seem particularly "warlike." He expresses regret and sadness at the deaths of his knights. His advice to Bedivere is not to carry on the fight but to pray for Arthur's soul.

"Rama's Initiation" from the *Ramayana* by R. K. Narayan

Selection Test (p. 223)

Critical Reading/Vocabulary and Grammar
1. c 2. d 3. a 4. c 5. b 6. d 7. c 8. d 9. b
10. a 11. a 12. b 13. b 14. a 15. c 16. d
17. a 18. b 19. d 20. a

Questions are classified in these categories:
Comprehension 1(A), 2(E), 4(A), 7(A)
Interpretation 5(C), 10(E), 12(C), 14(A)
Literary Analysis 6(A), 11(E), 13(A)
Reading Strategy 3(A), 8(C), 9(A)
Vocabulary 15(C), 16(A), 17(A)
Grammar Skill 18(E), 19(A), 20(A)
E = Easy, A = Average, C = Challenging

Essay Questions
Guidelines for student response:
21. (Easy) Students should note that an epic hero is brave, honorable, and strong. Like other epic heroes, Rama sets off on a long journey, not knowing what awaits him. He braves the forbidding desert and sets aside his fear of the horrific Thataka and his misgivings about killing a woman to defeat evil. He demonstrates skill with weapons. Students should also note that Rama is approved by the gods;

"Rama's Initiation" from the *Ramayana*
by R. K. Narayan *(continued)*

Viswamithra senses that Rama is destined for greatness, and after he kills Thataka, Rama is praised by the gods directly.

22. (Average) Primarily, the selection reveals a culture that values spirituality, bravery, discretion, and respect for the law. These values can be inferred, for example, from the respect given to the sage Viswamithra, the praise Rama receives for killing the evil Thataka, Rama's hesitation at killing a woman, and the harsh punishment that follows Sudra's destruction of the land.

23. (Challenging) Students might contend that Rama has little choice in becoming a hero. Rama has no choice in the decision to accompany the sage; the question is debated between Viswamithra and Dasaratha only. In a different light, students might argue that while Rama himself doesn't choose to make the journey, he still makes a choice as to whether he will perform heroic actions. Students might also explain that Rama is fated, through his abilities, to become a hero.

from *Sundiata: An Epic of Old Mali*
by D.T. Niane

Selection Test (p. 226)

Critical Reading/Vocabulary and Grammar
1. b 2. d 3. b 4. c 5. c 6. a 7. b 8. d 9. a
10. b 11. c 12. a 13. b 14. b 15. c 16. d
17. a 18. c 19. d 20. b

Questions are classified in these categories:
Comprehension 1(E), 5(E), 6(E), 13(A)
Interpretation 2(A), 3(A), 7(C), 9(A), 10(A),
   12(C), 14(A)
Literary Analysis 8(C), 11(A)
Reading Strategy 4(C)
Vocabulary 16(A), 18(A), 20(A)
Grammar Skill 15(E), 17(A), 19(A)
E = Easy, A = Average, C = Challenging

Essay Questions
Guidelines for student response:
21. (Easy) Students should say that Sogolon Djata is the most honorable character in the story. He withstands years of torment because he respects what the soothsayers tell him about the role he is destined to fill. He waits patiently until the right moment and then shows his strength by standing up for his mother and showing his community his strength. Naré Maghan is also honorable. Although he has personal doubts that his son will ever be a strong ruler, he eventually trusts what the soothsayer tells him and stands behind his son. Sassouma, on the other hand, shows herself to be jealous and vindictive. She ignores what destiny has dictated for Sogolon Djata so that she can satisfy her own selfish needs.

22. (Average) Students should describe the conflicts between Sogolon Djata and the people in his village; Sassouma, his mother; and himself as he waits patiently to claim his power. Students should also describe the conflict that takes place within Sogolon Djata's father as he tries to decide if his son, who cannot even walk, is truly destined to be a powerful king. Finally they should describe the conflict that takes place within Sogolon Djata's mother and between herself and Sassouma. Each of these conflicts is resolved when Sogolon Djata finally stands and claims his power. The difficult experiences endured by Sogolon Djata make him stronger and more committed to his role and to fulfilling his destiny.

23. (Challenging) Students should say that the main purpose in telling this story is to share important cultural events and inspire people to have respect for their god and destiny. The story is also told to entertain people and to illustrate the effects of certain actions and behaviors. The story informs when it focuses on the details of Sogolon Djata's difficult experiences and his rise to power. The drama of Sogolon Djata's rise to power and the excitement and suspense related to the moment in which he finally stands provides entertainment. The foolish and mean-spirited behavior of Sassouma is meant to persuade people to honor their beliefs even when they have doubts.

Unit Test (p. 229)

Critical Reading/Vocabulary and Grammar

1. a 2. c 3. d 4. b 5. c 6. a 7. b 8. c 9. a
10. b 11. c 12. b 13. a 14. c 15. d 16. a
17. c 18. b 19. b 20. c

Questions are classified in these categories:

Comprehension 1(E), 2(A)
Interpretation 4(A), 5(E)
Literary Analysis 3(A), 8(A), 9(C)
Reading Strategy 6(A), 7(A), 10(C)
Vocabulary 14(E), 15(A), 16(C), 17(A), 18(A), 20(A)
Grammar Skill 11(A), 12(C), 13(E), 19(C), 20(A)

E = Easy, A = Average, C = Challenging

Essay Questions

Guidelines for student response:

21. (Easy) Students should choose a specific hero from the unit and then identify the character's heroic qualities. Students should explain exactly why they find their character heroic, citing two or three specific details from the selection. For example, a student choosing King Arthur from Tennyson's *Morte d'Arthur* should first describe his or her impressions of King Arthur and then provide concrete details that support his or her opinion.

22. (Average) Students should focus on one selection from the unit, explaining how details of setting and the actions of characters taught them about a particular culture. For example, a student focusing on one of the tales of King Arthur should name details that are unique to this period of England. Students focusing on the excerpt from the *Ramayana* should focus on details that are unique to life in India 2,000 years ago.

23. (Average) Students' essays should focus on how one selection from the unit serves a particular purpose. For example, students might describe how the selection from *Sundiata* imparts valuable historical information, shares the beliefs of a culture, or entertains with exciting details.

24. (Average) Students should show a solid understanding of epic conflict in one of the selections. They should present concrete details to back up their ideas. For example, a student writing about the excerpt from *Sundiata* should focus on the obstacles faced by Sogolon Djata throughout his childhood, the calm way in which he handles these obstacles, and his triumphant moment at the end of the selection.

25. (Challenging) Students should display a complete understanding of at least three heroic characters from this unit. The student should explain the different experiences of each character and then, using concrete details from the selections, show how the characters are similar to or different from one another. Students should focus on the characters' values and interactions with other characters.